Great Americana

A Journal of Travels
into the Arkansa Territory

Thomas Nuttall

A Journal of Travels
into the Arkansa Territory

by Thomas Nuttall

READEX MICROPRINT

Foreword

A Journal of Travels Into The Arkansas Territory, During The Year 1819 by Thomas Nuttall was printed in 1821. Nuttall, then regarded in Europe as America's foremost botanist, undertook the trip to obtain scientific information about this little-known region of the West. His journal naturally reflected his educated background and his scientific purpose. Consequently it differed sharply from conventional travel accounts. Nuttall made clear in a preface to his journal that he intended it for "the scientific part of the community," and not for "those who vaguely peruse the narratives of travellers for pastime or transitory amusement."

Nuttall, who emigrated from England to Philadelphia in 1808, had journeyed widely in the United States prior to his Arkansas venture. Friends who sympathized with his desire to visit the Arkansas River country contributed financially. Nuttall's journey by flatboat down the Ohio River and then the Mississippi River to the junction of the Arkansas River is included in the journal. However, he reserved his greatest attention for the trip up the Arkansas River beyond the army posts and into Comanche Indian territory, and then for his subsequent descent to New Orleans.

Nuttall carefully noted in his journal the geological formation of the country and the plant and wildlife he had observed. The journal frequently contains statements

such as "To-day I went five or six miles to collect specimens of the Centaurea, which, as being...indigenous to
America, had excited my curiosity," as evidence of the
scientist's enthusiasm. However, he also interested himself in the people he met. He regretted the lack of education of those who lived on the frontier and speculated
that "the widely scattered state of the population in this
territory, is but too favourable to the spread of ignorance
and barbarism." The Indians and their culture fascinated
him, and he deplored the many instances of their mis-
treatment by whites. From a practical standpoint Nuttall
doubted that it would ever be possible to guarantee the
security of frontier settlements "until these wanton and
unprovoked cruelties of the whites, and their piratical
wars, be prevented." He felt a similar compassion for the
Negro slaves he encountered in the lower Mississippi Valley. To be sure, Negroes "may be inferior to us in intellect
and civilization, [but] they were undoubtedly born to the
possession of rational liberty," he thought. Yet he also
believed that "the abolition of domestic slavery must be
a work of time."

Several maps, illustration, and an appendix of scientific
and historical information relating to Nuttall's journey
accompany the text. Jeannette E. Graustein has supplied
additional information about Nuttall in her article "Nuttall's Travels into the Old Northwest," *Chronica Botanica*
(1950/1951), XIV, 9-15.

A Journal of Travels
into the Arkansa Territory

A

JOURNAL

OF

TRAVELS

INTO THE

ARKANSA TERRITORY,

DURING THE YEAR

1819.

WITH OCCASIONAL OBSERVATIONS ON THE MANNERS OF THE

ABORIGINES.

ILLUSTRATED BY A MAP AND OTHER ENGRAVINGS.

———————

BY THOMAS NUTTALL, F. L. S.

HONORARY MEMBER OF THE AMERICAN PHILOSOPHICAL SOCIETY, AND OF
THE ACADEMY OF NATURAL SCIENCES, &C.

———————

PHILADELPHIA:

PRINTED AND PUBLISHED BY THOS. H. PALMER.

1821.

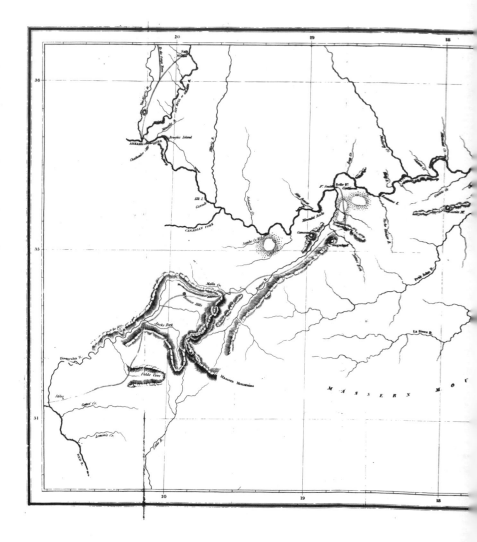

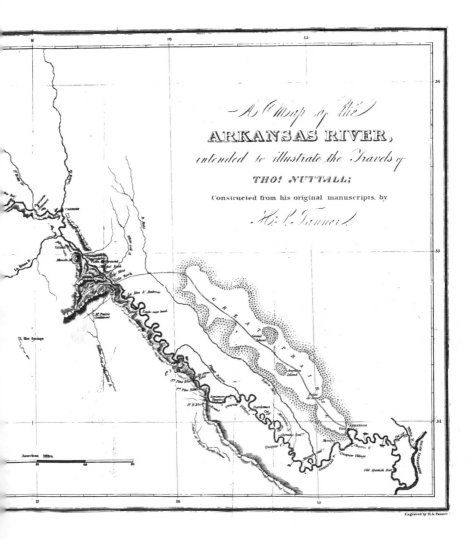

A Map of the
ARKANSAS RIVER,
intended to illustrate the Travels of
THO! NUTTALL;
Constructed from his original manuscripts, by
H. S. Tanner

Engraved by H.S.Tanner

TO

JOSEPH COREA DE SERRA,

MEMBER OF THE NATIONAL INSTITUTE OF FRANCE, OF THE
ROYAL SOCIETY OF LONDON, &c.

ZACCHEUS COLLINS, Esq.

MEMBER OF THE AMERICAN PHILOSOPHICAL SOCIETY, AND
VICE-PRESIDENT OF THE ACADEMY OF NATURAL
SCIENCES, &c.

WILLIAM MACLURE, Esq.

PRESIDENT OF THE ACADEMY OF NATURAL SCIENCES, AND
MEMBER OF THE AMERICAN PHILOSOPHICAL
SOCIETY, &c. &c.

JOHN VAUGHAN, Esq.

TREASURER AND LIBRARIAN OF THE AMERICAN PHILOSOPHI-
CAL SOCIETY, MEMBER OF THE ACADEMY OF NATURAL
SCIENCES, &c. &c.

Gentlemen,

PERMIT me to lay before you, the humble narrative of
a journey, chiefly undertaken for the investigation of
the natural history of a region hitherto unexplored. Excuse the imperfect performance of the gratifying task
which your liberality had imposed, but which was rendered almost abortive by the visitations of affliction.

If, in so tiresome a volume of desultory remarks, you
should meet with some momentary gratification, some
transient amusement, or ray of information, the author will
receive the satisfaction of not having laboured entirely in
vain.

PREFACE.

TO those who vaguely peruse the narratives of travellers for pastime or transitory amusement, the present volume is by no means addressed. It is no part of the author's ambition to study the gratification of so fastidious a taste as that, which but too generally governs the readers of the present day; a taste, which has no criterion but passing fashion, which spurns at every thing that possesses not the charm of novelty, and the luxury of embellishment. We live no longer in an age that tolerates the plain "unvarnished tale." Our language must now be crowded with the spoils of those which are foreign to its native idiom; it must be perplexed by variety, and rendered ambiguous and redundant by capricious ornament. Hermes, no longer the plain messenger of the gods, exercises all his deceit, and mingles luxury in the purest of intellectual streams.

Had I solely consulted my own gratification, the present volume would probably never have been offered to the public. But, as it may contain some physical remarks connected with the history of the country, and with that of the unfortunate aborigines, who are so rapidly dwindling into oblivion, and whose fate may, in succeeding generations, excite a curiosity and compassion denied them by the present, I have considered myself partly excused in offering a small edition to the scientific part of the community, just sufficient to defray the expenses of the printer, who kindly undertook the publication at his own risk. I may safely say, that hitherto, so far from writing for emolument, I have sacrificed both time and fortune to it. For nearly *ten* years I have travelled throughout America, principally with a view of becoming acquainted with some favourite branches of its natural history. I have had no other end in view than personal gratification, and in this I have not been deceived, for innocent amusement can never leave room for regret. To converse, as it were, with nature, to admire the wisdom and beauty of creation, has ever been, and I hope ever will be, to me a favourite pursuit. To communicate to others a portion of the same amusement and gratification has been the only object of my botanical publications; the most remote idea of personal emolument arising from them, from every circumstance connected with them, could not have been admitted into calculation. I had a right, however, reasonably to expect from Americans a degree of candour, at least equal to that which my labours had met with in Europe. But I have found, what, indeed, I might have reason to expect from human nature, often, instead of gratitude, detraction and envy. With such, I stoop not to altercate ; my endeavours, however imperfect, having been directed to the public good ; and I regret not the period I have spent in roaming over the delightful fields of Flora, in studying all her mysteries and enigmas, if I have, in any instance, been useful to her cause, or opened to the idle wanderer one fruitful field for useful reflexion.

Not wishing to enlarge the present publication, or retard it by the addition of a voluminous appendix, I reserve for a subsequent volume, which will shortly be issued, A *general view* and *description* of the *aboriginal antiquities* of the *western states*, and some *essays on the languages of the western Indians*, and their connection with those of other parts of the world, involving, in some measure, *a general view of language, both oral and graphical.*

The surveys and collections towards a history of the aboriginal antiquities, have remained unpublished in my possession for several years, and would have been longer withheld, in hopes of rendering them more complete, had not an unexpected anticipation obliged the author to hasten to do justice to himself, and claim, at least, that which was due to his personal industry.

The aboriginal languages of America, hitherto so neglected and unjustly consigned to oblivion as the useless relics of barbarism, are,

nevertheless, perhaps destined to create a new
era in the history of primitive language. In
their mazes is infolded a history of morals,
of remote connections, of vicissitudes and emi-
grations, which had escaped the circumstantial
pen of history; and yet, however strange it
may appear, are more durably impressed than
if engraven upon tablets of brass, and possessed of an intrinsic veracity nothing short of in-
spiration.

The literary character of the aboriginal languages of America, have, of late years, begun
to claim the attention of the learned both in
Europe and America.   The reports and cor-
respondence of the Historical committee appointed by the American Philosophical Society,
stand meritoriously preeminent in this re-
search; and it must be highly gratifying to the
public to know, that the same members continue still to labour in the field with unabated
vigour.   These various efforts united, I may
venture to predict, will be crowned with successful discoveries which could not have been
anticipated, and which will ultimately contribute towards the developement of that portion
of human history, which, above all others, appeared to be so impenetrably buried in oblivion.

Philadelphia, November, 1821.

CONTENTS.

1*

APPENDIX.

A JOURNEY

INTO THE

INTERIOR OF THE

ARKANSA TERRITORY.

———————

CHAPTER I.

*Departure from Philadelphia—Geological remarks—
Route through Harrisburgh and Carlisle to Cam-
mel's-town—Loudon, and the adjacent mountain
scenery—The North Mountain—Cove Mountain—
Passage of the Juniata, and surrounding scenery—
Bedford—Organic remains—The Alleghany Ridge
—Stoy's-town—First indications of bituminous
coal—Laurel Mountain—Greensburgh—Arrival
at Pittsburgh; manufactures; scenery, and peculiar character of its coal-mines.*

ON the morning of the second of October, 1818, I
took my departure from Philadelphia in the mail stage,
which arrived safely in Lancaster, sixty-three miles
distant, a little after sun-set. Though always pleas-
ingly amused by the incidents of travelling, and the
delightful aspect of rude or rural nature, I could not
at this time divert from my mind the most serious
reflections on the magnitude and danger of the journey which now lay before me, and which was, indeed,
of very uncertain issue.

2

Scarcely any part of the United States presents a more beautiful succession of hill and dale, than that which succeeds between Philadelphia and Lancaster; the valley, however, of Chester county, including Downingston, exceeds every other, except the site of Lancaster, in fertility and rural picture. It is about twenty-five miles in length by one in breadth, and pursues from hence a north-east direction. The rock throughout this valley is calcareous, and the soil is consequently of a superior quality. This lime-stone, which has been assiduously examined by the mineralogists and naturalists of Philadelphia, though not very dissimilar to that of the western states, except in the high inclination of the strata and the predominance of spar, has never yet been found to contain any kind of organic remains, and scarcely any metals more than traces of iron, manganese, titanium, and lead.

3d.] From Lancaster, I continued my route on foot, as affording greater leisure, and better opportunity for making observation. The rain, however, to-day prevented me from proceeding more than seventeen miles on the road to Harrisburgh. About twelve miles east of Middleton, I had again occasion to observe certain ledges of the prevailing calcareous rock, dipping at an angle scarcely under that of 45°, traversed by sparry veins, occasionally intermingled with epidote, in which are also imbedded bright, brown-red rhombic masses of felspar and amorphous quartz, a circumstance which had formerly fallen under my notice in a pedestrian tour on this road; I was now, however, enabled to trace this appearance into a connection with the transition formation which almost immediately succeeds, presenting masses of agglomerated rock, chiefly calcareous, of which the fragments are both angular and arrounded. Beyond this, on the first succeeding hill, occur layers of the old or transition sand-stone, not always red, though some of that colour appeared in the vicinity, interlayed with

brown-red slate-clay. Afterwards, and in connection
with this formation, appears the green-stone of the
Germans, and the bottoms of the valleys only are calcareous. Twelve miles west of Lancaster, we enter
the fine fertile tract, once known to the natives of the
Susquehannah by the name of *Pe-quay*, or the Pleasant Fields.

4th.] To Middleton, grunstein and argillaceous trap,
with sand-stone conglomerate, and Spanish-brown
slate-clay alternate and succeed each other, affording
an indifferent soil, and forming lofty hills, with precipitous declivities and narrow valleys. The sylvan
hills of the Susquehanna are, however, calcareous
and underlayed with common bluish grey and chlorite
slate, which as at Lancaster abounds with scattered
or inbedded cubic pyrites.* The long bridge of a
mile and a quarter, connecting with a small island,
crosses a wide and shallow part of the river, whose
bed is of slate (or argillite).

5th.] About half past seven, I left Harrisburgh, and
in the course of the day proceeded through Carlisle to
within five miles of Shippensburg, a distance of about
31 miles, over a deeply undulated country, evincing,
by the ease and comfort of its scattered population,
no inconsiderable degree of fertility in the soil, which
is calcareous. The first considerable chain of hills,
proceeding from north-east to south-west, clad with
unbroken forests, appeared on our left during most
part of the day, and indicated an approach to the
mountains.

6th.] This evening I arrived at Cammels'-town,
situated at the foot of the North Mountain. The intermediate and surrounding country is deeply undulated with hills of a softish sandstone and slate clay.
The more conspicuous hills of shale, accompanied

* The chlorite slate of the Wissahickon, near Germantown, considered as primitive, contains similar pyrites with octahedral crystals of iron
ore.

by organic remains, commence at Chambersburg, and, as in Virginia, are characterised by the appearance of Pine (*Pinus inops*), and scrub oak (*Quercus ilicifolia*); here also occurs the fragrant sumach (*Rhus aromaticum*).

The road, on which several bands of labourers were employed, was now nearly completed to Pittsburgh, affording that convenience and facility to the inland commerce of the state which had been so long neglected.   The states of New-York and Virginia, equally interested in the advancement of their internal trade, now begin to show themselves as the serious rivals of Pennsylvania, which, till lately, with the exception of New-Orleans, enjoyed the most considerable portion of the commerce of the west.

7th.] To-day I proceeded about 21 miles, over a very poor and mountainous country.   From the little village, or cluster of cabins, called Loudon, we commence the ascent over the North Mountain, by an easy and well-levelled turnpike.   From its summit appeared a wide and sterile forest extending across the glen, and, only at small and distant intervals, obscurely broken by scattered farms.   The soil is here argillaceous, a slate-clay passing into argillaceous trap and siliceous sandstone, occasionally changing into an almost homogeneous quartz, predominates.   At Loudon, there is a small iron-furnace, and ore in inconsiderable quantities found in the neighbourhood. Passing this range, sometimes called the Cove or North Mountain, we descend to M'Connels'-town, which now presents itself in bird's-eye view before us, here the soil is calcareous, but still, to all appearance, destitute of organic remains.   Deep and narrow valleys, steep hills every where presenting shale devoid of impressions, though often so far bituminous as to blaze, abound, but no coal is to be met with nearer than the valley of the Juniata, where organic impressions also commence.   Within the great valley of the

North Mountain, are several other lower and interrupted ranges. The chain also called the North
Mountain, proceeding much to the east in its southern
course, presents in that direction acuminated peaks,
and appears interrupted as towards Staunton in Virginia. From this summit we are distinctly enabled
to mark the direction of the South Mountain, so low
where we crossed it as to afford an almost impercepti-
ble ascent.

What still remained of the old road, appeared here
as bad as can well be imagined ; a mere Indian trace,
without any choice of level, over rocky ledges and
gullies, threatening at every instant the destruction
of the carriages which ventured over it.

8th.] After travelling about 28 miles, I arrived, in
the evening, at the very pleasant and romantically situated town of Bedford, hemmed in by a cove of mountains to the south and west, near whose declivity issue
the chalybeate springs, occasionally the resort of the
sick and convalescent. Very little of the road over
which I came to-day was yet turnpike, and as bad as
may naturally be supposed over a succession of mountain ridges, which, though scattered, and interrupted
by the passage of waters, scarcely fall short of the
North Mountain in point of elevation. These ridges,
of which in the above distance there are three or four,
are all often confounded in the name of Cove Mountain.

I crossed the Juniata by a wooden toll-bridge,
which, like all other private accommodations in the
United States, does not exempt the pedestrian traveller. The valley of the river is narrow and romantic,
embosomed by cliffs, rudely decorated with clumps
of sombre evergreens, particularly the tall Weymouth
pine and spruce, with the splendid Rhododendron and
the *Magnolia acuminata*. As we approach towards
Bedford the valleys widen, are more fertile, and present calcareous strata still inclined at a lofty angle, and
generally destitute of organic remains. Every eleva-

tion, and most of them short and steep, presents a
predominance of argillaceous earth, either red or greenish and slatey, as it may happen to contain an admixture of iron or chlorite ; there are, however, no iron
furnaces nor ore in this quarter nearer than the vicinity of Huntingdon.   Seams of coal have been discovered on the banks of the Juniata, but unworthy of notice or difficult to drain.   Fifteen miles from Bedford,
coal begins to appear.   Indeed, about a mile from the
town I observed in the siliceous sandstone made use
of for repairing the road, and which was obtained in
the vicinity, casts of *orthoceratites ?* or something resembling them, collected into fascicles or clusters, and
aggregated over the surface of the rocks in which they
are found ; the transverse septa or channels are all
proximate, and their circumference is about two inches.   Excepting a second impression, something similar, but much smaller (and which rather resembles some alcyonite), no other reliquiæ appeared in this
stone, which is also the first occurrence of the kind
on my journey to the westward.

The mountain scenery, at first so grand and im-
pressive, becomes at length monotonous ; most of the
cimes, terraces, and piles of rocks lose their effect beneath the umbrageous forest which envelopes them,
and which indeed casts a gloomy mantling over the
whole face of nature.

To judge of the inland commerce carried on betwixt Philadelphia and Pittsburgh, a stranger has but
to view this road at the present season.   All day I have
been brushing past waggons heavily loaded with merchandise, each drawn by five and six horses; the
whole road in fact appears like the cavalcade of a continued fair.

9th.] To-day I proceeded about 20 miles from
Bedford on the way to Pittsburgh, and in the evening
lodged at a tavern situated on the top of the Alleghany ridge.   About nine miles from Bedford I first ob-

served the occurrence of fossil shells, consisting of terebratulites, and amongst them the *Anomia trigonalis* of Martyn, with some other species. They occur in the sandstone employed for mending the road, with which also alternates much liver-brown argillaceous shale. From hence the dip of the strata gradually diminishes, and the hills are no longer so short and steep; slate-clay with appearances of coal are also visible, but as yet there are no *zoophytic*, or, as some consider them, *phytolithic* or vegetable impressions. The ascent to the summit of the Alleghany from the east is much more gentle than that of the North Mountain, or the other mountains scattered through this valley. The Alleghany, here from 10 to 20 miles broad, is apparently the boundary of the transition, and the long slopes and salient coves of its western declivity are within the range of the secondary formation. Much of the *Quercus Prinos monticola* (or mountain chesnut oak) presents itself on the mountain, together with the *Magnolia acuminata* and *Sorbus americana* or service-berry.

10th.] To-day I walked nine miles to Stoystown, if a handful of houses like this deserves such an appellation. The declivity of the surface is much more gentle and inconsiderable than that which I had passed. Indications of coal were also apparent along the margin of the road. The valleys are now broader, and the soil of a better quality. The inhabitants, however, chiefly Irish, are indigent, and considerably deficient in prudence and cleanliness. I spent most part of the day in collecting seeds of the *Magnolia acuminata*.

11th.] To-day I proceeded 18 miles to the little hamlet of Liganier lately begun, and passed though Loughlinstown, equally inconsiderable, except for dram shops, improperly called taverns, with which this road abounds. The turnpike is completed nearly throughout this distance, and also to Greensburgh. Towards evening I crossed the Laurel Mountain, and found abundantly on

its western declivity the *Circæa alpina.*   In the valley
on the eastern ascent I likewise saw the *Betula glauca,*
and a profusion of the common *Rhododendron,* which
gives the name of Laurel to this mountain.   Indications of coal, and a continued declension in the dip of
the strata are still obvious.   The sandstone, which is
almost the only rock I have seen throughout the course
of the day, is remarkable for the absence of organic
reliquiæ.   In some places it appears like grauwacke
blended with angular fragments of a soft slate.   Near
the western base of the Laurel ridge the usual zoophytes
make their appearance, chiefly *Culmaria striata**
(*Striaticulmis* of Martyn), also casts of enormous chan-
nelled *Culmariæ* like those of Bradford, in Yorkshire
(England).   Vegetation at this advanced season still
appeared very luxuriant on the western descent of the
Laurel, and the valleys bore the appearance of fertility.

   12th.] This evening I arrived at Greensburgh, 18
miles west of Liganier.   The last considerable mountain range to the west on this route is Chesnut Ridge,

---

* Although we are as yet unacquainted with the internal and essential
physical structure of these organic remains, which have been hitherto
considered as plants, I have thought it necessary to assume the above
generic name as preferable to the improbable, and at any rate merely
ordinal name of *Phytolithus.* The CULMARIÆ, as I have termed them, are
striated or grooved and somewhat compressed, cylindric, articulated
bodies, gradually attenuating from joint to joint, mostly undivided, or
simple, but occasionally bifid, and at length terminating in a point.   On
one of the sides they commonly possess a deep and central channel, and
in some species at the joints present alternate small protuberances and
cavities.   Their soboliferous propagation appeared to originate from
these joints, in the form of wart-like or areolate protuberances, and, unlike plants, they never seem to have produced any thing similar to
leaves, flowers, or seeds.
   The tessellated zoophytes, by others also considered as vegetable remains, which I have termed STROBILARIÆ are subcylindric and often
somewhat conic, but inarticulated ; some of the species protruded,
as occasion required, from the centre of those tessellæ, bodies resembling hollow spines, or (as would appear from a specimen in my possession from Bradford, in Yorkshire) suckers or hollow cylinders, with
circular contractile and striated mouths.   The whole of these processes,
when exserted mistaken for leaves, could also be withdrawn within the
body of the animal, and indeed most of the casts present this quiescent
or contracted state.   These bodies likewise exhibit in some specimens
a complicated internal structure.

which I crossed to-day. Here I met with the *Impera-
toria lucida* of Sprengel, also abundance of the *Cimi-
cifuga americana* and *Asplenium angustifolium*. The
dip of the strata becomes now more and more inconsiderable, but organic remains, except those peculiar
to the coal formation, are scarcely to be met with, and
there is a predominance of slaty and argillaceous sandstone.

13th.] The turnpike was now completed through
the last 40 miles up to Pittsburgh, and scarcely any
undertaking promises more advantage to the state in
general. It will tend to check the competition of the
inland navigation of the state of New York, as well
as that of the state of Virginia, through which the
United States have established a national road as far
as the town of Wheeling on the Ohio.

14th.] West of Greensburg, and indeed east of it,
from the base of the Chesnut Ridge, the surface of the
country is deeply undulated, and laborious to travel.
The land upon the height is sterile and thinly popula-
ted; still every five or six miles we meet with some
poor-looking hamlet, which commonly, out of 12 to 20
log cabins composing it, contains six or seven licensed
dram shops, besides three or four stores for the retail-
ing of merchandise. How much is a scattered and
independent population like that of the honest and industrious Germans inhabiting the eastern parts of
Pennsylvania to be preferred to these towns whose inhabitants are brought together by no prospect of general industry or economy. To say that coal is common
throughout this country, and that it is generally employed for fuel, is repeating a fact familiar to every
one who has ever visited the western country.

15th.] To-day I arrived again in Pittsburgh, and en-
deavour as I may to drive away my former prejudices
against this very important commercial and manufac-
turing city, I find it impossible. Nothing appears to

me to predominate but filth and smoke and bustle. The rivers and surrounding country are engaging and romantic—its situation—the Thermopylæ of the west, into which so many thousands are flocking from every christian country in the world—its rapid progress, and the enterprising character of its inhabitants, are circumstances which excite our admiration. In national industry, the true source of wealth and independence, Pittsburgh is now scarcely inferior to any of the older and larger towns in the Union. The shores of the Monongahela were lined with nearly 100 boats of all descriptions, steam-boats, barges, keels, and arks or flats, all impatiently and anxiously waiting the rise of the Ohio, which was now too low to descend above the town of Wheeling. A bridge was at this time nearly completed across this stream, and one of the piers of another across the Alleghany was also laid.

The day after my arrival I went through the flint-glass works of Mr. Bakewell, and was surprised to see the beauty of this manufacture, in the interior of the United States, in which the expensive decorations of cutting and engraving (amidst every discouragement incident to a want of taste and wealth) were carried to such perfection. The productions of this manufacture find their way to New Orleans, and even to some of the islands of the West Indies.

The president Monroe, as a liberal encourager of domestic manufactures, had on his visit to those works given orders for a service of glass, which might indeed be exhibited as a superb specimen of this elegant art.

Mr. Bakewell was now beginning to employ the beautiful white and friable sandstone which had been observed near to a branch of the Merrimec by Mr. Bradbury and myself, as well as others, in the winter of 1809. It promises every important requisite for the production of the purest flint-glass, and exists in inexhaustible quantities.

16—19th.] Still at Pittsburgh, waiting for an opportunity to descend the river, which was now almost
impracticable in consequence of the lowness of the
water.

19th.] This morning I took a walk to Grant's Hill,
from whence there is a delightful view of Pittsburgh,
and on the hill itself some very pleasing rural retire-
ments of the wealthy citizens.

My attention, as usual, was directed to the surrounding minerals and stratification, which are no un-
important matters in the economy of this settlement.
The coal basin, or rather bed, which has been so long
wrought on this hill, about six feet thick, is almost
exactly horizontal, and consequently worked by a
simple parallel drift without making any inconvenient
quantity of water. The coal bassets out towards the
edge of the hill, and so near the summit as to present
scarcely any other overlay than a thin shale, more or
less friable, and no sandstone. The dip, such as it
is, is to the north of east, but scarcely manifest. It is
bituminous or inflammable, and of a very good quality.
Beneath this single bed of coal, occurs a fine grained,
micaceous sandstone, rendered greenish from an admixture of chlorite earth; still lower in the series appears a compact calcareous rock, in which I did not
perceive any reliquiæ. At the southern extremity of
the hill, where it approaches the Monongahela, the
laminated micaceous sandstone, however, exhibits
great clusters of *culmariæ (striaticulmis* of Martyn),
almost ancipitally compressed, and with the striatures
very fine. Here the calcareous rock beneath the micaceous sandstone exhibits masses of terebratulites, some
of which are very minute, but in great quantities.
Near to the precipitous termination of Grant's Hill,
and in several other contiguous places, the sandstone
appears to have been disintegrated with violence, and
the angular fragments again to have been cemented by
a stalactitial deposition of calcareous spar, of a fibrous

texture, almost similar to Arragonite. Seams of fibrous gypsum, possessing a silky lustre, have also been discovered in this vicinity.

In the course of this ramble I found abundance of of the *Monarda hirsuta*, which as well as *M. ciliata*, do not much resemble the legitimate species of the genus.

CHAPTER II.

Departure from Pittsburgh—Autumnal Scenery— Georgetown—The unfortunate emigrant—Steuben- ville—Picturesque Scenery—Wheeling—Little Grave creek, and the Great Mound—Other Abori- ginal remains—Marietta—Belpré settlement— Other ancient remains—Coal—Galliopolis—Ancient level of the alluvial forest—Misletoe—Aboriginal remains—Big Sandy creek and commencement of Cane-land—Corn-husking—Salt creek—Mays- ville—Organic remains—Cincinnati—Lawrence- burgh—The French emigrant—Vevay—Ma- dison—Louisville—Prevalence of particular winds on the Ohio—Falls of the Ohio.

21st.] To-day I left Pittsburgh in a skiff, which I purchased for six dollars, in order to proceed down the Ohio. I was fortunate enough to meet with a young man who had been accustomed to the manage- ment of a boat, and who, for the consideration of a passage and provision, undertook to be my pilot and assistant. We set out after 11 o'clock, and made 19 miles. Here we were overtaken by a thunder-storm, accompanied by very heavy rain, which continued during most part of the ensuing night. We had no choice, and therefore took up our abode for the night in the first cabin which we came to, built of logs,

containing a large family of both sexes, all housed in
one room, and that not proof against the pouring rain.
Provided, however, with provision and beds of our
own, we succeeded in rendering ourselves comfortable, and were pleased with the hospitable disposition
of our landlord, who would scarcely permit any of
his family to receive from us the moderate compensation which we offered.

22d.] At day-break we again betook ourselves to
the voyage; but after proceeding about nine miles,
the strong south-west wind forced us to a delay of several hours.

In this distance from Pittsburgh the Ohio meanders through a contracted alluvial flat, thickly settled,
and backed with hills, which are often peaked and
lofty, fringed, at this season, by a forest of the diversified, but dying hues of autumn. The water was
extremely low, and we passed through several rapids,
in which bare rocks presented themselves in such
quantity, as to deny the passage of any thing but boats
drawing 9 or 10 inches of water.

After proceeding about two miles below Beaver-
town we landed in the dark, and went to the tavern
to which accident had directed us, but finding it
crowded with people met together for merriment, we
retired to a neighbouring hovel, in order to obtain rest
and shelter from the weather, which was disagreeably
cold. Our prospect of repose was soon, however,
banished, as our cabin, being larger than the tavern,
was selected for a dancing room, and here we were
obliged to sit waking spectators of this riot till after
one o'clock in the morning. The whiskey bottle
was brought out to keep up the excitement, and, without the inconvenience and delay of using glasses, was
passed pretty briskly from mouth to mouth, exempt-
ing neither age nor sex. Some of the young *ladies*
also indulged in smoking as well as drinking of drams.
Symptoms of riot and drunkenness at length stopped

the dancing, and we now anticipated the prospect of a little rest, but in this we were disappointed by the remaining of one of the company vanquished by liquor, who, after committing the most degrading nuisance, at intervals disturbed us with horrid gestures and imprecations for the remainder of the morning. On relating in the neighbourhood our adventure at this house, we were informed that this tavern was notorious for the assemblage of licentious persons.

23d.] After an hour or two of interrupted repose we again embarked, and found that there had been a slight fall of snow. The wind was still adverse, and so strong as perfectly to counteract the current; with some labour we got down to Georgetown, and warmed ourselves by a comfortable fire of coal. The tavern was very poorly accommodated, a mere cabin without furniture, of which its owner was from habit scarcely sensible. About two o'clock in the afternoon we again landed at a poor log-cabin to warm ourselves, and were very kindly welcomed by the matron of the house, who, without the benefit of education, seemed possessed of uncommon talents. I had read, in the first settlement of Kentucky, of remarkable instances of female intrepidity, brought forward by the exigencies of a residence on a dangerous frontier, and our hostess appeared to be equally an Amazon, modest, cool, and intrepid. I listened to her adventures with much interest. She and her husband, with a small family, had some years ago followed the tide of western emigration to the banks of the little Miami, near Cincinnati. Here, after a tedious and expensive journey, they had settled on a piece of alluvial land, and might probably have prospered, but for the dreadful effects of continued sickness (ague and bilious fever), which urged them to sacrifice every other interest for that of their emaciated offspring, and to ascend the Ohio in search of a situation which might afford them health. She pointed to some remains of decent furniture which the cabin scarcely sheltered, saying, with an affectionate look at her poor children, "we once had a decent property, but now we have nothing left; emigration has ruined us!" With six children around her, and accompanied by another family, ascending the Ohio in a flat-boat, they were struck by a hurricane. She herself and one of her children had taken their regular turn at the oar, the master of the boat, who had also his family around him, became so far alarmed and confused as to quit his post in the midst of the danger which threatened instantly to overwhelm them, tremendous waves broke into the boat, which the affrighted steersman knew not how to avoid. This woman seized the helm which was abandoned, and by her skill and courage saved the boat and the families from imminent destruction.

24th.] The wind still south-west, but abating a little. We proceeded at 11, and about 18 miles from Steubenville, landed and took up our lodging on an island, with no other shelter than the canopy of heaven; but we slept comfortably, with our feet to a warm fire, according to Indian custom.

25th.] This evening we arrived at Steubenville, which appears to be a place of industry and manufacture. Two miles below the town we lodged in the cabin of a poor tenant farmer.

The banks of the river are exceedingly romantic, presenting lofty hills and perpendicular cliffs of not less than 300 feet elevation, every where covered or fringed with belts of trees in their autumnal foliage, of every bright and varying hue, more beautiful even than the richest verdure of summer. The uplands being calcareous are found to be exceedingly fertile, and we consequently perceive houses and fences on the summits of the loftiest hills which embosom the river. From 50 to 70 dollars per acre was demanded for these lands, which are better for wheat than the

alluvial soils.   Flour was here four dollars per barrel,
and beef six cents per pound.

26th.] This evening we arrived at Wheeling, consisting of a tolerably compact street of brick houses,
with the usual accompaniment of stores, taverns, and
mechanics.   It is also the principal depot for the supply and commerce of the interior of this part of Virginia.   A number of boats had been fitted out here
this season, which could not navigate from Pittsburgh
in consequence of the lowness of the water.   At this
place the great national road into the interior, from
the city of Washington, comes in conjunction with
that of Zanesville, Chillicothe, Columbus, and Cincinnati.   At the northern extremity of the town there
is a very productive bed of coal, and equally horizontal with that of Pittsburgh ; its thickness is about
six feet, and as it occurs *beneath* the limestone it
must of course be considered as a *second* bed.   Every
where along the banks of the river, particularly at this
low stage we perceive adventitious boulders and pebbles of sienite, which cannot have originated nearer
than the mountains of Canada, situated beyond the
lakes.   Proceeding about four and a half miles from
Wheeling, we took up our night's residence at a
cabin near to the outlet of M'Mahon's creek.

27th.] To-day I again observed a bed of coal in
the bank of the Ohio, worked *beneath* the limestone,
situated nearly opposite to Little Grave creek.   This
superincumbent limestone does not appear to abound
with organic remains, and is nearly horizontal, with
a slight dip, perhaps 10°, to the south-east.   Ten or
12 miles further, the same coal bed still bassets out
from beneath the calcareous rock, and so near to the
present low level of the river as not to admit of being
worked at any other stage of the water.   The shale
(or bituminous slate clay) above and below the coal

is extremely superficial, being only a few inches in thickness, and interspersed with small masses of bitumen and reliquiæ which imitate charred wood, but are destitute of the characterizing cross grain.

At the mouth of Little Grave creek we landed, to view the famous mound, said to be 75 feet high. The ascent is extremely steep : it is indeed a pyramid, and of an elegant conic figure; at the summit there is a circular depression indicative of some excavation, and it is surrounded by a shallow ditch, across which, there are left two gateways. It appears to be elevated at about an angle of 60°, and the earth, as in many other similar monuments, has evidently been beaten down to resist the washing of rains. It is remarkably perfect and compleat, and would probably continue a monument as long as the walled pyramids of Egypt. Amongst other trees growing upon it, there was a white oak of not less than two centuries' duration. In the immediate vicinity, there is likewise a small ditched circle with two entrances, and a smaller ditched mound.

At this place, I took in a young man going down to Big Sandy creek, who assisted in working his passage with us. At dark we landed on the Ohio shore, and lodged with a poor but hospitable resident.

28th.] Tired of the boat, I got out and walked 10 or 12 miles, on the Virginia side of the river. Many of the settlers here appear to be Yankees, from Vermont and Connecticut, and in prosperous circumstances. A mile and a half above Sistersville, and 35 from Marietta, in Virginia, there is a small aboriginal station, consisting of five or six low mounds, and a circle containing an area of about an acre.

29th.] Twenty-six miles above Marietta, on the Virginia side, on the estate of Mr. Cohen, there was on the platform of the third, or most ancient alluvial bottom, a large, but low mound, grown over with brambles ; and, at the distance of about a quarter of a mile below, a small square embankment containing near an acre, with only one or two openings or entrances.

Most part of the afternoon, I continued walking along the Ohio bank, and observed, as I have done for near 30 miles above, the alluvial lands to be more extensive, occupying often both banks of the river, and a sensible diminution in the elevation of the hills. The bottoms here abound with elm, and there are also extensive and undrainable tracts covered with beech.

30th.] At day break, we again betook ourselves to our laborious journey, which, in consequence of the adverse wind, was nearly as toilsome as a voyage up, in place of down the stream; in addition to which, we had also to encounter the severe and benumbing effects of frost. We passed Marietta, remarkable for its aboriginal remains, and in the evening, encamped on the beach of the river, but did not rest very comfortably, in consequence of the cold.

31.] Passed Belpre settlement, an extensive portion of fertile alluvial land, and thickly settled. All the prevailing rock here, for some distance, is a massive sandstone, either brownish, greenish, or grayish, fine grained and micaceous, and occasionally exposing something like impressions of alcyonites, but appearing in no place indicative of coal. This evening we lodged at a house, four miles above the mouth of Shade river, where the bottoms are extensive and fertile. In a rocky situation, I found abundance of the *Seymeria macrophylla*, near six feet in height; also a new species of *Aster*, in full bloom, at this advanced season.

November 1st.] We proceeded about 19 miles without any material hindrance, when the south-west wind, which had so constantly opposed our descent, blew up a thunder-storm with rain, which detained us for the remainder of the day. Below Marietta, the

alluvial lands become still more extensive, and appear
to be held at a price considerably above their real
value by speculators, who thus prevent the population from accumulating. We scarcely, indeed, see
any thing in this quarter but the miserable log cabins
of tenants so poor and ill provided, even with the
common necessaries of life, that, had we not taken the
precaution of providing ourselves with provision, we
must often have had either to fast, or sit down to nothing better than mush and milk ; which, though an
agreeable, is not a sufficiently nourishing diet for a
traveller.

In descending the river, we uniformly find rapid
water along the islands and bars ; a circumstance appearing to indicate the former union of such islands
with the land.   Nearly all the sugar here made use of
by the inhabitants, is obtained from the maple *(Acer
saccharinum)*, which, by more careful management,
might be refined equal to muscovado.

2d.] We were again detained a considerable part of
the day by the contrary wind, and, during the delay,
fell in with a descending family, which had passed us
the preceding day. In a short time after meeting,
two hounds belonging to our companion, which had
been let loose in the woods, chased a buck to the river : my companion and the old migratory hunter instantly launched the skiff in the pursuit, and succeeded in shooting the unfortunate deer in the water ; a
method commonly resorted to in this country, where
the chase is more a matter of necessity than amusement.

3d.] This morning I walked up the right bank of
the river, to view an aboriginal station, said to be situated on the present estate of Mr. Warf, on Park's
bottom ; but, on proceeding about two miles through
an enswamped beech forest, I relinquished the undertaking, finding it to be more than three miles above
Mill creek, which I had crossed the preceding day.

I understood that this work was a circular embankment, including an area of three or four acres; and
in the vicinity of which, were several inconsiderable
mounds.　Beech woods, flanked by elevated cliffs,
still continued for four miles on the Virginia side, to
Le Tart's rapids, where the boat was to wait my arrival.　On the way I found abundance of the *Dracoce-
phalum cordifolium* with long slolons like ground ivy,
also *Hesperis pinnatifida*, but I was more particularly
gratified in finding the *Tilia heterophylla*.　Nothing
is here more abundant than the *Stylophorum (Cheli-
donium.* Mich.).　This evening, we were 16 miles
above Galiopolis;

4th.] About 11 miles from which, I observed a bed
of coal, now worked on the bank of the river, some
distance above the base of a high cliff, and overlaid
by a massive micaceous sandstone, constituting the
main body of the hill, and, as usual, horizontally
stratified.　Beneath the coal appeared a laminated
lime stone.　Not many miles from hence, nitre is also
obtained in caves.

The wind still continued against us, and with considerable labour we got five miles below Galiopolis,
at which and Point Pleasant there are several mounds
and aboriginal remains.*

5th.] This evening we had proceeded about 26
miles below Galiopolis.　Yesterday and to-day, I remarked, parallel with the present level of the river,
and often surmounted by a lofty and friable bank of
earth, beds of leaves compressed and blackened, giving out ferruginous matter to the water which oozed
through them.　On examination, they proved to be
the same kind of foliage as that of the trees which
compose the present alluvial forest; as platanus, beech,
oak, poplar, &c.

About Steubenville I observed the first occurrence

* A more particular account of these monuments is given in the latter part of this work.

of misletoe (the *Viscum verticillatum* of the West-
Indies), which now appears very prevalent and conspicuous. The fruit of the popaw (*Porcelia triloba*)
here comes to perfection, and is rich and finely fla-
voured, while above, and in a few localities where it
exists in Pennsylvania, it is scarcely eatable.

I was again informed of the existence of aboriginal
mounds and entrenchments on the fertile alluvial lands
called Messer's Bottom, which are of several miles
extent, commencing almost immediately below Galiopolis on the Virginia side, but after several unsuccessful inquiries, the ignorance and supineness of the
settlers, though numerous, prevented me from discovering them.

6th.] We proceeded about nine miles, and were
as usual prevented from continuing further by the
reiterated violence of the pertinacious south-west
wind, accompanied by a haze, which made every object appear as if enveloped in smoke.

7th.] This evening, we passed the mouth of Big
Sandy creek, the boundary of Kentucky. Near
to this line commences the first appearance of the
cane (*Arundinaria macrosperma*), which seems to indicate some difference in the climate and soil. The
settlements are here remote, the people poor, and
along the river not so characteristically hospitable as
in the interior of Kentucky. Landing rather late, we
took up our lodging where there happened to be a
corn-husking, and were kept awake with idle merriment and riot till past midnight. Some of the party,
or rather of the two national parties, got up and
harangued to a judge, like so many lawyers, on some
political argument, and other topics, in a boisterous
and illiberal style, but without coming to blows. Is
this a relic of Indian customs?

The corn-fields, at this season of the year, are so
overrun with cuckold-burs (*Xanthium strumarium*),
and the seeds of different species of Bidens or Span-

ish-needles, as to prove extremely troublesome to woollen clothes, and to the domestic cattle, which are loaded with them in tormenting abundance. In consequence of these weeds, the fleece of the sheep is scarcely worth the trouble of shearing. The best remedy for checking the growth of these noxious plants, would be to plough them in about the time of flowering, which would exterminate them, and improve the crop of corn.

The people here, living upon exigencies, and given to rambling about instead of attending to their farms, are very poor and uncomfortable in every respect; but few of them possess the land on which they live. Having spent every thing in unsuccessful migration, and voluntarily exiling themselves from their connections in society, they begin to discover, when too late, that industry would have afforded that comfort and independence which they in vain seek in the solitudes of an unhealthy wilderness. We found it almost impossible to purchase any kind of provision, even butter or bacon, nothing appearing to be cultivated scarcely but corn and a little wheat.

I was again informed of the existence of aboriginal remains in the vicinity of the place where we arrived this evening.

8th.] We were delayed nearly the whole of the day by the usual adverse wind.

9th.] To-day, however, we were fortunate enough, at last, to obtain the breeze in our favour, and proceeded about 28 miles, encamping three miles below the town of Portsmouth.

10th.] The wind still continuing in our favour, accompanied by a considerable current, we proceeded about 32 miles, and encamped 12 miles below Salt creek, and 17 above Maysville. In this course the river appears very meandering, and from Portsmouth, the hills, which are considerable, come up diagonally to the margin of the river and present serrated or conic summits. At the lowest stage of the water we perceive horizontal ledges of calcareous rock filled with terebratulites, &c. The salt at Adamsville appears to be made from water issuing out of the alluvial argillaceous soil near to the outlet of Salt breek, but in many parts of the Western country coring for salt water is frequently continued some hundreds of feet, (sometimes as much as 400 feet) below the surface, through calcareous and sand-stone rocks, and occasionally through beds of coal.

11th.] We proceeded seven miles below the thriving town of Maysville, formerly called Limestone from the rock in its neighbourhood, and experienced heavy rains during the whole day, which in our open skiff proved very unpleasant, and, to augment our uncomfortable situation, we encamped at a late hour on a very disagreeable muddy shore, where it was not possible to kindle a fire.

The farmers along the river for many miles down appear to be in thriving circumstances. Their houses are very decent in external appearance, but so badly finished and furnished that many of the rooms are unoccupied, or merely serve the purposes of a barn, and the family are commonly found living in the kitchen. Most of these ostentatious shells of frame houses are the work of the New-England settlers, who are very industrious, and not without more or less of their usual economy and sagacity.

12th.] We were again retarded by the south-west wind. The shore on which we landed was thickly strewed with fragments of calcareous rock filled with terebratulites, alcyonites, flustras, encrinal vertebræ, &c. &c. Some specimens which I here collected of the encrinal vertebræ were coated with a cellular epidermis, in appearance resembling a millepore ; they are also remarkably dichotomous. In one of the calcareous fragments which I broke occurred the *Trilobites paradoxus.*

The wind abating, we passed down to Augusta, and with our emigrant companions encamped on the opposite shore. Here the insolence of my companion rendered our separation absolutely necessary. It is to be regretted, that so many of those wandering New-Englanders (who, like the Jews in Europe, are to be met with in every part of the union), should prove so disgraceful to their country. My impression now was, that this young man was a refugee from justice or deserved infamy, and in all probability I narrowly escaped being robbed.

13th.] To day I arrived at Cincinnati, and was again gratified by the company of my friend Doctor I. Drake, one of the most scientific men west of the Alleghany mountains.

The town appeared to have improved much, both in appearance and population, since my last visit; it is, indeed, by far the most agreeable and flourishing of all the western towns. Here I had the good fortune, through Dr. D., to be introduced to Mr. H. Glenn, lately sutler to the garrison of Arkansa; from whom I had the pleasure to learn something more explicit concerning the probable progress of my intended journey.

A medical college was, I understood, about to be established in Cincinnati. Dr. D., who delivered a very appropriate introductory oration, will, probably, be the principal of the institution. But such undertakings are yet rather premature, and the student would derive many exclusive advantages by acquiring a medical education in the universities already established.

17th.] About 12 o'clock I left Cincinnati in my skiff, and was accidentally joined by two strangers going to Lawrenceburgh, 25 miles distant, where we arrived this evening. This a neat and thriving town, situated near the estuary of the Great Miami, and on the line of the state of Indiana.

18th.] I departed at day-break, but, after descending
five miles, discovered my gun had been forgotten at
the tavern where I lodged.   The day was dismal and
cloudy, with showers of snow and gales of wind, undissembled winter.   In the evening I arrived at a little town called the Rising Sun, from its tavern, 13
miles below Lawrenceburgh.

19th.] A fine morning and but little wind.—I now
continued alone to navigate the Ohio, which is here
exceedingly crooked.   The alluvial lands are extensive, with the hills low, and the rock, as usual, calcareous and filled with organic impressions.   I descended about 30 miles, and lodged with a very polite and
hospitable Frenchman, three miles above the Swiss
towns of Vevay and Ghent.   He informed me that he
had emigrated the last summer from Grenoble, and
had purchased land here at the rate of 10 dollars per
acre, including the house and improvements which
he occupied.   He complained how much he had been
deceived in his expectations, and that if he was home
again, and possessed of his present experience, he
would never have emigrated.   He did not give a very
favourable account of the settlement of Vevay, and he
and others, particularly a Swiss whom I called upon,
informed me that the wine here attempted to be made
was of an inferior quality.   It sold at 25 cents the
bottle, but soon became too sour to drink, and that
instead of obtaining the northern vines for cultivation,
as those around Paris, they had all along attended to
the southern varieties.   So the vineyards of Vevay, if
not better supported, will probably soon be transformed into corn-fields.   The wine which they have produced is chiefly claret, sometimes bordering on the
quality of Burgundy, for the preservation of which
their heated cabins, destitute of cellars, are not at all
adapted; we do not, however, perceive any obstacle
to the distillation of brandy, which could be disposed
of with great facility and profit.   The quantity of

5

wine said to be yielded to the acre, is about 500 gal.
lons, which, if saleable, ought to produce a considerable emolument, and materially benefit the country, by
diminishing the foreign demand. Several gentlemen
of science, wealth, and patriotism in Kentucky and
Mississippi Territory, are now also beginning to de-
vote their attention to this important and neglected
subject, and are commencing by the cultivation of
improved varieties of the native species of vine, which
promise, above those of Europe, every requisite of
fertility, hardihood, and improved flavour.

20th.] To-day I passed the rising town of Madison,
and the outlet of Kentucky river.—The sun was set-
ting when I arrived, and just served to disclose the
beauty of the surrounding scenery. On one side of
the river rose a lofty fascade of calcareous rocks, fretted like net-work; on the opposite extended the
low alluvial lands of Kentucky, thickly lined with an
almost unbroken rank of tall poplars, *(Populus angulisans,)* resembling a magnificent vista planted by
the hand of man.

21st.] Late in the evening I arrived at Bethlehem,
a miserable little hamlet in speculation, containing
about half a dozen houses.

22d.] To-day I came within 11 miles of Louisville,
and lodged with a hospitable and industrious Irishman,
who had emigrated from Belfast about 17 years ago.

23d.] At length I arrived at the large and flourishing
town of Louisville, but recently a wilderness. Labour
and provision rated here much above the value which
they commonly bore in the state and the surrounding
country. The markets were very negligently supplied,
and at prices little inferior to those of New Orleans.
In fact, the vortex of speculation, this commercial
gambling, absorbed the solid interests of the western
states, and destroyed all mercantile confidence. The
whole country was overrun with banks, which neither
deserved confidence nor credit. Not a note in Ken-

tucky commanded specie, the capital was altogether
fictitious, and ought to have been secured by every
species of property possessed by the stockholders.
A more ruinous and fraudulent system of exchange
was never devised in any Christian country; it is
truly a novelty to see a whole community, at least the
wealthy part of it, conspiring in a common system of
public fraud.

The love of luxury, without the means of obtaining it, has proved the bane of these still rude settlements of agriculturists, naturally poor in money by
reason of their remoteness from the emporium of commerce, and their neglect of manufactures. When
one heard a farmer demand a price for his produce in
Kentucky, equal nearly to that of Philadelphia, we
might be certain that he expected payment in depreciated paper.

A stranger who descends the Ohio at this season of
emigration, cannot but be struck with the jarring vortex of heterogeneous population amidst which he is
embarked, all searching for some better country,
which ever lies to the west, as Eden did to the east.
Amongst the crowd are also those, who, destitute of
the means or inclination of obtaining an honest livelihood, are forced into desperate means for subsistence.

In my descent from Pittsburgh to Louisville, I
found the wind, excepting about two days, constantly
blowing up the river. The north-west or south-west
winds, in fact, continue almost three quarters of the
year. The deep valley which the river has excavated
forms a vortex, into which the rarified air of the land
rushes for equilibrium. The south-west wind is uniformly, at this season of the year, attended with a
dense and bluish atmosphere, charged with vapours,
which appear like smoke, and sometimes accumulate
so as to obscure the land.

I was detained at Louisville until the 7th of December, trying various means of descending the river. The lowness of the water prevented the descent of the steam-boats, and the price of passage to Natchez was now no less than 50 dollars. Wearied by delay, I at length concluded to purchase a flat-boat, and freighted it nearly at my own cost, which, for an inexperienced traveller, was certainly an act of imprudence, as the destruction of the boat, which frequently happens, would probably have plunged me into penury and distress.

The wealth and population of Louisville are evidently on the increase, and a canal is now proposed, to obviate the difficulty of navigating by the Falls.

I perceive no material variation in the soil or river scenery. The surface is deeply undulated, fertile, and much sunk into circular depressions or water-swallows. The rock is all calcareous, but destitute of coal, or indeed any kind of overlaying stratum in this neighbourhood.

The Falls, at this stage of the water, roar in terrific grandeur; the descending surges resemble the foaming billows of the sea, and do not now admit the passage of vessels drawing more than 12 inches of water, though at other seasons there is a sufficiency for the largest boats on either side of the island which divides the falls. The calcareous ledge over which the water thus pours is nearly as horizontal as a floor, and filled with the reliquiæ of terebratulites, caryophillites, corallines, encrinites, &c. It also contains an unusual portion of pyrites, illinitions of blende ore of zinc, and a bluish green pulverulent substance, which is perhaps an ore of copper, or an oxide of nickel. Wood in a state of petrifaction has been discovered near the island which divides the cataract, and that in considerable quantity. The steam-boats, which ascend as far as Shippingsport, below the Falls, are of no less than 3 to 500 tons burthen, and are handsomely fitted up for the accommodation of passengers. Sometimes they descend to New Orleans in eight or ten days, affording a facility of communication heretofore unprecedented.

CHAPTER III.

Departure from Shippingsport—Velocity of the current—Troy—Owensville—Indigence of the hunting emigrants—Mounds—Evansville—The Diamond island—Shawneetown—Grandeur of the river and the uncultivated state of the surrounding country—Fort Massac—Arrival at the mouth of the Ohio—Delayed by the ice of the Mississippi--A visit from the Delaware and Shawnee Indians—Observations on their mutual jealousy and improvidence.

On the 7th, towards evening, I left Shippingsport in the flat-boat which I had purchased, accompanied by an elderly gentleman and his son, who intended to proceed to New Orleans. The river had now taken a sudden and favourable rise of eight or ten feet perpendicular. We floated all night, keeping an alternate watch, and before the expiration of 24 hours, on the 8th, the current alone had carried us without labour near 80 miles ! We accompanied another vessel of the same kind, and, for mutual convenience, our boats, according to custom, were lashed together side by side, thus also facilitating our progress by obtaining a greater scope of the current.

9th.] We continued at the same rate, floating along without any labour, except that of occasionally rowing out from the shore, or avoiding submerged trunks of trees, called snags or sawyers, as they are either stationary or moveable with the action of the current; by the French they are called *chicos*. In the night

we passed the town of *Troy*, an insignificant handful
of log-cabins, dignified by this venerable name ; here
we stopped a few moments to unload some salt, which,
in consequence of the scarcity, incident to the low
stage of water, sold at four dollars per bushel. Nearly
all the salt which supplies this country descends the
Kanhaway.

On the 10th we arrived at Owensville, more commonly called Yellow Banks, from the ochraceous
appearance of the argillaceous friable bank of the
river. This is another insignificant cluster of log-
cabins, and the seat of a county. Flour sold here at
10 dollars per barrel. In consequence of the want of
mills, they depend altogether on the upper country for
their supplies of this important article. Mills are
much wanted, and, in order even to obtain corn-meal,
every one has to invent something of the kind for
himself. At this place the store-keepers were busily
collecting pork for the market of New Orleans, at the
rate of five dollars per hundred, in exchange for dry-
goods and groceries. No other produce appeared in
this place. No orchards are yet planted, and apples
were worth one dollar and a half the bushel.

We floated as usual till towards midnight, but the
north-west wind arising, at length put a stop to our
progress. Having proceeded about 18 miles below
Owensville, we endeavoured to land on the Kentucky
side, but, in the attempt, ran an imminent risk of
grounding on an extensive bar; with considerable
labour we rowed our unmanageable flat to the opposite shore, where we found deep water, and a good
harbour from the wind.

11th.] About day-break we were accosted by a
back-woods neighbour, anxious for a dram of whiskey, which we had foreseen and provided for. We
were detained all day by the wind, and the hunters
went out in quest of turkeys. The improvidence of
these hunting farmers, is truly remarkable : annually

mortgaging their produce for the meanest luxuries of civilized life; still destitute of flour, of the produce of the orchard, of country spirits, and, indeed, of coffee and sugar for a great part of the year; at the same time, that they might become independent, with even moderate industry.

Potatoes are very indifferent in this country, but pulse and all kinds of grain excellent and productive.

Here, at Mountplace as it is called, there are two or three Indian mounds, upon one of which our visitor had built his house, and in digging had discovered abundance of human bones, as well as several stone pipes, and fragments of earthen ware.

12th.] About 9 o'clock, we pushed out and proceeded. Towards evening, 15 miles from Hendersonville, in Indiana, we passed a small town called Evansville, apparently a county seat, by the appearance of a court house. We continued to float through-out the night, which was very fine and moonlight, but cold, the thermometer being down at 20°. We passed Henderson in the night, and, about 5 o'clock in the morning of the 13th, came in sight of the large and beautiful broad island, called the Diamond, with the river, on either side of it, apparently a mile in breadth. At two intervals of 10 miles each, we had passed two other islands, and about one o'clock, found ourselves carried by good fortune, and at an easy rate, opposite to the Wabash and its island, which mark the commencement of the territory of Illinois.

From Owensville, cane begins to be tall and abundant. The prospect of an approaching storm caused us to come to shore at an early hour, where we remained for the night, having our boat tied to a stout branch or stem of the *Borya acuminata*,* which grows here in abundance, and is nearly as thorny as a

---

* Now *Forestiera acuminata*.

sloe bush, sending up many straight stems from the same root.

14th.] We rowed over to Shawneetown, a handful of log cabins, with some of them shingled, commanding an agreeable view of the river, but not situated beyond the reach of occasional inundation. I learned, on inquiry, that Mr. Birkbeck's settlement was not so unhealthy as had been reported, and that it was continually receiving accessions of foreigners. After floating some distance, we came up with three other flat boats, and lashing to them proceeded all night. The river is here very wide and magnificent, and checquered with many islands. The banks at Battery Rock, Rock in the Cave, and other places, are bold and rocky, with bordering cliffs. The occidental wilderness appears here to retain its primeval solitude ; its gloomy forests are yet unbroken by the hand of man, they are only penetrated by the wandering hunter, and the roaming savage.

15th and 16th.] Got down below fort Massac, and remained ashore most part of the night, being detained by the wind. On the night and morning of the 15th, the thermometer fell to 10°. In a cypress swamp, near to the shore, grew the *Gleditsia monosperma* and the *Cephalanthus*, with pubescent leaves and branchlets, which grows in Georgia and Louisiana, also the *Asclepias parviflora*.

17th.] Between 2 and 3 o'clock in the afternoon, we arrived at the mouth of the Ohio, and were considerably mortified on perceiving the Mississippi to be full of floating ice. Governed by the conduct of the boats which we had for three days accompanied, we came to on the Kentucky shore, and remained in company with several other boats, this and the whole of the following day.

The summit of the bank, at the foot of which we had landed, was surmounted by an almost impenetrable and sempervirent cane brake ; we measured seve-

ral canes upwards of 30 feet in height. These wilds
afford but little gratification to the botanist, their extreme darkness excluding the existence of nearly every
herbaceous plant. Among the trees, we still continue to observe the coffee-bean (*Gymnocladus canadensis*), now loaded with legumes, the seeds of which,
when parched, are agreeable to eat, but produce a
substitute for coffee greatly inferior to the *Cichorium*.

The whole country here, on both sides of the Mississippi and the Ohio, remains uninhabited in consequence of inundation, and abounds with various
kinds of game, but particularly deer and bear, turkeys, geese, and swans, with hosts of other aquatic
fowls; though, with the exception of the white peli-
can, they are such as commonly exist in many other
parts of the Union.

While amusing ourselves on the 17th, we were
visited by a couple of the Delaware Indians, and shortly after by a hunting party of Shawnees, who reside
some miles west of St. Louis. I invited one of them
into our cabin, and prevailed upon him to take sup-
per, with which he appeared to be well satisfied and
grateful. On the following day, a number of the
Shawnees came with our evening guest, and desired
to purchase gun-powder. They behaved with civility,
and almost refused to taste of spirits, but their reluct-
ance was at length overcome by some of our neighbours, and the night was passed at their camp with
yells and riot. Although the Delawares and Shawnees are proximately allied to each other, yet we perceive the existence of that jealousy among them,
which has ever been so fatal to the interest of the aborigines, from the conquest of Cortes to the present moment. The Delawares cautioned me against
the Shawnees, among whom they were continually
hunting, and stigmatized them as rogues; I found
them, however, all equally honest in their dealings, as
far as I had any intercourse with them; still the history

6

of the Shawnees, on many occasions, has long proved the truth of the character which is given of them by the Delawares. Scarcely any of the Indian tribes have migrated so often and so far, as the restless and intriguing Shawnees; who, since their first discovery on the banks of the Savannah, in Georgia, have, in the space of a century, successively migrated through the western states to the further bank of the Mississippi. Ever flying from the hateful circle of civilized society, which, probably in their own defence, they have repeatedly scourged, so as, indeed, to endanger their safety; averse to agriculture and systematic labour, they still depend upon the precarious bounty of the chase for their rude subsistence. Retreating into the forests of the western interior, according to their own acknowledgment destitute of lands, they are reduced to the misery of craving the favour of hunting ground from the Cherokees and Osages, excepting the uninhabitable wilds of the Mississippi, which, as in former times, still continue the common range of every tribe of native hunters.

These Indians possess the same symbolical or pantomimic language, as that which is employed by most of the nations with which I have become acquainted. It appears to be a compact invented by necessity, which gives that facility to communication denied to oral speech.

CHAPTER IV.

*Embark amidst the ice of the Mississippi—Run
aground on Wolf's island in attempting to land—
relieved from this situation--but find ourselves again
involved in it, and are imposed upon by the extor-
tion of a neighbouring voyager—Pass the Iron
banks—Cypress—Solitude of the country—New
Madrid—Oscillations of the earth still frequent—
Point Pleasant—Vestiges of the great earthquake
—The Little Prairie settlement almost destroyed
by it—The Canadian reach—A dangerous and difficult pass of the river—The first Chicasaw Bluffs
—Additional danger and uncertainty of the navigation—Stratification of the Bluff—A dangerous accident—The second Chicasaw Bluffs—Observations
on their stratification.*

19th.] This morning, after breakfast, our more
than usually timid neighbours and ourselves ventured
into the floating ice of the Mississippi, which we soon
found to be less formidable than we had imagined,
though still not without some danger of drifting im-
perceptibly or unavoidably upon some sunken tree, of
which there are no small abundance throughout the
bed of the Mississippi. Carried upon these by the
rapid current, our boats might be staved or entirely
overturned, accidents which not unfrequently happen
to those who give way to negligence or incaution.

About half an hour before sun-set, our company
came to alongside a breaking sand-bar, where lay
also two other boats; governed by their example we
attempted to land, but floated by the current to a distance below, and here, unfortunately, attempting to
make a landing, and trusting too confidently to the
lightness of our boat, we were instantly carried upon
a shallow and miry bar. I was sensible of the dilem-

ma into which we had fallen, and lost no time to plunge
into the water, though at the point of freezing, attempting, but in vain, to float off the boat by a lever.
The effort was beyond my strength, and after remaining in the water nearly an hour, I had reluctantly to
submit to our situation. At length, two boatmen offered their assistance, for the consideration of five
dollars, with which I complied, and in a few moments
we again floated. They took us in the dark about
100 yards further down, and there made a landing. I
still felt suspicious of our situation, notwithstanding
their assurances of safety: and at day-light, we
found ourselves (in consequence of the rapid falling of the river) as fast as ever grounded upon
the bar; to obviate which, all our strength and ingenuity availed nothing. The boatmen also, who had
assisted us the preceding night, and put us off our
guard by false assurances, now passed us with indif-
ference, and denied us the assistance which they had
promised. We immediately commenced unloading,
and had proceeded pretty far in our labour, when we
were visited by the owner of a neighbouring boat,
who, pretending to commiserate our situation, offered
to assist us gratuitously; and hearing how we had
been cheated out of five dollars, expressed his dis-
like at any boatmen having acted with such want of
fellow-feeling. We had scarcely time to breakfast,
before our yankees arrived with two skiffs; and one
of them now assured us that we should never be able
to get off until the rise of the river; though, as appeared in the sequel, merely with the friendly view of putting a good price upon his services. The other, instead of the gratuitous assistance which he had offered, made a tender of his services at three dollars. At
length, like genuine Arabs, they demanded the value
of eight dollars, with which I was reluctantly obliged
to comply. After about ten minutes further unloading, a lever placed under the bow, set us readily afloat

in one minute; so much had these kind gentlemen
deceived us, as to our real situation. They now also
refused to fulfil the bargain of assisting us to reload,
until brought to some sense of duty by remonstrance.—
I shall not indeed soon forget Wolf's island, and its
harbour of sharpers.

20th.] The day was far advanced when we got off,
and after floating 10 miles we moored for the night,
taking care to have deep water.

The land appears low and uninhabited on every side,
except at the Iron-banks (called Mine au Fer by the
French) we passed yesterday, and which are cliffs of
friable and argillaceous earth, the upper bed being ferruginous, beneath which occurs a very conspicuously-
coloured band of pink clay about 12 inches thick, and
below are white beds of the same material, improperly
considered chalk.

The cyprus (*Cupressus disticha*) which continues
some distance along the Ohio above its estuary, is
here much more common, and always indicates the
presence of annual inundation and consequent swamps
and lagoons, but we do not yet meet with the long
moss (*Tillandsia usneoides*), a plant so characteristic of
the prevalence of unhealthy humidity in the atmosphere.

21st.] We commenced our voyage at the dawn of
day, and continued to float along without interruption.
The river here appears truly magnificent, though generally bordered by the most gloomy solitudes, in
which there are now no visible traces of the abode of
man. It is indeed a sublime contrast to the busy hum
of a city, and not altogether destitute of interest. In
the course of the day we passed a number of capacious
islands, but all as they ever were from their creation,
and most of them even without names, the property
of any one who will assume the possession; but they
are in general, I suspect, annually submerged by inundation.

This evening we were 10 miles above New Madrid, and moored opposite to one of the islands which
had been convulsed by the earthquake of 1811.

22d.] We commenced our voyage early, and arrived before noon at New Madrid. We found both
sides of the river unusually lined with sunken logs,
some stationary and others in motion, and we narrowly avoided several of considerable magnitude.

New Madrid is an insignificant French hamlet, containing little more than about 20 log houses and stores
miserably supplied, the goods of which are retailed at
exorbitant prices: for example, 18 cents per pound
for lead, which costs seven cents at Herculaneum;
salt five dollars per bushel; sugar 31 1-4 cents per
pound; whiskey one dollar 25 cents per gallon; apples 25 cents per dozen; corn 50 cents per bushel;
fresh butter 37 1-2 cents per pound; eggs the same
per dozen; pork six dollars per hundred; beef five
dollars. Still the neighbouring land appears to be of
a good quality, but people have been discouraged from
settling in consequence of the earthquakes, which, besides the memorable one of 1811, are very frequently
experienced, two or three oscillations being sometimes
felt in a day. The United States, in order to compensate those who suffered in their property by the catas-
trophe, granted to the settlers an equivalent of land in
other parts of the Territory.

The site of the town, as we learn from La Vega,
the historian of Soto, bears unequivocal marks of an
aboriginal station; still presenting the remains of some
low mounds, which, as usual, abound with fragments
of earthen ware.*

23d.] We proceeded about six miles, and came to
at another small French hamlet called Point Pleasant.

---

* See the Appendix, and the account of De Sotos incursion.
In the immediate vicinity of the town I met with *Bæbera glandulosa,*
Erigeron (Cænotus) divaricatum, Verbena stricta, V. Aubletia, Croton
capitatum, and *Helenium quadridentatum.* On the banks of the river
Oxydenia attenuata and the *Capraria multifida* of Michaux.

Here I saw the Catalpa (*Catalpa cordifolia*) in the forests, apparently indigenous, for the first time in my life, though still contiguous to habitations.

This place and several islands below were greatly convulsed by the earthquake, and have in consequence been abandoned. I was shown a considerable chasm still far from being filled up, from whence the water of the river, as they say, rushed in an elevated column. The land is here of a superior quality, but flat, and no high grounds have made their appearance since we passed the Iron-Banks, no rock is any where to be seen; the banks of the river are deep and friable; islands and sand-bars, at this stage of the river connected with the land, are almost innumerable. In the midst of so much plenty provided by nature, the Canadian squatters* are here, as elsewhere, in miserable circumstances. They raise no wheat, and scarcely enough of maize for their support. Superfine flour sold here at 11 dollars per barrel.

The dresses of the men consist of blanket capeaus, buckskin pantaloons, and mockasins.

25th.] Christmas-day. We left Point Pleasant, and floated along without encountering any material obstacle, except glancing against an enormous moving log (or sawyer), which for the moment threw us into terror. Indeed the submerged trees become more and more numerous.

In the evening we arrived at the remains of the settlement called the Little Prairie, where there is now only a single house, all the rest, together with their foundations, having been swept away by the river, soon after the convulsion of the earthquake, in consequence (as the inhabitants say, and as they also affirm in New Madrid) of the land having sunk 10 feet or more below its former level.†

---

* Such as cultivate unappropriated land without any species of title.

† For a historical account of this country, once thickly inhabited by the natives, see the abridged relation of its discovery, and pretended conquest, by Ferdinand de Soto, in the APPENDIX.

26th.] After continuing about 10 miles below the
Little Prairie, we were detained for the remainder of
the day by the commencement of a storm, which towards evening increased to violence, and continued
so throughout the night. I felt under some apprehension that we should break our cable, and so be cast
away upon some of the many snags and sawyers
which obstruct the river.

27th.] Towards noon, the north-west wind mode-
rating, we continued as usual, and proceeded about
12 miles through a portion of the river filled with islands and trunks of trees. No habitations whatever
appeared since we left the Little Prairie.

28th.] Proceeded a few miles, to the head of the
25th island, as marked in the Pittsburgh Navigator,
and remained about four hours, waiting the abatement
of the wind, which did not permit us to proceed in
safety. Our company did not appear inclined to advance towards the Canadian reach until the following
morning; but not wishing to spend any time unneces-
sarily, we continued about five miles further.

29th.] Proceeding at day-break, we looked with
apprehension for the dangers described by the Navigator, but passed along with so little difficulty as almost to doubt our actual situation. A few miles below, however, we observed the river contracted within a narrow space by a spreading sand-bar (or island),
and planted almost across with large and dangerous
trunks, some with the tops, and others with the roots
uppermost, in a perpendicular posture. The water
broke upon them with a noise which I had heard distinctly for two miles, like the cascade of a mill-race,
in consequence of the velocity of the current; with
all our caution to avoid them, the boat grazed on one,
which was almost entirely submerged, and we received a terrific jar. All day we had experienced uninterrupted rain, but it was now pouring down in torrents. About two o'clock in the afternoon, as soon

as the fog had cleared away, we perceived ourselves again moving towards the field of danger. I counted, in the space of a minute, about 100 huge trees fixed in all postures, nearly across the whole river, so as scarcely to leave room for a passage. We proceeded towards a bank of willows on the Louisiana side, thinking to land for the night, in consequence of the unremitting and drenching rain, but found it impracticable, by reason of the rapid current. At length we descended to water which had the appearance of an eddy, and here I was strongly urged to land, in which attempt the boat would, in all probability, have been sunk amidst a host of snags and half-concealed trunks which lined the shore. With all our exertions in rowing off, we but narrowly escaped from being drawn into the impassable channel of a sand island which spread out into the river, presenting a portion of water resembling a sunken forest. The only course which we had left appeared no less a labyrinth of danger, so horribly filled with black and gigantic trunks of trees, along which the current foamed with terrific velocity—Scylla on one hand, and more than one Charybdis on the other. Fortunately, however, our voyage was not destined to end here, and, after an hour's drenching amidst torrents of rain, we at length obtained a landing place about 10 miles above the first Chicasaw Bluffs.* On the point of one of these bars at Flour island, we observed the wreck of two large flat boats which we supposed might have been lost during the earthquake. Nothing still appeared on every hand but houseless solitude, and gloomy silence, the inundation precluding the possibility of settlement.

30th.] We proceeded as soon as the dense fog this morning would permit, but could not ascertain our situation any longer by the vague trifling of the Navi-

---

* Called by the first French settlers the Cliffs of Prud'homme.

gator, and after proceeding some distance at the beck of the current, came in sight of Flour island. Here the Navigator says, "the channel is on the right side, but some prefer the left," but the very sight of the right-hand channel was to me sufficient, and finding the main body of the river carrying us to the left, I felt satisfied to go farther round rather than venture through such a horrid pass, which indeed resembled a submerged forest, and through which no flat boat, I should suppose, could ever proceed with safety, however deep might be the water. That we had got a passable channel to the left, I was fully satisfied on perceiving the intersection of the first Chicasaw Bluffs or hills, all the high lands of the Mississippi being uniformly washed at their base by a deep and rapid current. Here we landed for a few moments, to survey those hills, the only ones we had seen since leaving the Iron banks. The ascent was steep, and the elevation between 2 and 300 feet above the level of the river. These banks appeared to consist of a stratified, ferruginous, and bluish sandy clay, probably a disintegrated sandstone, which it perfectly resembled to the eye, though altogether friable to the touch. In some places, lower down the river, we observed masses of ferruginous conglomerate blackened by the atmosphere, the pebbles chiefly hornstone, and some of them quartz. The *debris* of which this conglomerate consists is entirely adventitious, or unconnected with the existing rocks, which form the basis of this ancient deposit.

At this place, we saw the first cabin since our departure from the Little Prairie. On approaching the 34th island from the mouth of the Ohio, which presents itself rounding, and nearly in the middle of the river, we had at first determined to take the left-hand side, set down by the Navigator as the channel, but finding ourselves to float very slowly, we rowed a little, and then submitted to the current. It was soon

observable, that we drifted towards the right-hand
channel, though much the narrowest, and my companion advised that we should keep the left, especially as it was the nearest, and as the wind accompanied
by rain blew strongly up the river. However, on
finding still that the current drew to the right, even
against the wind, and having arrived at the commencement of the bar of the island, I determined, at all
events, to keep to the right. At length, after considerable labour, we landed at a neighbouring cabin, and
were informed that the left channel had not in places
more than 12 inches of water, being nearly dry, and
almost destitute of current. Here, again, we made a
fortunate escape. We also learnt, that not more than
two days ago, a flat boat was sunk by the snags, which
filled the right-hand channel of Flour island.

At this place, we met with two or three families of
hunters, with whom were living some individuals of
the Shawnees and Delawares. They had lately caught
an unusual abundance of beaver in the neighbourhood, and were anxious to barter it for whiskey,
though scarcely possessed either of bread or vegetables. Amongst their furs, I also saw a few skins of
the musk-rat, (*Arctomys monax*, L.) which are never
met with further to the south.

31st.] We continued our voyage as usual at day-
light, and floating with a brisk current down the right
side of the 34th island, had nearly cleared ourselves of
a host of snags and sawyers, when at last, puzzled on
which side of one of these terrific objects to steer, we
unfortunately struck it with considerable force, and
the young man who accompanied us (the son of Mr.
G.), an amiable youth of 16, was precipitated headlong into the river, together with the steering oar,
which was suddenly jerked off by the snag; our boat
was at the same instant careened over so far, as at first
to appear overturning, but I instantly had the satisfaction to see that she was free, had received no

injury, and that Edwin on this emergency could swim, and, though much alarmed, had come within our reach, and got safely on board. As to our steering oar it remained across the snag, and was now become a sawyer; working horizontally upon the back of the black and fearful trunk which had so justly thrown us into consternation.

The wind springing up against us, we came to under the second Chicasaw Bluff, and had time to examine and contemplate these romantic cliffs, now doubly interesting after such a monotonous and cheerless prospect of solitary brakes and enswamped forests. This fasçade, or perpendicular section, precisely of the same materials and consistence as that of the Iron banks above, continues, I think, uninterruptedly for near two miles, and is about 150 feet high. The uppermost bed (all of them as nearly horizontal as may be), 12 to 20 feet thick, commencing immediately below the present vegetable loam, consists of a yellowish, homogeneous, now friable, sandy, and argillaceous earth, which is succeeded by a thinner and more ferruginous bed; below occurs a layer or band of *pink*-red clay, now and then variegated with white specks, and, though constant in its appearance and relative position, no where exceeding 18 inches in thickness; below again occur ferruginous earths and clays more or less sandy, then a bed of a brownish-black colour, and about 18 inches in thickness, which, on examination, I found to be lignite, or wood-coal, containing less bitumen than usual, and so distinctly derived from the vegetable kingdom, exhibiting even the cross grain of the wood, as to remove all doubts of its origin. To the taste it was sensibly acid, and smelt in burning like turf. Beneath this coal, and in connection with it, occurs a friable bed of dark-coloured argillaceous and sandy earth, in which I could very distinctly perceive blackened impressions of leaves of an oak, like the red oak and the willow oak, with

Equisetum hiemale or Shave-rush, and other vegetable remains, not much unlike the black beds of leaves which occur along the banks of the Ohio, but much more intermingled with earth. In this bed also occur masses or nodules of a hard and very fine-grained light gray sandstone, bordering almost upon hornstone, likewise charged with vegetable remains, resembling charred wood, together with leaves of oaks and of other forest trees. Nearly on a level with the present low stage of the river, there was a second bed of this coal, more interrupted than the first in its continuity, though constant in its locality, no less in some places (like basins) than 8, 12 or 15 feet in thickness. Below, clays again succeeded, and terminated the visible stratification.

In two or three places, I observed that the mud, which was very deep, had been boiling up into circular masses like fumeroles, and have no doubt, but that the decomposition of this vast bed of lignite or wood-coal, situated near the level of the river, and filled with pyrites, has been the active agent in producing the earthquakes, which have of late years agitated this country. The deposition of vast rafts of timber, thus accidentally brought together by the floods of the river, are continually, even before our eyes, as I may say, accumulating stores of matter, which, in after ages, will, no doubt, exert a baneful influence over the devoted soil, beneath which they are silently interred! How much has the vegetable kingdom to do with the destiny of man! The time, though slowly, is perhaps surely approaching, which will witness something like volcanic eruptions on the banks of the Mississippi. The inhabitants frequently, and almost daily, experience slight oscillations of the earth: I have even witnessed them myself, while descending the river.

CHAPTER V.

Pass the third Chicasaw Bluff—Dangers of the navigation, and solitude of the country—The fourth Bluff of the Chicasaws—Lignite prevalent—Chicasaw Indians—St. Francis river—depopulation of the neighbouring country—Trees of the alluvial forest—Destruction of the Big Prairie settlement—Scrub-grass—Difficulties of the navigation—Changes of the soil, produced by the agency of the river—A visit from three of the Arkansa Indians—A dense fog over the river; the cause of it—Arrival near the mouth of the Arkansa and White river.

January 1st, 1819.] We proceeded slowly, in consequence of adverse wind; and, at length, came in sight of the third Chicasaw Bluff, quite similar in appearance and conformation with that of the second above described. The 35th island of the Navigator intervened betwixt us and the cliff, there being no water to the left of it; the channel at this stage of the river, was completely choked up by a bed of sand.

We came to for the night on a sand-bar, opposite the centre of the island, resembling an Arabian desert, and scattered in every direction with lignite or bovey coal, washed probably from the basis of the Bluffs. The shore of the island was horribly strewed with the wreck of the alluvial forest, brought down by the overwhelming current of the river at its highest stage, and thrown confusedly together in vast piles.

In the course of the day, we stopped awhile at a Shawnee camp, and bartered for some venison and wild honey, which they had in plenty. The honey, according to the Indian mode, was contained in the skin of a deer taken off by the aperture of the neck, thus answering, though very rudely, the purpose of a bottle.

On the 2d, we passed the " Devil's Race-ground," as it has been very formidably termed, but observed no obstructions in the river equal to that at Plumb point, where we saw the wrecked boats. We observe, however, every day, wrecks of flat boats, drifted along the shores. We continued to the lower end of the "Devil's Elbow," and again found the difficulty greatly exaggerated. The whole surrounding coun- try still continues a desolate wilderness, abandoned to inundation, presenting impenetrable cane brakes and gloomy forests : none of the trees, however, attain that enormous magnitude, which they so frequently present along the borders of the Ohio. This appear- ance may perhaps be attributed, in part, to the per- petual revolutions of the soil, occasioned by the over- whelming force and inundations of the river.

A dog lost in the forest, and perishing with hunger, came up to the bank of the river, yelling most pite- ously ; but would not enter our skiff, which was sent for it, and continued to follow us for some distance, but the danger of the shore, and the rapidity of the current, rendered our endeavours to assist the misera- ble animal perfectly useless, and, after some time, he fell back, stopped and yelled, till he reluctantly disap- peared.

3d.] We proceeded only a few miles in conse- quence of the wind, and came to at the point of a sand-bar, seven miles above the fourth Bluffs. Here we observed a flat-boat lying aground, and dry upon the bar, for want of precaution in landing during the falling state of the river.

4th.] This morning we descended to the fourth Chicasaw Bluffs, and, after endeavouring in vain to proceed, were obliged to desist for the wind, and come to under fort Pickering. The strata are here again similar to those of the second Bluffs, even the seam of pink clay occurs, and near the level of the river we likewise perceive the lignite in a béd of about six feet thickness ; but not probably continuous. Along the shore we saw masses which looked precisely like burnt logs, but all this coal, at length, blazes in the fire, and gives out, as usual, a smoke partaking of the odour of coal and turf.

We found a store here for the supply of the Indians and the settlers of the neighbourhood, besides that of the United States. The advance upon articles sold to the natives is very exorbitant : for example, a coarse Indian duffell blanket four dollars, whiskey, well watered, which is sold almost without restraint, in spite of the law, two dollars per gallon, and every thing else in the same proportion. Yet the Indians get no more than 25 cents for a ham of venison, a goose, or a large turkey.

On visiting a neighbouring encampment of the Chicasaws, we found many of them in a state of intoxication. They are generally well dressed, extravagantly ornamented, and, from the fairness of many of their complexions, and agreeable features, appear to have profited by their intercourse with the whites. Several of them possessed some knowledge of English, and a considerable number are making advances towards civilization. General Jackson purchased from them a tract of land, said to be of more than 300 miles extent, and bounded by Wolf river, a small stream which enters the Mississippi at the commencement of the Bluffs. On the river lands I here first noticed the occurrence of *Brunichia, Quercus lyrata,* and *Carya aquatica (Juglans,* MICH.)

On the 5th we passed President island, of considerable magnitude, contiguous to which there is a rapid current. The left channel was now choked up with sand at its entrance. Here we again observed a settlement of two or three families. In the evening we came to alongside a sand-bar or willow island, at least so in high water, though now connected with the land by a dry sand-bar, like many other of the transient islands noticed in the Navigator. We, at length, began to observe a rise in the bed of the river.

6th.] To-day we saw a few widely-scattered log-cabins along the bank, and came within 14 miles of the mouth of St. Francis.

7th.] We proceeded by the left channel of St. Francis island, and found it very shallow and difficult, abounding with snags and bars, upon one of which lay a flat-boat aground, which had been detained here 12 days. We endeavoured to make a landing at the uppermost house of the settlement, near the mouth of the St. Francis, but found the water much too rapid ; we succeeded, however, in eddy water half a mile below, but found a considerable difficulty in ascending the broken bank.

I made some enquiries respecting the Arkansa, 95 miles from hence. The Osages bear a very bad character with these hunting farmers, of whom we saw but two individuals, and one inhabited house, excepting that we had first endeavoured to make. This settlement appears to be nearly abandoned, and very undeservedly. I walked out two or three miles into the woods, and found the land considerably elevated above the reach of inundation, and of a good quality. Nearly opposite island 60, a few miles below, we were informed of the existence of hills within a quarter of a mile of the river.

How many ages may yet elapse before these luxuriant wilds of the Mississippi can enumerate a population equal to the Tartarian deserts! At present all is irksome silence and gloomy solitude, such as to inspire the mind with horror.

I was greatly disappointed to meet with such a similarity in the vegetation, to that of the middle and northern states. The higher lands produce black ash, elm *(Ulmus americana)*, hickory, walnut, maple,

8

hackberry (*Celtis integrifolia*, no other species), honey-locust, coffee-bean, &c. On the river lands, as usual, grows platanus or buttonwood, upon the seeds of which flocks of screaming parrots were greedily feeding,* also enormous cotton-wood trees (*Populus angulisans*), commonly called yellow poplar, some of them more than six feet in diameter, and occasionally festooned with the largest vines which I had ever beheld. Here grew also the holly (*Ilex opaca*), *Aplectrum hiemale*, (*Ophrys hyemale*, Lin.), *Botrychium obliquum*, and *Fumaria aurea*. Nearly all the trees throughout this country possessing a smooth bark, are loaded with misletoe (*Viscum verticillatum*).

8th.] About a mile below the place where we spent the last night, is the settlement called the Big Prairie, consisting of three or four log-cabins, and two families, but in a state of abandonment since the shock of the earthquake, which the inhabitants assert to have produced a depression of the ordinary level, that exposed the settlement to inundation ; and, in fact, by a sudden encroachment of the river, which carried off the land for more than a quarter of a mile in breadth, all the habitations, except the two now surviving, were swept into the river. About a mile and a half below commences the 60th island of the Navigator ; the right channel was now choked up with sand at its outlet. A little distance below we landed at a store to purchase some necessaries. Considerable tracts of good and elevated land, once numerously peopled by the natives, appear in this quarter, over which the conspicuous devastations of a hurricane now added horror to solitude.

The scrub-grass or rushes, as they are called here (*Equisetum hiemale*), from about 50 to 60 miles above, to this place, appear along the banks in vast fields, and, together with the cane, which is evergreen,

---

* Their most favourite food in the autumn is the seeds of the cuckold bur (*Xan'hium strumarium*).

are considered the most important, and, indeed, the only winter fodder for all kinds of cattle. The cane is unquestionably saccharine and nutritious, but the scrub-grass produces an unfavourable action on the stomach, and scours the cattle so as to debilitate and destroy them if its use be long continued.

We proceeded, without any accident worthy of re-mark, about six miles, below the " Little Round island," noticed in the Navigator, which from its un-common aspect affords a pretty good local object for the boatman. While passing the island we were ac-costed by some, to us, suspicious characters, mimick-ing distress to draw us to land, but in vain. We had been well assured of the existence of gangs of pirates occasionally occupying these solitudes.

9th.] We continued, as usual, soon after day-break, and were about to stop by reason of the wind, when it unexpectedly abated, so far as to prevent us, and we proceeded to the *Three Islands*, as they ought to be called for the sake of distinction, and which are not intelligible as the 62d and 63d of the Navigator. These islands lie nearly parallel, and present them-selves at the commencement of a left hand bend in the river. Two of them which first appear are small wil-low islands, with adjoining sand-bars. The channel of the first was now dry ; that of the second smooth, but apparently shallow. The principal insulated forest is crescent-formed like Flour island, or deeply and circularly indented on the right-hand side. We had proceeded past the two willow islands nearly to the principal one, when we perceived, unexpectedly, that the greater part of the river was pouring along with headlong velocity between the main and second wil-low island. To the left, the channel round the third island appeared broad and shallow, indeed nearly de-serted by the river. We now entered the torrent al-most too late for precaution, which, towards the main island, the side to which we had been inadvertently drawn, was planted full of black and fearful logs. It was only with the utmost exertion that we saved ourselves (by rowing out towards the bar) from the fate of some unfortunate boatmen, which presented itself to us with more than usual horror. This was a large flat-boat, which hung upon the trunk of an implanted tree, by which it had been perforated and instantly sunk.

We passed islands 64 and 65, and came to the shore in the bend opposite the middle of 66, which appeared to be about three miles in length. From New Madrid to this place the river appears singularly meandering, sweeping along in vast elliptic curves, some of them from six to eight miles round, and constantly presenting themselves in opposite directions. The principal current pressing against the centre of the bend, at the rate of about five miles per hour, gradually diminishes in force as it approaches the extremity of the curve. Having attained the point or promontory, the current proceeds with accumulating velocity to the opposite bank, leaving, consequently, to the eddy water, an extensive deposition in the form of a vast bed of sand, nearly destitute of vegetation, but flanked commonly by an island or peninsula of willows. These beds of sand, for the most part of the year under water, are what the boatmen term bars. The river, as it sweeps along the curve, according to its force and magnitude, produces excavations in the banks ; which, consisting of friable materials, are perpetually washing away and leaving broken and perpendicular ledges, often lined with fallen trees, so as to be very dangerous to the approach of boats, which would be dashed to pieces by the velocity of the current. These slips in the banks are almost perpetual, and by the undermining of eddies often remarkable in their extent. To-day we witnessed two horrid sinkings of the bank, by each of which not less than an acre of land had fallen in a day or two

ago, with all the trees and cane upon them, down to
the present level of the river, a depth of 30 or 40 feet
perpendicular. These masses now formed projecting
points, upon which the floating drift was arrested, and
over which the current broke along with more than
ordinary velocity. Just after passing one of these
foaming drifts, we narrowly escaped being drawn into
a corresponding eddy and vortex that rushed up the
stream, with a fearful violence, and from which we
should not have been easily extricated. I now sufficiently saw the reason why the flat-boats were always
kept out from the shore, and towards the bars which
occupy the opposite side of the river.

The encroachments in the centre of the curves of
the meanders, proceeding to a certain extent, at
length break through and form islands, in time the
islands also disappear, and so the river continually augmenting its uncontroulable dominion over the friable
soil, alternately fills up one channel, and more deeply
excavates or forms another, in proportion to the caprice of the current.

In regard to landing, eddy or silent water is constantly to be found beyond the point of the bends or
curves of the river. The bars are also generally safe,
when sufficiently high, and the water deep. In such
situations, the counter current, though inconsiderable,
affords also a singular facility to vessels which are ascending.

A rude cabin, which we passed to-day, was the
only habitation we had seen for 30 miles.

This evening we were visited by three young men,
a boy, and a squaw of the Osarks, a band of the
Quapaws or Arkansa Indians. Their aspect was
agreeable, their features aquiline, and their complexion comparatively fair; my first impression was that
they somewhat resembled the Osages. Their errand
was whiskey, and I regretted that it was not possible
to satisfy them without it. They drank healths in

their own language, and one of them could mumble out a little bad English. They informed me, partly by signs, that their company was about five or six families or fires, as they intimated, out on a hunting excursion. I was sorry to find that they were beggars, and that one of them proved himself to be a thief.

10th.] This morning we left the 66th island, opposite the middle of which we came to last evening, but found our situation hazardous from the sliding in of the bank around, and which might easily have involved us in difficulty. By the time we had proceeded about a mile and a half along the bend or right hand channel of 67 and 68, which lie opposite to each other, a fog sprung up, so very dense as to render our situation amidst almost unseen obstacles extremely dangerous. We had no alternative but rowing over to the bar of the island on our left, in which attempt we at length succeeded, not, however, without a risk of grounding. Here we lay until towards evening, when we proceeded to the termination of the 68th island, and made an indifferent landing. On exposing the thermometer to the air, it rose and remained at 62°. In the water it fell to 42°; the difference being 20°, which readily accounted for the dense fog that exclusively enveloped the river. This coldness of the water was no doubt occasioned by the thawing of ice in the upper part of the river, or some of its more considerable tributary streams, in consequence of which, the vapours of the moist and warm air were perpetually precipitated over it. The air, of unequal temperature, now and then felt extremely warm.

On the 11th we were again detained by the fog and heavy rain, but turned out about 10 o'clock. After proceeding opposite the commencement of the 69th island we stopped in consequence of the fog. Here, on ascending the bank, I found the woods almost impenetrably laced with green briars (*Smilax*), supple-jacks *(Œnoplia volubilis)*, and the *Brunichia,* and for the first time recognised the short-podded honey-locust *(Gleditscia brachycarpa)*, a distinct species, intermediate with the common kind *(G. triacanthos)*, and the one-seeded locust *(G. monosperma)*, differing from *G. triacanthos* in the persisting fasciculated legumes, as well as in their shortness and want of pulp.

We proceeded a few miles further amidst torrents of rain, and were again obliged to land in consequence of the fog. Here we met with two hunters, who informed us of the existence of a considerable settlement on the banks of White River.

The wind springing up in the evening from the north-west, the thermometer fell to 52°, and the water to 40°, from which time the dense fog that had exclusively enveloped the river began to disperse, and in the night we had a storm.

12th.] Coming along the bend of the 71st island, we struck upon an enormous planter, or immoveable log, but again escaped without accident. About noon we landed at Mr. M'Lane's, a house of entertainment. Here I was advised to proceed with my small cargo and flat-boat to the port of Osark, on the Arkansa, by the bayou, which communicates between the White and Arkansa rivers, in both of which it was now conjectured there was back-water from the Mississippi. Concluding upon this measure, I hired a man at five dollars to assist me, and parted here with Mr. G—— and son, who soon, to my satisfaction, got a further passage on board a flat-boat. The idea of so soon arriving on the ground which I more immediately intended to explore, did not fail to inspire me with hope and satisfaction.

CHAPTER VI.

*Proceed up White river for the Arkansa—Suspicious
conduct of one of the boatmen—Pass through the
connecting bayou, and proceed up the Arkansa;
its navigation; soil and surrounding scenery—A
small French settlement—Extraordinary mildness
of the season—Mounds—Changes in the alluvial
lands produced by the agency of the river—Land
speculators—Vegetation of the alluvial lands—The
town or Post of Arkansas—Enormous land claims
—Difficulty of navigating against the current—
The Great Prairie—First settlement on the Arkansa; its present state—Agricultural advantages
arising from the mildness of the climate—Storax—
Aboriginal remains—The Quapaws or Arkansas—
Their traditions and character.*

13th.] To-day I was detained at Mr. M'Lane's,
waiting the drunken whim of the Yankee, whom necessity had obliged me to hire.   In the course of a
few hours he had shifted from two bargains.   At first,
I was to give him five dollars for his assistance, and
in case that should prove inadequate, I had agreed to
hire an additional hand on the Arkansa.   Now he
wished to have the boat for bringing her completely
to the Port, and next he wanted 10 dollars!

I endeavoured to amuse myself in the neighbourhood, by a ramble through the adjoining cane-brake.
Here I found abundance of the *Celtis integrifolia* (en-
tire-leaved nettle tree) and the common and one-seeded honey-locust; also *Forrestiera acuminata* of Poi-
ret *(Borya acuminata*, WILD.).   The day was as
mild and warm as the month of May, and the *Senecio
laciniata*, so common along the banks of the Mississippi, already showed signs of flowering.

14th.] To-day we proceeded up White river with

considerable difficulty, and hard labour, the Mississippi not being sufficiently high to produce any eddy. The course which we made, in the two miles that we ascended, was west by north. I now found the boatman whom I had hired, one of the most worthless and drunken scoundrels imaginable; he could not be prevailed upon to do any thing but steer, while myself and the other man I had hired, were obliged to keep constantly to the oar, or the cordelle (tow-rope). In the evening we left the boat without any guard, intending to repair to it in the morning from Mr. M'Lane's, where we returned again this evening, being only three miles distant across the forest. Here I discovered that the Yankee intended to proceed to the boat in our absence and rob me, pretending some business to the mouth of the Arkansa, for which he must depart by moon-light. Unknown to him, however, and accompanied by a young man whom I had hired in his place, we repaired to the boat, waiting under arms the approach of the thief, but unable to obtain a boat, he had relinquished the attempt, and saved himself from chastisement.

In the neighbouring woods I was shewn a scandent leguminous shrub, so extremely tenacious as to afford a good substitute for ropes, and commonly employed as a boat's cable. A knot can be tied of it with ease. On examination I found it to be the plant which I have called *Wisteria speciosa* (*Glycine frutescens*. WILLD.) the Carolina kidney-bean tree.*

15th.] We continued with hard labour ascending White river to the bayou, said to enter seven miles up that stream. The latter proceeds from the bayou, in a direction of west to north-west, the bayou or cut-off continuing to the south-west. In this distance, there are no settlements, the land being overflowed by the back water of the Mississippi. We passed nearly

---

* The name of *Thyrsanthus*, given by Mr. Elliott, has been already employed for another genus.

through the bayou, in which there are four points of land and a half; the current carrying us almost three miles an hour towards the Arkansa, which it entered nearly at right angles, with a rapid current, and a channel filled with snags. The length of the bayou appears to be about eight or nine miles.

16th.] Leaving the bayou, we entered the Arkansa, which was very low, but still red and muddy from the freshets of the Canadian. Most of the larger streams which enter into it from the south, are charged with red and turbid water, while those of the north are clear. Every where I observed the chocolate or reddish brown clay of the salt formation, deposited by the southern freshets. The Arkansa had here a very gentle current, and was scarcely more than 200 yards wide, with its meanders, on a small scale, similar to those of the Mississippi. In consequence of the unrestrained dominion of the inundation, no settlements yet appeared in this quarter. We proceeded chiefly by means of the cordelle, but at a very tedious and tiresome rate, for, after the utmost exertion, with our unwieldly boat, we were this evening only six and a half miles above the outlet of the bayou.

17th.] We found the labour of towing our boat exceedingly tiresome, in consequence of the sudden falling of the river, produced by a corresponding ebb of the Mississippi. With painful exertions, and after wading more than three hours in the river, we passed only two bars in the course of the day.

18th.] To-day we towed along two bars, much more considerable than any preceding bends, but had the disappointment to spend the night only a single mile below Madame Gordon's, the place of our destination with the boat, and only 16 miles above the bayou, by which we entered the Arkansa. This house is the first which is met with in ascending the river. Nearly opposite to the foot of the last bar but one which we passed, a vast pile of drift wood marks the outlet of a bayou, which is open in high water, and communicates with the Mississippi.

The three last bends of the river, like the four first, tending by half circles to the north-west, are each about two and three miles in circuit. As in the Mississippi, the current sets with the greatest force against the centre of the curves; the banks of which are nearly perpendicular, and subject to a perpetual state of dislocation. In such situations we frequently see brakes of cane; while, on the opposite side, a naked beach of sand, thinly strewed with succulent and maritime plants, considerably wider than the river, appears to imitate the aridity of a desert, though contrasted at a little distance by skirting groves of willows and poplars.

No other kind of soil appears than a friable loam, and the beds of red clay, which so strongly tinge the water at particular periods of inundation. The sand of the river appears to be in perpetual motion, drifting along at the beck of the current; its instability is indeed often dangerous to the cattle that happen to venture into the river, either to drink or traverse the stream.

The land, although neglected, appears in several places, below Madame Gordon's, high enough to be susceptible of cultivation, and secure from inundation, at least for some distance from the immediate bank of the river.

No change, that I can remark, yet exists in the vegetation, and the scenery is almost destitute of every thing which is agreeable to human nature; nothing yet appears but one vast trackless wilderness of trees, a dead solemnity, where the human voice is never heard to echo, where not even ruins of the humblest kind recal its history to mind, or prove the past dominion of man. All is rude nature as it sprang into

existence, still preserving its primeval type, its unre-
claimed exuberance.

19th.] This morning we had extremely hard labour, to tow the only mile which remained of our
tiresome voyage. I was obliged to plunge into the
water up to the waist, and there work for some time,
to disengage the boat from a hidden log upon which
it was held; the men I had employed, being this
morning scarcely willing to wet their feet, although I
had to pay them exorbitant wages.

A mile and a half from Madame Gordon's, there
was a settlement, consisting of four or five French
families, situated upon an elevated tract of fertile land,
which is occasionally insulated by the overflowings
of the White and Arkansa rivers.

20th] To-day, and indeed for more than a week
past, the weather, except being cloudy, has felt to me
like May ; towards mid-day, the thermometer rose to
67°. The birds had commenced their melodies ; and
on the high and open bank of the river near to Madame Gordon's, I had already the gratification of finding flowers of the same natural family as many of the
early plants of Europe ; the Cruciferæ ; but to me
they were doubly interesting, as the first fruits of a harvest never before reaped by any botanist.

In the afternoon, I walked about a mile from the
river to the house of Monsieur Tenass, an honest and
industrious farmer. The crop of cotton, and of corn,
here the last summer was, I understand, very indifferent, for want of rain. The first sold here, at five
to six dollars per hundred weight, in the seed ; and
flour at 10 dollars per barrel.

The climate, is said to be too warm for apples, but
quite suitable for peaches. The land on which this
gentleman and his neighbours resided, in tolerable independence, is very considerably elevated and open,
bearing a resemblance to the lands about the Chica-

saw Bluffs, and at first view, I thought I discovered
a considerable hill, but it was, in fact, an enormous
mound, not less than 40 feet high, situated towards
the centre of a circle of other lesser mounds, and elevated platforms of earth. The usual vestiges of earth-
enware, and weapons of hornstone flint, are here also
met with, scattered over the surrounding soil.

In any other direction from this settlement, the
lands are totally overflowed in freshets as far as the
Mississippi. On this side of the Arkansa, the floods
cover the whole intermediate space to White river, a
distance of 30 miles. Within this tract, cultivation
can never take place without recourse to the same industry, which has redeemed Holland from the ocean.
The singular caprice of the river, as it accidentally
seeks its way to the sea, meandering through its
alluvial valley, is truly remarkable. The variation of
its channel is almost incredible, and the action which
it exercises over the destiny of the soil, can scarcely
be conceived. After pursuing a given course for
many ages, and slowly encroaching, it has, at length,
in many instances cut through an isthmus, and thus
abandoned perhaps a course of six or eight miles, in
which the water stagnating, at length becomes totally
insulated, and thus presents a lagoon or lake. One of
these insulated channels, termed a lake, commences
about two miles from hence, and approaches within
four miles of the Arkansas or the Post of Osark, affording a much nearer communication than the present course of the river.

Towards evening, two keel boats came in sight,
one of which was deeply loaded with whiskey and
flour ; the other, a small boat fitted out by a general
Calamees and his brother, two elderly men out on a land
speculation, who intended to ascend the river as far as
the Cadron, which is 300 miles from hence by water,
or to the Fort, which is 350 miles further. I perceived that they noted down every particular which

came to their knowledge, but appeared to be illiterate men, and of course, I found them incapable of appreciating the value of science. On application, they merely condescended to offer me a passage, provided I would find my own provision, and work as a boatman. Such was the encouragement, which I at length wrung from these generous speculators; not, I dare say, exploring the Missouri territory with the same philanthropic views as the generous Birkbeck.

21st.] About 12 o'clock, the thermometer was again at 67°. In the course of the forenoon, I took a solitary ramble down the bank of the river, and found along its shelving border, where the sun obtained free access, abundance of the *Mimosa glandulosa* of Michaux; also *Polypremum procumbens, Diodia virginica, Verbena nodiflora,* Lin. *Eclipta erecta,* Mich. *Poa stricta, Panicum capillaceum, Poa reptans* as usual in vast profusion, and *Capraria multifida.* The trees and shrubs are chiefly the Pecan, *(Carya olivæformis) C. aquatica;* the black walnut, *(Juglans nigra),* but very rare; *Fraxinus quadrangulata, Liquidamber* and *Platanus,* but rarely large or full grown; also *Celtis integrifolia;* the swamp oak *(Quercus aquatica),* nearly sempervirent, the red oak *(Q. rubra),* the scarlet oak *(Q. coccinea),* Spanish oak *(Q. falcata); Populus angulisans,* the cotton wood, of greater magnitude than any other tree in this country, with the wood yellowish, like that of the Tulip tree, answering the purpose of fence rails, and being tolerably durable. The smaller white poplar *(P. monilifera),* never so large as the preceding, commonly growing in groves like the willows, and presenting a bark which is white and even. Different kinds of honey locust, as the common species *Gleditscia triacanthos,* the one-seeded *G. monosperma,* and the short podded *G. brachyloba.* There is no sugar-maple, as I understand, nearer than the upper parts of the St. Francis and White river.

The alluvial soil is here sandy and light; by no means luxuriant, except on the very margin of the river. We no where see such enormous trees as those which so frequently occur along the banks of the Ohio; this, however, may in part be occasioned by the instability of the soil, from whence they are occasionally swept at no very distant intervals. The tulip tree *(Lyriodendron tulipifera)*, which attains the acme of its perfection and magnitude in Kentucky, is not met with on the banks of the Arkansa.

In consequence of the many saline streams which fall into this river, its waters are frequently found to be almost impotable.

22d.] The path, which I this morning pursued to the Post, now town of Arkansas, passed through remarkably contrasted situations and soil. After leaving the small circumscribed and elevated portion of settled lands already noticed, and over which were scattered a number of aboriginal mounds, I entered upon an oak swamp, which, by the marks on the trees, appeared to be usually inundated, in the course of the summer, four to six feet by the back water of the river. The species are principally *Quercus lyrata, Q. macrocarpa* (the over-cup oak) ; *Q. phellos* (the willow oak); *Q. falcata* (the Spanish oak) ; and *Q. palustris* (the swamp oak) ; with some red and scarlet, as well as black and post oak on the knolls, or more elevated parts. In this swamp, I also observed the *Nyssa aquatica, N. pubescens* (Ogechee lime, the fruit being prepared as a conserve), as well as *N. biflora,* and *Gleditscia monosperma.* After crossing this horrid morass, a delightful tract of high ground again occurs, over which the floods had never yet prevailed ; here the fields of the French settlers were already of a vivid green, and the birds were singing from every bush, more particularly the red bird *(Loxia cardinalis)*, and the blue sparrow *(Motacilla sialis)*. The ground appeared perfectly whitened with the *Alyssum bidentatum.* The *Viola bicolor,* the *My-osurus minimus* of Europe, (probably introduced by the French settlers) and the *Houstonia serpyllifolia* of Michaux, (*H. patens* of Mr. Elliott) with bright blue flowers, were also already in bloom. After emerging out of the swamp, in which I found it necessary to wade about ankle deep, a prairie came in view, with scattering houses spreading over a narrow and elevated tract for about three miles parallel to the bend of the river.

On arriving, I waited on Monsieur Bougie, one of the earliest settlers and principal inhabitants of the place, to whom I was introduced by letter. I soon found in him a gentleman, though disguised at this time in the garb of a Canadian boatman. He treated me with great politeness and respect, and, from the first interview, appeared to take a generous and active interest in my favour. Monsieur B. was by birth a Canadian, and, though 70 years of age, possessed almost the vigour and agility of youth. This settlement owes much to his enterprise and industry.

The town, or rather settlement of the Post of Arkansas, was somewhat dispersed over a prairie, nearly as elevated as that of the Chicasaw Bluffs, and containing in all between 30 and 40 houses. The merchants, then transacting nearly all the business of the Arkansa and White river, were Messrs. Braham and Drope, Mr. Lewis, and Monsieur Notrebe, who kept well-assorted stores of merchandize, supplied chiefly from New Orleans, with the exception of some heavy articles of domestic manufacture obtained from Pittsburgh. Mr. Drope, to whom I was also introduced by letter, received me with politeness, and I could not but now for awhile consider myself as once more introduced into the circle of civilization.

The improvement and settlement of this place proceeded slowly, owing, in some measure, as I am informed, to the uncertain titles of the neighbouring

lands. Several enormous Spanish grants remained
still undecided ; that of Messrs. Winters, of Natchez,
called for no less than one million of acres, but the
congress of the United States, inclined to put in force
a kind of agrarian law against such monopolizers, had
laid them, as I was told, under the stipulation of settling upon this immense tract a certain number of
families.

The cotton produced in this neighbourhood, of a
quality no way inferior to that of Red river, obtained this
year from six to six and a half dollars per cwt. in the
seed, and there were now two gins established for its
preparation, though, like every thing else, in this infant
settlement of the poor and improvident, but little attention beyond that of absolute necessity, was as yet
paid to any branch of agriculture. Nature has here
done so much, and man so little, that we are yet totally unable to appreciate the value and resources of
the soil. Amongst other kinds of grain, rice has been
tried on a small scale, and found to answer every expectation. The price of this grain, brought from New
Orleans, was no less than 25 to 37½ cents per lb. by
retail. Under the influence of a climate mild as the
south of Europe, and a soil equal to that of Kentucky, wealth will ere long flow, no doubt, to the
banks of the Arkansa.

I again made application to the land speculators,
trying to prevail upon them on any terms, to take up
my baggage, as far as the Cadron, which would have
enabled me immediately to proceed on my journey,
across the great prairie, but they remained inexorable.

23d.] To-day, I returned to Madame Gordon's,
which, though only six miles distant by land, is not
less than 15 by water. I was now obliged more deeply to wade through the enswamped forests, which sur-
round the habitable prairie lands, in consequence of
the late rain. In these ponds, I am told, the Proteus

10

or Syren is occasionally met with. There are also alligators, though by no means numerous.

24th.] This morning I again proceeded up the river with my flat boat, by the assistance of two French boatmen, full of talk, and, at first, but indifferently inclined to work ; we succeeded, however, by night, to get to the third of the five sand-bars or bends, which intervene between this place and the village of Arkansas. The following day in the evening, after a good deal of hard labour and wading, on my part, and that of the negro in my employ, we arrived at Monsieur Bougie's, and the next day I parted with a sort of regret from the boat, which, with all its difficulties, had afforded me, through the most inclement season of the year, no inconsiderable degree of comfort and convenience.

On the 26th, I proceeded with my baggage and property to the village in Monsieur Bougie's perogue, accompanied by one boatman. Near to the town, we grounded on the inner side of a recent, and still augmenting bar, and, after falling a little back, we crossed over, but here the current would not permit us to advance with the oars. The shore was high, and the water too deep for poles, so that we had again to attempt the side we had left ; here, in drifting with velocity again on the bar, our fickle boat or canoe was so near overturning, notwithstanding our exertions, that, for a moment I considered every thing as lost ; getting out, however, into the water, we with some difficulty set the perogue afloat, and for safety dragged her along, up to our waists in water. The sand was here so moveable, as to bury our feet at every step. We at length succeeded, and came to shore, under a bank 100 feet high, without any kind of practicable landing for merchandise, that of last year being now choked up with moving sand.

In the meanest garb of a working boat-man, and

unattended by a single slave, I was no doubt considered, as I had probably been by the land speculators, one of the canaille, and I neither claimed nor expected attention; my thoughts centered upon other
objects, and all pride of appearance I willingly sacrificed to promote with frugality and industry the objects
of my mission.

An insignificant village, containing three stores,
destitute even of a hatter, a shoe-maker, and a taylor,
and containing about 20 houses, after an existence of
near a century, scarcely deserved geographical notice,
and will never probably flatter the industry of the
French emigrants, whose habits, at least those of the
Canadians, are generally opposed to improvement and
regular industry.   During my stay, I took up my residence with Dr. M'Kay, and found in him an intelligent and agreeable companion ; but such is the na-
tionality of these ignorant people, that French quackery
has hitherto been preferred to the advice of a regular
physician.   Blanket capeaus, mocassins, and overalls
of the same materials, are here, as in Canada, the prevailing dress ; and men and women commonly wear
a handkerchief on the head in place of hats and bonnets.

28th.] This morning I accompanied the doctor to
shoot wild geese, as they passed to a neighbouring lake,
about two miles in the rear of the town.   Here a vast
prairie opens to view, like a shorn desert, but well
covered with grass and herbaceous plants.   Over this
vast plain, which proceeds a little to the west of north,
computed to be not less than 30 leagues in length, by
10 to 15 in breadth, passes the road to the Cadron,
and the settlements of Red river.

Among other plants already in flower in these natural meadows, we saw abundance of a new and fragrant species of *Allium* with greenish-white flowers,
and destitute of the characteristic odour of the genus
in common with *A. fragrans*, to which it is allied.

The *Houstonia serpyllifolia* and *Claytonia caroliniana*
were also in full bloom at this early season.

February 3d.] This afternoon I walked to Mr.
Mosely's, six miles distant by land, and 15 by water.
The prairie, in consequence of the late rains, appeared
almost one continued sheet of water. I observed
springing up, the *Eryngium aquaticum*, occasionally
employed as a medicine by the inhabitants, acting as
a diuretic, and in larger doses proving almost emetic.
Crossing the prairie, which is bordered with settlements, we entered the alluvial forest, containing oak,
hickory, box, elder *(Acer negundo)*, elm, &c. nearer
the river cotton-wood appears as usual. I saw here a
prickly-ash *(Zanthoxylion Clava Herculis)*, the size
of an ordinary ash, but the same species as that of the
southern states, and the bark proving equally effica-
cious for allaying the tooth-ache.

The first attempt at settlement on the banks of the
Arkansa, was begun a few miles below the bayou which
communicates with White river. An extraordinary
inundation occasioned the removal of the garrison to
the borders of the lagoon near madame Gordon's, and,
again disturbed by an overflow, they at length chose
the present site of Arkansas. The first band of hunters who attempted to reside here, were, it is said,
obliged to remove, in consequence of the swarms of
rats, with which they found the country infested.
These animals, which are native, differ specifically
from the European species, are much larger, and com-
mit the most serious depredations.*

* A much earlier settlement was made by Chevalier de Tonti, who,
in 1685, proceeding from the fort of the Illinois, recently established,
down to the mouth of the Mississippi, in order to second the unfortunate
La Salle, and not finding him, ascended the river in order to return to
his post. In his way he entered the Arkansa, and proceeded up to the
village of that nation, with whom he made an alliance, and left 10 of his
people, at their earnest request, to settle among them. This small
party, occasionally augmented by the Canadians who descended the
river, keeping on peaceable terms with the natives, and intermarrying
amongst them, continually maintained their ground, though rather by

The poverty of the land in the immediate vicinity of this place, will probably operate as a perpetual barrier to its extension. The encroachments of the river upon the precipitous and friable bank in front of the town, and the enlargement of the ravines by which it is intersected, renders the site altogether precarious, and prevents the practicability of any thing like a convenient landing for merchandise. During the period of high water, however, the adjoining bayou, or channel of communication with a neighbouring lake, affords this convenience.

The love of amusements, here, as in most of the French colonies, is carried to extravagance, particularly gambling, and dancing parties or balls. But the sum of general industry is, as yet, totally insufficient for the support of any thing like a town.

The houses, commonly surrounded with open gallerics, destitute of glass windows, and perforated with numerous doors, are well enough suited for a summer shelter, but totally destitute of comfort in the winter. Without mechanics, domestic conveniences and articles of dress were badly supplied at the most expensive rate. Provision produced in the country, such as beef and pork, did not exceed six cents per pound ; but potatoes, onions, apples, flour, spirits, wine, and almost every other necessary article of diet, were imported at an enormous price, into a country which ought to possess every article of the kind for exportation to New Orleans. Such is the evil which may always be anticipated by forcing a town, like a garrison, into being, previous to the existence of necessary

adopting the manners of the Indians, and becoming hunters, than by any regular industry or attention to the arts and conveniences of civilized life. Families of this mixed race are now scattered along the banks of the Arkansa, to the extremity of the present Quapaw reservation.

Had the unfortunate grant of Mr. Law been carried into effect, which proposed to settle at, and round the present village of Arkansas, 9000 Germans from the Palatinate, we should now probably have witnessed an extensive and flourishing colony, in place of a wilderness, still struggling with all the privations of savage life.

supplies. With a little industry, surely every person
in possession of slaves might have, at least, a kitchen
garden ! but these Canadian descendants, so long nur-
tured amidst savages, have become strangers to civilized comforts and regular industry. They must,
however, in time give way to the introduction of more
enterprising inhabitants.

The enormous claim of Messrs. Winters, containing about a million of acres of this territory, and which
will yet probably for some time remain undetermined,
proves a considerable bar to the progress of the settlement. Besides a great portion of the neighbouring prairie, it embraces much of the finest land
on the northern border of the river, and continues
for near one hundred miles along its bank.

The great prairie of which we have already spoken,
said to be 90 miles in length, contains an invaluable
body of land, and, where sufficiently drained, which is
pretty generally the case, except during the rains of
winter, would produce most species of grain in abundance. As a pasture it is truly inexhaustible, though
in the hottest months of summer occasionally deprived
of water.

The cattle throughout this country are generally
left to provide for themselves, and suffered to range at
large, excepting such as are in domestic use. That
they may not become entirely irreclaimable, they are
now and then enticed to come up to the fold by a
handful of salt, or a few ears of corn. No hay is provided for fodder, nor does it indeed appear necessary,
except to assist in fattening for the stall, but this piece
of economy, like almost every thing else which might
promise comfort, is neglected, and the cattle are killed
just as they are hunted up from the prairie or the
cane-brake. It is from the prevalence of the cane, and
the shave-rush *(Equisetum hiemale)*, that the cattle
are kept in tolerable condition, and often even fat,
through the severest part of the winter. Indeed, at

this early, but perhaps uncommonly advanced season of the year (not yet the middle of February), there was already a few inches of green herbage, and only one night during this month have I seen any ice. The thermometer, towards noon, rises to 70°, and the peach and plum-trees, almost equally naturalized, have nearly finished blooming. The fig, however, unprotected by the shelter of a wall, though sufficiently vigorous, appears every year to die down nearly to the ground. Grapes succeed so as to promise wine, but without the advantage of cellars it soon becomes subjected to the acetous fermentation.

The sweet gum tree *(Liquidambar styraciflua)*, which produces no resin in the northern states, where it is equally indigenous, here, as in Mexico and the Levant, exudes the odoriferous Storax of the shops.

As to the breed of domestic animals, no selection of those commonly raised has yet been attended to, nor any foreign ones introduced from parallel climates, so as to afford us any idea of the resources and conveniences which might here be brought into existence. The horned cattle increase and fatten without any labour or attention, more than the trouble of occasionally ascertaining their existence in the wilderness through which they are at liberty to roam without limit. It is in consequence of this unrestrained liberty, and the advantage of a perpetual supply of food, that the horse has become already naturalized in the southern parts of this territory, and the adjoining province of Spain. By this means, however, the domestic breed has been in some respects considerably deteriorated; the horses of this country are rather small, though very hardy, and capable of subsisting entirely upon cane or grass, even when subjected to the hardest labour. They were commonly sold from 30 to 50 and 100 dollars a piece, though paid for in the depreciated currency of the country, bearing a discount of from 10 to 20 per cent.

The singular temperature and general mildness of this climate, which may be presumed from a cursory inspection of its flora and agriculture, and then again the occurrence of considerable frosts in the winter, are circumstances which justly excite astonishment when we survey the same parallels of latitude in the trans-atlantic regions. Here, in the latitude of the Cape of Good Hope, in that of Sidon, and even south of Candia and Cyprus, with its groves of myrtle, near to the latitude of Madeira, and in that of the empire of Morocco, we find the fig annually levelled to the ground by frosts. Not even the low palmetto *(Sabal minor)* indigenous, consequently no prospect of naturalizing the date, so common in the same parallels of Africa; no olive, nor any well-grounded prospect of its success; wines, for which Madeira has so long been celebrated (at least any of superior quality), appear also proscribed from this part of America. No evergreens of any description, except the holly, appear throughout the dreary forests. The north-western winds, sweeping over the arctic deserts of eternal winter, have extended the temperature of northern Europe over all the regions of the United States, nearly to the very limits of the tropic. The climate of Arkansas, scarcely elevated more than 5 or 600 feet above the level of the sea, is not more ardent and less temperate than that of the south of France.

For several miles in and round the town, the accumulation of low mounds or Indian graves, scattered with those fragments of pots, which were either interred or left on the graves with offers of food, by the affectionate friends of the deceased, mark the ancient residence of the natives. In one of the tumuli, on the bank towards the bayou, intersected by the falling away of the earth, a pot of this kind, still employed by the Chicasaws and other natives for boiling their victuals, had fallen out of the grave, and did not appear to be of very ancient interment. Whether these monuments had been the slow accumulation of natural and casual mortality, or the sad remains of some overwhelming destruction, was now impossible to determine. From the ashes of fires, and fragments of charcoal, besides the accompaniment of many indestructible weapons, utensils, and pots broken into fragments by force, I suspect that these mounds are merely incidental, arising from the demolition of the circular dwelling in which the deceased had been interred, a custom which was formerly practised by the Natchez, Cherokees, and other of the natives. Indeed, the sacrifices and offerings which the Indians formerly made to the manes of the deceased father, were sometimes almost ruinous to his family, though no longer blackened by the immolation of human victims. Father Charlevoix relates, that stopping, as he descended the Mississippi, at a village of Ouyapes (or Wyapes), the same with the Quapaws (or, as they call themselves, O-guah-pas), then living near the confluence of White river with the Mississippi, he found them in great distress from the ravages of the small-pox. Their burying-place appeared " like a forest of poles and posts newly set up, and on which there hung all manner of things : there is every thing which the savages use." The men and women both continued lamenting throughout the night, and repeating without ceasing, " *Nihahani*, as the Illinois do, and in the same tone." A mother weeping over the grave of her son, poured upon it a great quantity of Sagamitty (or hominy). Another kindled a fire near one of the tombs,* probably for the purpose of sacrificing food, as I have seen practised by the Pawnee-Rikasrees of the Missouri.

The aborigines of this territory, now commonly called Arkansas or Quapaws and Osarks, do not at this time number more than about 200 warriors. They

* Charlevoix's Historical Journal, p. 307, London Edition.

were first discovered about the year 1685, by Chevalier de Tonti.   From what source Father Charlevoix
ascertains that they were very numerous in the time
of Ferdinand de Soto, I am unable to learn.   In the
abridged relation of this expedition by Purchas, I cannot possibly discover any thing relating to them.   The
people of Quigaute must have occupied a country not
far from the Arkansa, and are said by La Vega to
have been numerous and powerful, but that they were
the same people as the Arkansas or O-guah-pas,
seems by no means probable.   From their own tradition it does not appear that they were visited by the
whites previous to the arrival of La Salle ; they say,
that many years had elapsed before they had any interview with the whites, whom they had only heard of
from their neighbours.

In a council held with the Quapaws some years ago,
concerning the boundaries of the lands which they
claimed, a very old chieftain related to the agent, that
at a very remote period his nation had descended the
Mississippi, and after having proceeded in one body
to the entrance of a large and muddy river (the Missouri), they had there divided, one party continuing
down the Mississippi, and the other up the miry river.
The descending band were checked in their progress
by the Kaskaskias, whose opposition they at length
subdued.   In their further descent they were harassed
by the Chicasaws and Choctaws, and waged war with
them for some considerable time, but, at length, over-
coming all opposition, they obtained the banks of the
Arkansa, where they have remained ever since. Some
of them, reverting apparently to the period of creation, say, that they originally emerged out of the water, but made many long and circuitous journeys
upon that element, previous to their arrival on the
banks of this river.

As their language scarcely differs from that of the
Osages, Kanzas, Mahas, and Poncas of the Missouri,
it is presumable that these sprung from the band

which ascended the Missouri. They say, they remained separated from a knowledge of each other for many years, until mutually discovered on a hunting party, taking each other at first for enemies, till assured to the contrary by both uttering the same language.

They bear an unexceptionably mild character, both amongst the French and Americans, having always abstained, as they say, from offering any injury to the whites. Indeed, to do them justice, and to prove that this opinion concerning them is no modern prejudice, I cannot do less than quote the testimony of Du Pratz, made about a century ago. Speaking of the Arkansa territory, he adds, " I am so prepossessed in favour of this country, that I persuade my self the beauty of the climate has a great influence on the character of the inhabitants, who are at the same time very gentle, and very brave. They have ever had an inviolable friendship for the French, uninfluenced thereto, either by fear or views of interest ; and live with them as brethren, rather than as neighbours."* They say, that in consequence of their mildness and love of peace, they have been overlooked by the Americans ; that they are ready enough to conciliate by presents those who are in danger of becoming their enemies, but neglect those who are their unchangeable friends.

The complexion of the Quapaws, like that of the Choctaws and Creeks, is dark, and destitute of any thing like the cupreous tinge. The symmetry of their features, mostly aquiline, often amounts to beauty, but they are not to be compared in this respect to the Osages, at least those of them which now remain. Charlevoix says, " The Akansas (as he calls them) are reckoned to be the tallest and best shaped of all the savages of this continent, and they are called, by way of distinction, *the fine men.*" I question, however, whether this epithet is not similar to that of the

* Du Pratz, History of Louisiana, p. 61.

Illinois, and the Llenilenape, or " original and genu.
ine men," as it is translated, of the Delawares. The
name of Akansa or Arkansa, if ever generally assumed by the natives of this territory, is now, I am persuaded, scarcely ever employed; they generally call
themselves O-guah-pa or Osark, from which last epithet, in all probability, has been derived the name of
the river and its people; indeed, I have heard old
French residents in this country, term it Riviere des
Arks or d'Osark.

They employ artificial means to eradicate that pubescence from their bodies, which is, indeed, naturally scanty. The angle of the eye is usually elongated,
but never turned up exteriorly, as it is said, in common with the Tartars, by Humboldt, to be the case
with the Mexicans.

Although they may be said to be taciturn, compared with Frenchmen, their passions are not difficult
to excite.

As hunters, they are industrious, but pay little attention to agriculture; and pleased by intercourse
with the whites, they are not unwilling to engage as
boatmen and hunters.

About a century ago, father Charlevoix describes
the Arkansas as occupying four villages; that which
he visited was situated on the bank of the Mississippi, in a little meadow, which was (in 1819) M'Lane's
landing, the only contiguous spot free from inundation. The people called Akansas by this author, were
then made up of the confederated remnants of ruined
tribes. The villages which he visited, called themselves Ouyapes, evidently the O-guah-pa. On the
Arkansa, six miles from the landing, there was a second village, consisting of the Torimas and Topin-
gas. Six miles higher were the Sothouis, and a little
further was the village of the Kappas;* these are
again the same people as the Quapaws or O-guah-pas.

* Charlevoix, Hist. p. 306, 307. Lond. Ed.

In the time of Du Pratz, the Arkansas had all retired up the river of this name, and were living about
twelve miles from the entrance of White river. They
were still said to be pretty considerable in numbers,
and had been joined by the Kappas, the Michigami-
as, and a part of the Illinois. He likewise remarks,
that they were no less distinguished as warriors than
hunters, and that they had succeeded in intimidating
the restless and warlike Chicasaws.* Indeed, the
valour and the friendship of the Arkansas is still
gratefully remembered by the Canadians and their
descendants, and it is much to be regretted that they
are making such evident approaches towards total destruction. The brave manner in which they opposed
the Chicasaws, has long ensured them the quiet possession of their present country. Among the most
extraordinary actions which they performed against
those perfidious Indians, is the story which has been
related to me by major Lewismore Vaugin, one of
the most respectable residents in this territory. The
Chicasaws, instead of standing their ground, were retreating before the Quapaws, whom they had des-
cried at a distance, in consequence of the want of
ammunition. The latter understanding the occasion,
were determined to obviate the excuse, whether real
or pretended, and desired the Chicasaws to land on
an adjoining sand-beach of the Mississippi, giving
them the unexpected promise of supplying them with
powder for the contest. The chief of the Quapaws
then ordered all his men to empty their powder-horns
into a blanket, after which, he divided the whole with
a spoon, and gave the half to the Chicasaws. They
then proceeded to the combat, which terminated in
the killing of 10 Chicasaws, and the loss of five prisoners, with the death of a single Quapaw.

I am informed, that it is a custom of the Quapaws,
after firing the first volley, to throw aside their guns,
and make a charge with their tomahawks.

* Du Pratz, Hist. Louisiana, p. 318.

The treacherous Osages, to whom they are naturally allied by the ties of consanguinity, at one period
claimed the assistance of the Quapaws, with the secret intention of betraying them to destruction.   Arriving near the scene of action, and discovering, as
was said, the encampment of the supposed enemy,
the Osages parted from their friends, under pretence
of ambuscading the enemy.   Their conduct, however guarded, had not, it seems, been sufficient to remove the suspicions of the wary leader of. the Quapaws, who now concerted measures of security.   The
Quapaws made their fires as usual, but secretly left
them, in order to watch the motions of the Osages,
who, as it had been suspected, crept up to their encampment in the dead of night, and fired a volley
near the fires, not doubting but they had destroyed
those who had seemingly confided in their friendship.
But at this instant, the Quapaws, sufficiently prepared,
arose from their concealment, and exercised a just
chastisement on the traitors.

The social regulations, as well as the superstitions
and ideas of the supernatural entertained by the Quapaws, are no way materially distinct from those which
are practised by their eastern and northern neighbours.
The most simple testimonies of attachment, without
the aid of solemn vows, are thought sufficient to complete a conjugal felicity, which, where all are equal, in
wealth and property, can only be instigated through
the desire of personal gratification or mutual attachment, and can but seldom be attended with that coldness and disgust, which is but too common, where
this sacred tie is knit by avarice.   Neither is this contract controlled by any unnatural and overruling policy.   The obligation to decorum and the essential ties
of society are not abandoned by the Indian, in consequence of his being freed from that perpetual restraint, which appears to have been requisite in civilized society.   The father can recall his daughter from

the habitation of one who has rendered himself odious
to his child. The husband can abandon the wife who
has made herself obnoxious to his house and family.
They are only united by the bonds of mutual esteem
and reciprocal friendship; they will, of course, endea-
vour to deserve it of each other, as affording a gratification to themselves, no less than to their parents
and relatives.

As the marriage is never ostentatious, or strictly
ceremonious, so its disavowal, when not induced by
any thing flagrant, is not a matter to alarm the repose
of society. The male children go with the father, the
females attend upon the mother. Children, however
begotten, are dear to a society ever on the brink of
extermination,

That any ceremonies, more than the celebration of
a frugal and sober feast, are constantly practised by
any of the natives of this country, is much more than
can be satisfactorily proved. Among the Quapaws,
I have been informed, that the husband, on the consummation of his marriage, presents his wife with the
leg of a deer, and she, in return, offers him an ear of
maize, both of which are so many symbols of that
provision against the calls of necessity, which they
are mutually accustomed to provide.*

The young and unmarried women of the Quapaws,
according to a custom equally prevalent among many
other tribes of Indians, wear their hair braided up
into two parts, brought round to either ear in a cylindric form, and decorated with beads, wampum, or
silver. After marriage these locks are all unfolded,
the decorations laid aside for her daughters, and her
hair, brought together behind in a single lock, becomes no longer an assiduous object of ornament.
According to the History of the Costume of all
Nations, this manner of braiding the hair appears
to have been equally prevalent among the women of

---

* A ceremony similar to this, was also, according to Adair, practised
among the Creeks.

Siberia, Tartary, Turkey, and China. As an expression of the greatest grief and misfortune, anciently practised by many other nations of the world, I have, amongst the aborigines of the Missouri, not unfrequently seen both men and women shave away their hair. It is not, however, I believe, practised by the Indians of the Mississippi, nor among the Quapaws and Osages.

The ideas of supernatural agency, entertained by the Arkansas, are very similar to those which prevail among the natives of the Missouri. Every family, for example, chooses its *penates*, or guardian spirit, from among those various objects of creation which are remarkable for their sagacity, their utility, or power. Some will perhaps choose a snake, a buffaloe, an owl, or a raven; and many of them venerate the eagle to that degree, that if one of those birds should happen to be killed during any expedition, the whole party immediately return home. The large feathers of the war-eagle, which they consider talismanic, are sometimes distributed throughout the nation, as sacred presents, which are expected to act as sovereign charms to those who wear them.

The cure of diseases, though sometimes attempted with rational applications, is not unfrequently sought, among the Quapaws, and many other natives of the continent, in charms and jugglery.

As to the future state, in which they are firm believers, their ideas are merely deduced from what they see around them. Their heaven for hunters is at least as rational as that of some of our own fanatics.

For some considerable time after the interment of a warrior and hunter, his grave is frequented with provision, which, if still remaining, after a reasonable lapse of time, is considered as a sure presage that the deceased has arrived at a bountiful hunting ground, and needs no further supply from the earth.

The Quapaws, though no greater proficients in music than the rest of the Indians, have, however, songs appropriated to love, to death, and to battle, but which are merely so many simultaneous effusions of the heart, accompanied by rude and characteristic airs and dances.

It is hardly necessary to detail the dress of the Arkansas, which scarcely, to my view, in any respect, differs from that of the Delawares, Shawnees, or Chipeways. Its component parts are, as usual, mocasins for the feet; leggings which cover the leg and thigh; a breech-cloth; an overall or hunting shirt, seamed up, and slipped over the head; all of which articles are made of leather, softly dressed by means of fat and oily substances, and often rendered more durable by the smoke with which they are purposely imbued. The ears and nose are adorned with pendents, and the men, as among many other Indian tribes, and after the manner of the Chinese, carefully cut away the hair of the head, except a lock on the crown, which is plaited and ornamented with rings, wampum, and feathers. Many of them, in imitation of the Canadian French, wear handkerchiefs around their heads, but in the manner of a turban. Some have also acquired the habit of wearing printed calicoe shirts next to the skin.

The younger Indians, as I am informed, notwithstanding the neglect of renewing their dress, are so partial to cleanliness of the skin, that they practice bathing both winter and summer.

12

CHAPTER VII.

Departure from Arkansas—Indian villages—Moo-
ney's settlement—Curran's settlement—Interview
with the Quapaw chief.—The Pine Bluffs—Soil,
climate, and productions--The Little Rock--Roads--
Mountains—Vegetation—The Mamelle—-Cadron
settlement—Tumuli—Soil and climate--Pecannerie
settlement—Mountains—Cherokees—The Maga-
zine mountain—Dardanelle settlement--Manners
and customs of the Cherokees—Their war with the
Osages.

From Arkansas to the Cadron, a distance of about
300 miles by water, I now understood there existed
a considerable line of settlements along the north
border of the river, and that the greatest uninhabited interval did not exceed 30 miles. Though
the spring was premature, and the weather still subject to uncomfortable vicissitudes, the want of society
and of employment induced me to embrace the earliest
opportunity of continuing my journey into the interior of
the territory, where I hoped to find additional employment and gratification in my researches connected
with natural history. For this purpose I again embarked on the river in a large skiff, which was proceeding to the Baird's-town settlement; but as most
of our company were fond of whiskey, the only bever-
age in the country, except water or milk, it was difficult to get them parted from their companions and
conversation; however, after many efforts to make a
start, we at last got off, though merely to make one
or two miles, so as to be disengaged, at any rate, for
the morning. Our encampment was a sand-bar or
beach, skirted by willows, and though in itself a situation by no means interesting, yet far from disagreea-

ble to him who can enjoy the simple fare of the hunter, and the calm and unsullied pleasures of nature.

On the following day (*February* the 27th) we proceeded about 21 miles, or seven points up the river, and in some places against a current of considerable velocity, which had been augmented by a southern freshet, communicating a muddiness and chocolate-brown colour to the stream. In the evening, to avoid the attacks of musquitoes, we again chose a sand-beach for our place of encampment.

In the course of the day we passed the outlet of the bayou, or rather river, Meta, which diagonally traverses the Great Prairie, also two Indian villages on the south bank, which continues to be the Quapaw line as far as the Little Rock. The first was the periodical residence of a handful of Choctaws, the other was occupied by the Quapaws. On this side of the river there appeared to be considerable bodies of very fertile land elevated above inundation.

The peach-trees, now in bloom, were considerably disseminated beyond the immediate precincts of the Indian villages, and seemed to be almost naturalized, but, in common even with the wild fruits of the country, they are occasionally robbed of fruit by the occurrence of unseasonable frosts.

On the 28th, after ascending about 13 miles, we arrived at the settlement begun by colonel Mooney, consisting of three or four families. I was here very hospitably entertained by Mr. Davison. Near this house, and about 200 yards from the river, there was a fine lake of clear water, of considerable extent, communicating with the river by a bayou, which enters a few miles below. Its bed appeared to be firm and sandy. The neighbouring land was of a superior quality, either for corn or cotton, but all conditionally held on the uncertain claim of Messrs. Winters. Notwithstanding the extent of inundated lands, the climate was considered unusually healthy, and the

soil, with but little labour, capable of insuring a comfortable independence to the cultivator.

March 1st.] This morning a slight white frost was
visible, though, yesterday and the day before, the thermometer rose, at noon, to 70°, and the Red-bud
(Cercis canadensis) was commonly in flower. We
proceeded about 10 miles, and encamped oppposite
to an island ; the water now falling as rapidly as it had
risen. Leaving the boat, and walking through the
woods, I was surprised to find myself inadvertently at
the Quapaw village we had passed yesterday, situated
upon a small prairie, constituting the isthmus of a
tongue of land, which, six or seven miles round,
was here scarcely half a mile across. Endeavouring now to obtain a nearer route to the river, than
that of returning by the path, I found myself in a horrid cane-brake, interlaced with brambles, through which
I had to make my way as it were by inches. The
delay I thus experienced created alarm among my
companions, who fired three guns to direct me to the
spot where they waited, and where I soon arrived,
pretty well tired of my excursion.

2d.] A slight frost appeared again this morning. We
proceeded slowly, passing in the course of the day three
points of land, one of which was about six miles, the
others three each, and in the evening encamped a mile
below Morrison's bayou. Nearly opposite to this
stream there was another village of the Quapaws, containing about 15 cabins, and called, by the French,
ville de Grand Barbe, from their late chief, who, contrary to the Indian custom, wore a long beard. It
stands on the edge of the forest, surrounded by good
land, and elevated above the overflows.

3d.] To-day we arrived at Curran's settlement, consisting of six families, who had chosen for their residence a body of very superior land. From 1000 to
1500 pounds of cotton have been produced upon the
acre, and of a staple no way inferior to that of Red

river. As to maize, it is as luxuriant as possible.
But what most recommended this settlement, in my
estimation, was the unequivocal appearance of health
and plenty. We landed for the night nearly opposite
what is called the Old River, four miles above Curran's, an elliptic curve of the river, 11 miles in circuit,
cut off at the isthmus in the course of a single night,
as was witnessed by a French trader encamped on the
spot, who fled in terror from the scene of devastation.
On the borders of this bend, now become a lake, and
which explains the origin of similar bodies of water
along this river, there were three families now settled.

4th.] The middle of the day, and early part of the
afternoon, felt warm and sultry as summer. About
noon I arrived at the cabin of Mr. Joseph Kirkendale,
four miles above the cut off in the river, where I
tasted nearly the first milk and butter which I had
seen since my arrival on the banks of the Arkansa.
This farm, like those below on Old River, was
situated upon a small and insulated prairie or open
and elevated meadow, about 15 miles from the Great
Prairie. The drought which was experienced last
summer throughout this territory, proved, in many
places, nearly fatal to the crops of corn and cotton, so
that the inhabitants were now under the necessity of
importing maize for provision, at the rate of one dollar and a quarter per bushel.

At Mr. Kirkendale's I had an interview with the
principal chief of the Quapaws, who landed here on
his way down the river. His name, to me unintelligible, was Ha-kat-ton (or the *dry man*). He was not
the hereditary chief, but received his appointment as
such, in consequence of the infancy of the children of
the Grand Barbe. His appearance and deportment
were agreeable and prepossessing, his features aquiline
and symmetrical. Being told that I had journeyed a
great distance, almost from the borders of the great
lake of salt water, to see the country of the Arkansa,

and observing the attention paid to me by my hospitable friend, he, in his turn, showed me every possible
civility, returned to his canoe, put on his uniform
coat, and brought with him a roll of writing, which
he unfolded with great care, and gave it me to read.
This instrument was a treaty of the late cession and
purchase of lands from the Quapaws, made the last
autumn, and accompanied by a survey of the speci-
fied country. The lines of this claim, now conceded
for the trifling sum of 4000 dollars in hand, and an
annuity of a thousand dollars worth of goods, pass up
White river, until a south line intersects the Canadian river of Arkansa, then continuing along the
course of this river to its sources, afterwards down
Red river to the Great Raft, and thence in a north-east
direction to point Chicot, on the Mississippi, and so
in a north-west line to the place of commencement,
near White river. Their reservation (situated exclusively on the south bank of the Arkansa) commences at the post or town of Arkansas, and continues up that river to the Little Rock, thence in a
southern direction to the Washita, which continues
to be the boundary, to a line intersecting the place of
commencement. To this deed were added the names
of no less than 13 chiefs. This tract contains probably more than 60,000 square miles. Such are the
negociating conquests of the American republic, made
almost without the expense of either blood or trea-
sure!

Hakatton informed us, that he had lately returned
from the garrison, where, in concert with a fellow
chief and the commander, they had succeeded in
rescuing from bondage some unfortunate prison rs
and females of the Caddoes, of whom about 15 or 20
had been killed by the Osages. The former reside on
the banks of Red river, into whose territory the Osages
occasionally carry their depredations. This chief
warned me from trusting myself alone amongst the

Osages, who, if they spared my life, would, in all probability, as they had often done to the hunters, strip
me naked, and leave me to perish for want. But in
his nation, he took a pride in assuring me, if I was
found destitute, I should be relieved to the best of
their ability, and conducted, if lost, to the shelter of
their habitations, where the stranger was always welcome. His late journey to the seat of government,
appeared to have inspired him with exalted ideas of
the wealth and power of civilized society.

To my inquiries, respecting the reputed origin of
the O-guah-pas, he answered candidly, that he was
ignorant of the subject; and that the same question
had been put to him at St. Louis, by governor Clarke.

This morning I observed the wife of the chief,
preparing for her family a breakfast from the nuts of
the Cyamus (or Nelumbium). They are first steeped
in water, and parched in sand, to extricate the kernels,
which are afterwards mixed with fat, and made into
a palatable soup. The tubers of the root, somewhat
resembling batatas or sweet potatoes, when well boiled, are but little inferior to a farinaceous potatoe, and
are penetrated internally and longitudinally, with from
five to eight cavities or cells.

5th.] We were again visited by the Quapaw chief,
who appeared to be very sensible and intelligent,
though much too fond of whiskey. I took an opportunity to inquire of him, whether the Quapaws considered smoking as in any way connected with their
religion, to which he answered, that they merely regarded it as a private gratification or luxury; but that the
Osages smoked to God, or to the sun, and accompanied it by a short apostrophe: as, " Great Spirit,
deign to smoke with me, as a friend! fire and earth,
smoke with me, and assist me to destroy mine enemies, the Caddoes, Pawnees, Mahas, &c.! my dogs
and horses, smoke also with me!"

Among the most remarkable superstitious ceremonies practised by the Quapaws, is that which I now found corroborated by Hakatton. Before commencing the corn-planting, a lean dog is selected by the squaws, as a sacrifice to the Indian Ceres, and is, with terrific yells and distorted features, devoured alive. This barbarous ceremony, which we derided, he assured us gravely, was conducive to the success of the ensuing crop. After the harvest of the maize, and subsequent to the Green-corn Dance, they have also a succession of dances and feasts, which they support like our Christmas mummers, by going round and soliciting contributions.

The Quapaws are indeed slaves to superstition, and many of them live in continual fear of the operations of supernatural agencies.

On the 7th, we proceeded to Mr. Morrison's, a few miles distant, but did not accomplish it until the succeeding morning, in consequence of the prevalence of a violent storm from the south-west.

On the 6th, I remained at Mr. Morrison's farm, agreeably situated on a small prairie, contiguous to the river, surrounded with an extensive body of good land, continuing a considerable distance from the bank. These small prairies often appear to have been the sites of ancient Indian stations.

A number of Quapaw canoes passed down the river, and several drunken Indians, accompanied by Paspatoo, their chief, now 75 years of age, were straggling about in quest of whiskey, which if not *prohibited*, would, in all probability, be less plentifully supplied.

The adjoining forest was already adorned with flowers, like the month of May in the middle states. The woods, which had been overrun by fire in autumn, were strewed in almost exclusive profusion with the *Ranunculus marilandicus*, in full bloom, affording, with other herbage, already an abundant pasture for the cattle. Towards evening, Mr. Drope, with his large and commodious trading boat of 25 tons burthen, passed this place on his way to the garrison, with whom I was to embark on the following morning.

9th.] I walked about four miles to Mr. Dardennes', where there were two families residing on the bank of the river, which is agreeably elevated, and here I had the satisfaction of joining Mr. Drope. Lands of the same fertile quality as that on the border of the river, extend here from it for eight miles without interruption, and free from inundation. The claim of Winters' still continues up to an island nearly opposite Mr. Lewismore's, but the survey of all this land, now ordered by Congress, seems to imply the annihilation of this claim, which for the benefit of the settlement ought promptly to be decided.

Four miles above Dardennes', commences the first gravel-bar, accompanied by very rapid water.

10th.] We now passed Mr. Mason's, 18 miles above Dardennes', where likewise exists an extensive body of rich and dry land, along the borders of Plum bayou. We encamped at the upper point of the sand-beach, about three miles above Mason's, on the margin of a small and elevated prairie, which, from the abundance of Chicasaw plum bushes forming a grove, I fancied might have been an ancient aboriginal station. The day was exceedingly wet, accompanied with thunder, which had continued with but little intermission since the preceding night.

11th.] Passed Mr. Embree's, and arrived at Mr. Lewismore's. Six miles above, we also saw two Indian villages, opposite each of those settlements. The land is here generally elevated above the inundation, and of a superior quality ; the upper stratum a dark-coloured loam, rich in vegetable matter.

The Indians, unfortunately, are here, as usual, both poor and indolent, and alive to wants which they have

13

not the power of gratifying. The younger ones are
extremely foppish in their dress; covered with feathers, blazing calicoes, scarlet blankets, and silver pendents. Their houses, sufficiently convenient with
their habits, are oblong square, and without any other
furniture than baskets and benches, spread with skins
for the purpose of rest and repose. The fire, as usual, is in the middle of the hut, which is constructed
of strips of bark and cane, with doors also of the
latter split and plaited together.

The forest was already decorated with the red-bud,
and a variety of humble flowers. A species of *Vitis*,* called the June grape, from its ripening at that
early period, was also nearly in blossom. It does
not appear to exist in any of the eastern states; in
leaf it somewhat resembles the *vigne des batures* (or
Vitis riparia of Michaux), while the fruit, in the composition of its bunches, and inferior size, resembles
the winter grape.

We spent the evening with major Lewismore Vaugin, the son of a gentleman of noble descent, whose
father formerly held a considerable post under the
Spanish government.

Fifteen miles above this place, Monsieur Vaugin
informed me of the remains of an aboriginal station
of considerable extent, resembling a triangular fort,
which the Quapaws on their first arrival in this country say, was inhabited by a people who were white,
and partly civilized, but whom, at length, they con-
quered by stratagem. The hunters possess an opinion, by no means singular, that this embankment is
of antediluvian origin.

12th.] This morning we met captain Prior and
Mr. Richards, descending with cargoes of furs and
peltries, collected among the Osages. The former

---

* The infertile plant cultivated in the vicinity of the city of London,
has received the name of *Vitis odoratissima,* by the gardeners, an epithet which does not express any peculiar character.

was one of those who had accompanied Lewis and Clarke across the continent. Six miles above Mr. Vaugin's, at Monsieur Michael Le Boun's, commences the first appearance of a hill, in ascending the Arkansa. It is called the Bluff, and appears to be a low ridge covered with pine, similar to the Chicasaw cliffs, and affording in the broken bank of the river the same parti-coloured clays. Mr. Drope remained at the Bluff, trading the remainder of the day with the two or three metif families settled here, who are very little removed in their habits from the savages, with whose language and manners they are quite familiar. In the evening, a ball or dance was struck up betwixt them and the *engagées*. The pine land is here, as every where else, poor and unfit for cultivation. Over this elevated ground were scattered a considerable number of low mounds.

13th.] To-day I walked along the beach with Mr. D., and found the lands generally dry and elevated, covered with cotton-wood *(Populus angulisuns)*, sycamore *(Platanus occidentale)*, maple *(Acer dasycarpa)*, elm *(Ulmus americana)*, and ash *(Fraxinus sambucifolia* and *F. platicarpa)*. We observed several situations which appeared to have been formerly occupied by the Indians. A canoe of the Quapaws coming in sight, we prevailed on them to land, and, during the interval of our boat's arriving, I amused myself with learning some of their names for the forest trees. While thus engaged, I observed, that many of their sounds were dental and guttural, and that they could not pronounce the *th*. In the evening we came to a little above the second Pine Bluff.

14th.] We proceeded to Mons. Bartholome's, where Mr. D. stayed about two hours. Mons. B. and the two or three families who are his neighbours are entirely hunters, or in fact Indians in habits, and pay no attention to the cultivation of the soil. These, with two or three families at the first Pine Bluffs, are the remains of the French hunters, whose stations have found a place in the maps of the Arkansa, and they are in all probability the descendants of those ten Frenchmen whom de Tonti left with the Arkansas, on his way up the Mississippi in the year 1685. From this place we meet with no more settlements until our arrival at the Little Rock, 12 miles below which, and about 70 from hence, by the meandering course of the river, we again meet with a house. We proceeded about eight miles from Bartholome's, and about sun-set came in sight of another pine bluff of about 100 feet elevation, and a mile in length. On the right hand bank the land appeared fertile and elevated. Near our encampment there was a small lake communicating with the river by a bayou. The horizontal beds of clay in this cliff or precipice are precisely similar to those of the Chicasaw Bluffs.

15th.] The land appeared still, for the most part, on either bank, elevated above inundation. Some cypress* clumps, however, were observable on the Quapaw side. On the opposite we saw a cluster of Hollies (Ilex opaca), which were the first we had seen any way conspicuous along the bank of the river. The forests every where abound with wild turkeys, which at this season are beginning to be too poor for food. We came about 16 miles above the last pine bluff, and were there detained the remainder of the evening by the commencement of a strong southwest wind, which in the night veered round to the north-west. The land on the Indian side, contiguous to the river, abounded with thickets of Chicasaw plum-trees, which appear to have overgrown the sites of Indian huts and fields, but, except in a few elevated places, the first alluvial platform or terrace is subject to inundation. The second bank, where the large cane commences, is, however, free from water. The

---

* *Cupressus disticha.*

right side of the river appeared universally high, and rich cane land with occasional thickets and openings.

Throughout this country there certainly exists extensive bodies of fertile land, and favoured by a comparatively healthy climate. The cultivation of cotton, rice, maize, wheat, tobacco, indigo, hemp, and wine, together with the finest fruits of moderate climates, without the aid of artificial soils or manures, all sufficiently contiguous to a market, are important inducements to industry and enterprize. The peach of Persia is already naturalized through the forests of Arkansa, and the spontaneous mulberry points out the convenience of raising silk. Pasturage at all seasons of the year is so abundant, that some of our domestic animals might become naturalized, as in Paraguay and Mexico; indeed several wild horses were seen and taken in these forests during the preceding year.

The territory watered by the Arkansa is scarcely less fertile than Kentucky, and it owes its luxuriance to the same source of alluvial deposition. Many places will admit of a condensed population. The climate is no less healthy, and at the same time favourable to productions more valuable and saleable. The privations of an infant settlement are already beginning to disappear, grist and saw-mills, now commenced, only wait for support; and the want of good roads is scarcely felt in a level country meandered by rivers. Those who have large and growing families can always find lucrative employment in a country which produces cotton. The wages of labourers were from 12 to 15 dollars per month and boarding, which could not then be considered as extravagant, while cotton produced from five to six dollars per hundred weight in the seed, and each acre from 1000 to 1500 pounds.

16th.] At sunrise the thermometer was down to 28°, and the wind at north-west. This sudden transition, after such a long continuance of mild wea-

ther, felt extremely disagreeable, and foreboded the
destruction of all the fruit in the territory. This
morning we passed the fifth Pine Bluff, and the last
previous to our arrival at the Little Rock ; the fasçade
was about the same height and of the same materials
as the preceding. Among the pebbles of a gravel
beach which I examined were scattered a few fragments of cornelian, similar to those of the Missouri,
and abundance of chert or hornstone containing organic impressions of entrocites, caryophillites, &c. here
and there were also intermingled a few granitic fragments, which, if not more remotely adventitious, had
probably descended from the mountains.—We proceeded to-day about 17 miles.

17th.] This morning we had the disagreeable prospect of ice, and the wind was still from the north-
west, but abating. To-day we progressed about 20
miles. The sixth point we passed, since our encampment of the preceding night, was called the
Eagle's Nest, which is here seen situated on the opposite side of the bend before us, of six miles in circuit,
and only about 100 yards across at the isthmus.

The almost uninterrupted alternation of sand-bars
in the wide alluvial plain of the Arkansa afford, as on
the Mississippi, great facilities to navigation, either in
propelling the boat by poles, or towing with the cordelle. As the bars or beaches advance, so they continually change the common level of the river, and
driving the current into the bend with augmenting
velocity, the curve becomes at length intersected, and
the sand barring up the entrances of the former bed
of the river, thus produces the lakes which we find interspersed over the alluvial lands.

In the present state of the water, which is remarkably low, considering the rains which have fallen, it
is difficult to proceed with a large merchant boat more
than 18 or 20 miles a-day.

18th.] We now passed an island or cut-off two miles long, and forming a point four or five miles round. Near its commencement we were again gratified with the sight of a human habitation.

Although the lands along the bank of the river here, appear elevated above the inundation, yet, betwixt the lower settlement and Mr. Twiner's, where we now arrived, the surveyor found considerable tracts subject to the overflow, and in one place a whole township so situated. On the opposite side, or Indian reservation, the hills approach within six or eight miles of the river, and, like most of the southern pine lands, promise but little to the agriculturist, but the intermediate alluvion is as fertile as usual. The Great Prairie, as I am told, on our right, lies at the distance of about 18 or 20 miles ; the intermediate space, unbroken by hills, must necessarily afford an uninterrupted body of land little removed from the fertile character of alluvial.

Towards evening we arrived at Monsieur La Feve's, where two families reside, at the distance of about eight miles above Mr. Twiner's ; these are also descendants from the ancient French settlers.

19th.] This morning we met with a boat from the garrison, commanded by lieutenant Blair, on his way to Arkansas. We also passed Trudot's island, and Mr. D. stopped awhile at the elder La Feve's, for the purposes of trade. Monsieur F. by his dress and manners did not appear to have had much acquaintance with the civilized world. In the evening, we arrived at the house of Mr. Jones, where we were very decently entertained.

20th.] Two miles further lived Mr. Daniels, in whose neighbourhood a second family also resided. The land in this vicinity appeared to be of a very superior quality, and well suited for cotton. Some of it, obtained by the grant of the Spaniards, and since confirmed by the United States, is held as high

as ten dollars the acre. From this place proceeds
the road to St. Louis, on the right, and Mount Prairie settlement, and Natchitoches on Red river, on the
left. From all I can learn, it appears pretty evident
that these extensive and convenient routes have been
opened from time immemorial by the Indians; they
were their war and hunting-paths, and such as in
many instances had been tracked out instinctively by
the bison in their periodical migrations. It is in these
routes, conducted by the Indians, that we are to trace
the adventurers De Soto and La Salle, and by which
we may possibly identify the truth of their relations.
From the appearances of aboriginal remains around
Mount Prairie we may safely infer the former existence of the natives on that site, and it appears also
probable, that this must have been the fertile country
of the Cayas or Tanicas described by La Vega, a
people who are at this time on the verge of extermination.

The distance from Mr. Daniels', on the banks of
the Arkansa, to Red river, is believed to be about 250
miles. The Great Prairie, bearing from hence to the
north-east, is said to be 40 miles distant, and there is
likewise a continuation of open plains or small prairies, from hence to the Cadron settlement. White
river lies about 100 miles distant to the north.

In the course of the day we passed the sixth Pine
Bluff, behind which appeared the first prominent hill
that occurs to view on the banks of the Arkansa. The
fasçade or cliffs, in which it terminates on the bank
of the river, is called the Little Rock, as it is the
first stone which occurs in place. The river, no
longer so tediously meandering, here presents a stretch
of six miles in extent, proceeding to the west of
north-west. In the evening we arrived at Mr. Hogan's, or the settlement of the Little Rock, opposite
to which appear the cliffs, formed of a dark greenish
coloured, fine-grained, slaty, sandstone, mixed with

minute scales of mica, forming what geologists commonly term the *grauwacke slate*, and declining beneath the surface at a dip or angle of not less than 45° from the horizon. The hills appear to be elevated from 150 to 200 feet above the level of the river, and are thinly covered with trees.

There are a few families living on both sides, upon high, healthy, and fertile land ; and about 22 miles from Hogan's, there is another settlement of nine or ten families situated towards the sources of Saline creek of the Washita, which enters that river in 33° 27' ; this land, though fertile and healthy, cannot be compared with the alluvions of the Arkansa ; notwithstanding which, I am informed, they were receiving accessions to their population from the states of Kentucky and Tennessee. The great road to the southwest, connected with that of St. Louis, already noticed, passing through this settlement, communicates downwards also with the post of Washita, with the remarkable thermal springs near its sources, about 50 miles distant, and then proceeding 250 miles to the settlement of Mount Prairie on Saline creek of Red river, and not far from the banks of the latter, continues to Natchitoches. The whole of this country, except that of the hot-springs, which is mountainous, consists either of prairies or undulated lands thinly timbered, and possessed of considerable fertility.

21st.] For three or four nights past, we experienced frost sufficient to destroy most of the early grape, plum, popaw, and red-bud bloom. At 6 o'clock this morning, the thermometer was down to 22°. In the distance of two miles we arrived at the younger Mr. Curran's, nearly opposite to whose house appeared gentle hills, presenting along the bank of the river beds of slate dipping about 45° to the northwest. About 2 miles above, commence on the right bank of the river, the first hills, or rather mountains,

being not less than 4 or 500 feet high, and possessing
a dip too considerable to be classed with the secondary formation. Their character and composition refer them to the transition rocks, and, as far as I have
had opportunity to examine, they appear, at all events,
generally destitute of organic reliquiæ. Similar to
what we had already examined, they are a stratum of
slate made up of the detritus of more ancient rocks,
and frequently traversed with crystalline quartzy veins.
I cannot, in fact, perceive any difference betwixt this
rock and that of the greater part of the Alleghany mountains in Pennsylvania and Virginia, and particularly
those which are of like inconsiderable elevation. About
eight miles from Mr. Curran's, appeared again, on the
left, very considerable round-topped hills, one of them,
called the Mamelle, in the distance, where first visible, appeared insulated and conic like a volcano.
The cliffs bordering the river, broken into shelvings,
were decorated with the red cedar *(Juniperus virginiana)*, and clusters of ferns.

After emerging as it were from so vast a tract of
alluvial lands, as that through which I had now been
travelling for more than three months, it is almost
impossible to describe the pleasure which these romantic prospects again afforded me. Who can be
insensible to the beauty of the verdant hill and valley,
to the sublimity of the clouded mountain, the fearful
precipice, or the torrent of the cataract. Even bald
and moss-grown rocks, without the aid of sculpture,
forcibly inspire us with that veneration which we justly
owe to the high antiquity of nature, and which appears to arise no less from a solemn and intuitive reflection on their vast capacity for duration, contrasted
with that transient scene in which we ourselves only
appear to act a momentary part.

Many of the plants common to every mountainous
and hilly region in the United States, again attracted
my attention, and though no way peculiarly interest-

ing, serve to show the wide extension of the same
species, under the favourable exposure of similar soil
and peculiarity of surface. To me the most surpris-
ing feature in the vegetation of this country, existing
under so low a latitude, was the total absence of all
the usual evergreens, as well as of most of those plants
belonging to the natural family of the heaths, the
rhododendrons, and the magnolias; while, on the
other hand, we have an abundance of the arborescent
Leguminosæ, or trees which bear pods, similar to the
forests of the tropical regions. Here also the *Sapin-
dus saponaria*, or soap-berry of the West Indies, attains the magnitude of a tree.

On the banks of the river, near the precise limit of
inundation, I met with a new species of *Sysimbrium*,
besides the *S. amphibium*, so constant in its occurrence along the friable banks of all the western rivers.
This plant, which is creeping and perennial, possesses
precisely the taste of the common cabbage *(Brassica
oleracea)*, and, from its early verdure, being already
in flower, might perhaps be better worth cultivating
as an early sallad, than the *Barbarea americana*, or
winter sallad.

22d.] From Mr. Blair's, at which place and in the
neighbourhood Mr. D. spent the remainder of the
day, I proceeded down the river about eight miles,
in order to examine the reported silver mine of that
place. My route along the banks of the river lay
through rich and rather open alluvial lands, but, in
many places, not free from transient inundation.

The pretended silver-mine is situated about one
mile below White Oak bayou or rivulet. The search
appears to have been induced by the exposure of
the rocks in the bank of the river, which present indeed an appearance somewhat remarkable. The dip
of the strata, about 45° to the north-west, and the
whole texture of the rock, is similar to that which we
have already noticed. The principal and lowest stra-

tum, is a dark coloured, sandy, but fragile slate-clay ; the upper beds are a fine-grained, siliceous sandstone, containing grains of mica, and occasionly traversed with veins of quartz. In one of these veins, about a foot in breadth, were abundance of rock crystals, scattered over with round masses or imperfect crys. tals of a white and diaphanous talc, collected into ra-dii, each plate forming the segment of a circle.

I was for some time unable to ascertain the charac-ter of the pretended ore of silver, as the whole con-cern lay abandoned. I observed, however, that the slags of their furnace betrayed a considerable propor-tion of iron in their operations, and at length I dis-covered a heap of what appeared to have been the ore, containing pyrites, some of the crystals of which were cubic, like those so common around Lancaster (Penn-sylvania), in the chlorite slate. Whether these pyri-tes did indeed contain silver or not, I could not ab. solutely determine, though nothing extraordinary could reasonably have been expected from their very common appearance and unequivocal character. On showing these specimens to the neighbours, they in-formed me, that the pyrites was the ore in question, while others asserted it to be sulphur, and considered the siliceous matrix as the silver ore. It did not, however, to the microscope betray the smallest me-tallic vestige which could be taken for silver. Like all the rest of this rock, it indeed contained abun-dance of magnetic iron-sand, which on the disintegra-tion of the stone, appeared scattered along the strand of the river. Upon the whole, I am inclined to be-lieve that some imposition had been practised upon the ignorance and credulity of those who were enticed into this undertaking. Monsieur Brangiere is the person who first made the experiment, or attempted to bring the project into execution.

Ever since the time of Soto, reports concerning the discovery of precious metals in this territory have

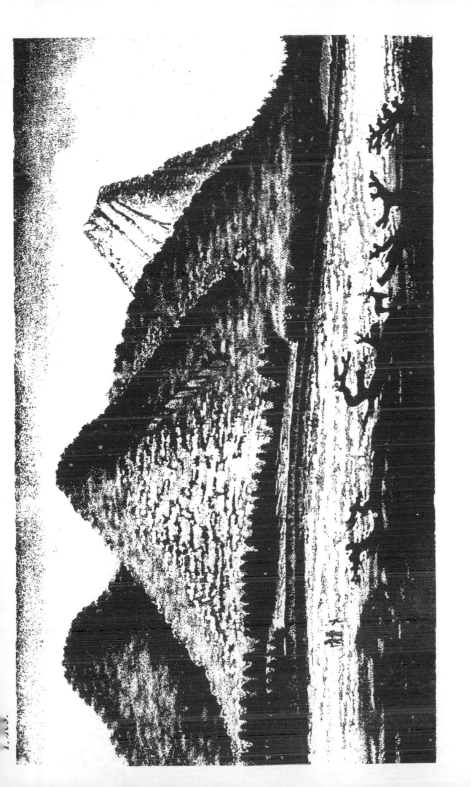

been cherished ; we see them marked upon the maps, and although the places are easily discoverable, the gold and silver they were said to afford has entirely vanished like a fairy dream. It is indeed averred that about 60 dollars worth of silver were obtained from this rock, but that it was relinquished in consequence of the labour exceeding the profits. A furnace and several temporary sheds proved that some earnest attempts had been made, either really or fictitiously, to obtain silver. If any silver was obtained, it may be considered as connected with the magnetic iron-sand, which at St. Domingo and in India is found occasionally mixed with gold and silver.

Du Pratz, after animadverting on the visionary reports of the wealth of this territory, himself adds; " I found, upon the river of the Arkansas, a rivulet that rolled down with its water, gold-dust." " And as for silver mines, there is no doubt but that they might be found there, as well as in New Mexico, on which this province bordered."*

Near to these hills reported to afford silver, I observed two low aboriginal mounds, though the situation did not appear favourable to the residence of the natives.

23d.] Mr. D. remained nearly the whole day at J. Piat's, where a second family also resides, as well as a third on the opposite side of the river, and several others in the vicinity. About a quarter of a mile above Piat's I amused myself in sketching a view of the romantic hills that border the river, and which are not less than 5 to 800 feet high, with the strata inclined about 45° to the south-east.

In the afternoon I crossed the river, and ascended to the summit of these lofty cliffs of slaty and siliceous sandstone, where, from an elevation of about 600 feet, I obtained a panorama view of the surrounding coun-

* Hist. Louisian. p. 219, London Edition.

try, checquered with low mountains running in chains
from the north of west to the south of east. The meanders of the river appeared partly hid in the pervading
forests of its alluvial lands, still fertile and expansive.
To the west, the lofty, conic, and broken hill called
the Mamelle now appeared nearly double the elevation
of that on which I stood, probably more than 1000
feet in height. Two miles above, it presented the
appearance of a vast pyramid, hiding its summit in
the clouds. In this direction opened an extensive alluvial valley, probably once the bed of the river, which
from hence makes a general curve of about 20 miles
towards the north. These mountains appear to be
connected with the Mazern chain of Darby, as they
continue from hence towards the sources of the Pottoe of Arkansa, and the Little river, and Kiamesha of
Red river.

Amidst these wild and romantic cliffs, and on the
ledges of the rocks, where, moistened by springs,
grew a cruciferous plant, very closely allied, if not
absolutely the same, with the *Brassica napus* or the
Rape-seed of Europe, and beyond all question indigenous.

24th.] After taking a second sketch of the Mamelle mountain, from a different point of view, I proceeded to join the boat, and crossed a poor and rocky
Pine hill. Here the sandstone is scarcely slaty, and,
as usual, more or less ferruginous. Crossing the
bayou Palame (or rather rivulet), I joined the boat at
Mr. Gozy's, in whose neighbourhood there were also
two other families. This evening we proceeded
nearly to the termination of Grand island, which is
four miles in length.

25th.] About a mile below Grand island, 'on our
left, the hills again come in upon the river, presenting
the most romantic cliffs. In one place particularly, an
unbroken fascade not less than 150 feet of slaty sandstone presents itself, the lamina of which, about 12 or

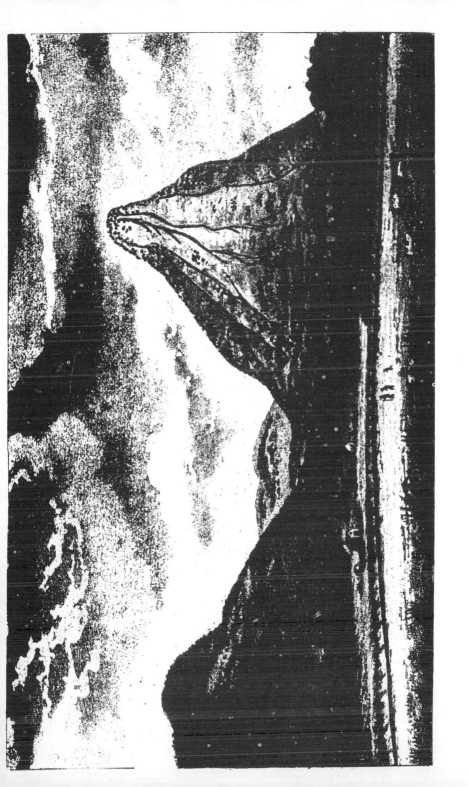

18 inches in thickness, dipping to the south-east, are elevated at an angle of near 80° from the horizon, and altogether resemble the basis of some mighty pyramid. In four miles further we passed the outlet of Fourche La Fève, said to proceed in a western direction for 200 miles, and to take its sources in the mountains of the Pottoe. A north-western range of hills here in the whole distance border the river, the strata of which, still lamellar, dip north-north-east, and are inclined about 45°. This evening, at Mr. Montgomery's, the Cadron hills appear before us, at the distance of about six miles.

26th.] A strong north-west wind arose in the night, accompanying a rise in the river of two and a half feet, and a current of the velocity of four or five miles per hour.

On the 27th we arrived at the Cadron settlement, containing in a contiguous space about five or six families. Mr. M'Ilmery, one of the first, is at present the only resident on the imaginary town plot. A cove of rocks here affords a safe and convenient harbour, and a good landing for merchandize.

No village or town, except Arkansas, has yet been produced on the banks of this river, though I have no doubt, but my remarks may ere long be quoted and contrasted with a rising state of more condensed population. Town-lot speculations have already been tried at the Cadron, which is yet but a proximate chain of farms, and I greatly doubt whether a town of any consequence on the Arkansa will ever be chosen on this site. Some high and rich body of alluvial lands would be better suited for the situation of an inland town, than the hills and rocks of the Cadron. Modern cities rarely thrive in such romantic situations. There is scarcely a hundred yards together of level ground, and the cove in which Mr. M'Ilmery lives is almost impenetrably surrounded by tiresome and lofty hills, broken into ravines, with small rills of water. It is true, that here may be obtained a solid foundation on which to build, without danger of dislocation by the perpetual changes and ravages of the river, but in an agricultural settlement something more is wanting than foundations for houses.

The Cadron was at this time in the hands of four proprietors, who last year commenced the sale of town-lots to the amount of 1300 dollars, and the succeeding sale was appointed to take place in the approaching month of May.

What necessity there may be for projecting a town at this place, I will not take upon myself to decide, but a house of public entertainment, a tavern, has long been wanted, as the Cadron lies in another of the leading routes through this territory. It is one of the resorts from St. Louis, and the settlements on White river, as well as to the hot springs of the Washita, and the inhabitants of Red river. From Arkansas to this place, about 150 miles by land, there is a leading path which proceeds through the Great Prairie.

To those southern gentlemen who pass the summer in quest of health and recreation, this route to the hot springs of the Washita, which I believe is the most convenient, would afford a delightful and rational amusement.

In the course of the day I amused myself amongst the romantic cliffs of slaty sand-stone, which occupy the vicinity of the Cadron. Here I found vestiges of several new and curious plants, and among them an undescribed species of *Eriogonum*, with a considerable root, partly of the colour and taste of rhubarb. The *Petalostemons*, and several plants of the eastern states, which I had not seen below, here again make their appearance. The *Cactus ferox* of the Missouri, remarkably loaded with spines, appears to forebode the vicinity of the Mexican desert.

The dip of the strata is here south-east, and the mountains, generally destitute of organic remains, pass off in chains from the north of west to the south of east.

28th.] The river still continued rising. This morning I walked out two or three miles over the hills, and found the land, except in the small depressions and alluvion of the creek, of an inferior quality, and chiefly timbered with oaks and hickories thinly scattered. Ages must elapse before this kind of land will be worth purchasing at any price. Still, in its present state, it will afford a good range of pasturage for cattle, producing abundance of herbage, but would be unfit for cotton or maize, though, perhaps, suited to the production of smaller grain ; there is not, however, yet a grist-mill on the Arkansa, and flour commonly sells above the Post, at 12 dollars per barrel. For the preparation of maize, a wooden mortar, or different kinds of hand or horse-mills are sufficient. Sugar and coffee are also high priced articles, more particularly this year. In common, I suppose, sugar retails at 25 cents the pound, and coffee at 50. Competition will, however, regulate and reduce the prices of these and other articles, which, but a few years ago, were sold at such an exorbitant rate, as to be almost proscribed from general use. There is a maple in this country, or rather, I believe, on the banks of White river, which has not come under my notice, called the sugar-tree (though not, as they say, the *Acer saccharinum*), that would, no doubt, by a little attention afford sugar at a low rate ; and the decoctions of the wood of the sassafras and spice bush *(Laurus benzoin)*, which abound in this country, are certainly very palatable substitutes for tea.

It is to be regretted that the widely scattered state of the population in this territory, is but too favourable to the spread of ignorance and barbarism. The means of education are, at present, nearly proscribed, and the rising generation are growing up in mental darkness, like the French hunters who have preceded

15

them, and who have almost forgot that they apper-
tain to the civilized world.   This barrier will, however, be effectually removed by the progessive acces-
sion of population, which, like a resistless tide, still
continues to set towards the west.

Contiguous to the north-eastern, or opposite declivity of the chain of hills, which flank the settlement of
Mr. M'Ilmery, I observed in my ramble, a considerable collection of aboriginal tumuli, towards the centre of which, disposed in a somewhat circular form,
I thought I could still discern an area which had once
been trodden by human feet;—but, alas! both they
and their history are buried in impenetrable oblivion!
their existence is blotted out from the page of the
living! and it is only the eye which has been accustomed to the survey of these relics, that can even distinguish them from the accidental operations of nature.   How dreary is this eternal night which has
overtaken so many of my fellow-mortals!—a race,
perhaps brave, though neither civilized nor luxuri-
ous, and who, like the retreating Scythians pursued
by Darius, made, perhaps, at last, an obstinate resistance around their luckless families, and the revered
tombs of their ancestors!

* * *

Besides these tumuli scattered through the forests,
there are others on the summits of the hills, formed
of loose stones thrown up in piles.   We have no reason to suppose, that these remains were left by the
Arkansas; they themselves deny it, and attribute them
to a people distinct and governed by a superior policy.

29th and 30th.] Still at Mr. M'Ilmery's, during
which time the weather has been cold and stormy.

The United States have now ordered the survey of
all the alluvial and other saleable lands of the Arkansa,
which are to be ready for disposal in about two years
from the present time.   One of the surveyors, Mr.
Pettis, was now laying out the lands contiguous to the

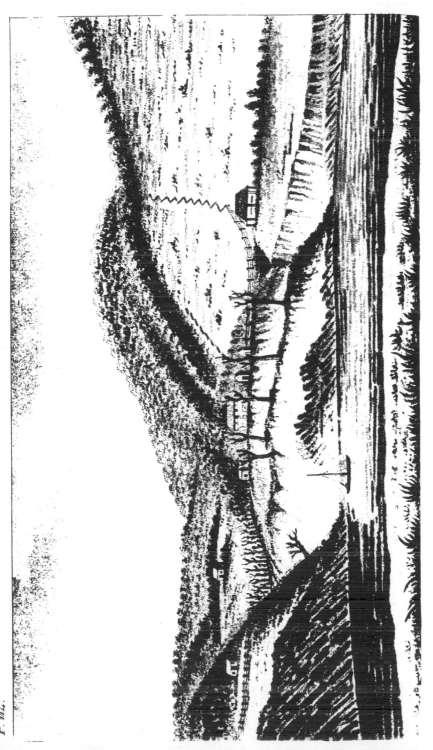

Cadron into sections. Another surveyor is also employed in the Great Prairie, and proceeding, at this time, from the vicinity of Arkansas to this place. The poorer and hilly lands, generally, are not yet thought to be worth the expense of a public survey. Some of these surveys, however, extend as far to the north as the banks of White river. Mr. P. obtains three dollars per mile, for surveying the river lands, which are extremely difficult, from the density and extent of the cane-brakes, and the multiplicity of lagoons or portions of the deserted channel of the river, which, as we have had already occasion to remark, are still continually forming.

These fine cotton lands have not altogether escaped the view of speculators, although there is yet left ample room for the settlement of thousands of families, on lands, which, except the few preemption rights, will be sold by the impartial hand of the nation, at a price as reasonable as the public welfare shall admit of, which has heretofore been at the rate of two dollars the acre, and as no lands on this river are now surveyed and offered for sale, but such as are considered to be of the first and second rate, there can consequently be no room left for imposition, and though there is, indeed, a considerable proportion of inundated land unavoidably included, yet in general, as I understand from the surveyor, there will be in almost every section, a great portion of elevated soils.

The preemption rights, as they are called, are a certain species of reward or indemnification for injuries sustained in the late war, and afforded to such individuals only, as had made improvements in the interior of the territories, prior to the year 1813. Such individuals, if able to pay, are entitled to one or more quarter sections, as the lines of their improvements may happen to extend into the public lines when surveyed, of one or more such plots or fractional sections of land. These rights have been bought up by speculators, at from 4 or 500 to 1000 dollars, or at the positive rate of from 3 to 10 dollars the acre, including the price of two dollars per acre to the United States; a certain proof of the growing importance of this country, where lands, previous to the existence of any positive title, have brought a price equal to that of the best lands on the banks of the Ohio, not immediately contiguous to any considerable town. The hilly lands, which have not been thought worthy of a survey, will afford an invaluable common range for all kinds of cattle, while the alluvial tracts are employed in producing maize, cotton, tobacco, or rice. I must, here, however, remark by the way, that there exists a considerable difference in the nature of these alluvial soils. They are all loamy, never cold or argillaceous, but often rather light and sandy; such lands, however, though inferior for maize, are still well adapted for cotton. The richest soils here produce 60 to 80 bushels of maize per acre. The inundated lands, when properly banked so as to exclude and introduce the water at pleasure by sluices, might be well employed for rice, but the experiment on this grain has not yet been made, on an extensive scale, by any individual in the territory, although its success, in a small way, has been satisfactorily ascertained. Indigo is occasionally raised for domestic use, but would require more skill in its preparation for the market. Indeed, as yet, the sum of industry calculated to afford any satisfactory experiment in agriculture or domestic economy, has not been exercised by the settlers of the Arkansa, who, with half the resolution of the German farmers of Pennsylvania, would ensure to themselves and their families comfort and affluence.

After the most diligent inquiries concerning the general health of this country, I do not find any substantial reason to alter the opinion which I have already advanced. I am, however, firmly persuaded,

that the immediate banks of the Arkansa, in this respect are to be preferred to the prairies, and I can only
account for this remarkable circumstance, by the unusual admixture of common salt, or muriate of soda,
in its waters, which prevents it from becoming dan-
gerously putrid in the neighbouring ponds and lagoons; and I would farther recommend its use to the
inhabitants in preference to any fountain water, however convenient. The pellucid appearance of the
water, in most of the lagoons which have come under
my notice, is, in all probability, attributable to this
circumstance.

I was indeed informed that instances of the ague
were known at some seasons, but that this disease
had been principally confined to those who were des
titute, through indolence or accidental poverty, of the
proper means of nourishment, and who, after its commencement, neglected the aid of medicine. A better
proof, than the general healthy appearance of the inhabitants, and the total absence of doctors, whose aid
must of course be unnecessary, need not be adduced
in favour of the prevailing salubrity of the banks of
the Arkansa.

From Mr. M'Ilmery, I learn that there exists very
considerable tracts of fertile land, along the banks of
La Feve's creek, which proceeds in a south-west direction towards Red river for about 200 miles, deriving its source with Little river of the latter, as
well as with another contiguous stream of the Arkansa, called Petit John, and likewise with the Pottoe.
It is also said to be navigable near 100 miles, and
possessed of a gentle current.

From Mr. Pettis, the surveyor, I obtained two
small specimens of the oil-stone, or hone of the
Washita. It is a siliceous slaty rock, of a conchoi-
dal and sometimes splintery fracture, bordering on
hornstone; some of it is as white as snow, and it
splits so evenly as to afford hones without any addi-

tional labour. Occasionally it appears divided by ferruginous illinitions, presenting muscoid ramifications
in relief, but scarcely discolouring the surface. It
feebly absorbs oil or water, and then becomes somewhat diaphanous. It is infusible by the common
blowpipe.*

31st.] This evening we proceeded to David M'Ilmery's, about three miles above the Cadron, who
lived about a mile and a half from the bank of the
river, at the head of a small alluvial plain or prairie,
apparently well calculated for a superior farm. While
passing through this prairie, I observed five deer
feeding, and passed almost without disturbing them.

Wild cats of two kinds, both striped and spotted,
as well as panthers, bears, and wolves (black and
grey), are in considerable abundance in this country.
The bison (improperly called buffaloe) is also met
with occasionally in the distance of about a day's ride
towards the Washita.

The inhabitants were just beginning to plough for
cotton, an operation here not very laborious, except
when breaking up the prairies, as the soil is friable
and loamy.

In a small prairie adjoining, where a second family
were residing, a single tree of the bow-wood (or *Maclura*) existed, having a trunk of about 18 inches
diameter.

April 1st.] The Arkansa after a sudden rise had now
commenced again to fall; its inundations being chiefly
vernal, taking place from February to May, are less
injurious than those of the Missouri and Mississippi,
which occur in mid-summer, and are consequently
unavoidably injurious to the advancing crops. This
circumstance also tends to prove, that no considerable

* For a further account of this mineral, which appeared to be undescribed, see a note in the Essay on the Geological Structure of the Valley of the Mississippi, which I published in the first part of the second
volume of the Journal of the Academy of Natural Sciences of Philadelphia.

branch of this river derives its source within the region of perpetual snow, which dissolves most in the warmest season of the year, and that its inundations are merely the effect of winter rains; its rising and falling, from the same cause, is also much more sudden than that of the Missouri.

About eight miles from the Cadron, we passed Mr. Marsongill's, pleasantly situated on the gentle declivity of a ridge of hills, which commence about a mile from the river. Three miles further, we passed Mr. Fraser's, the commencement of the Pecannerie settlement. Here, at the distance of more than 12 miles, the hills of the Petit John appear conspicuous and picturesque. In three miles more, seven or eight houses are seen, situated along either bank of the river, and sufficiently contiguous for an agreeable neighbourhood.

From the Cadron upwards, the falls of the rivulets afford conveniences for mills. A grist-mill did not, however, as yet exist on the banks of the Arkansa, though a saw-mill had been recently erected.

2d.] Mr. D. proceeded about eight miles above Fraser's, and remained the rest of the afternoon nearly opposite to the bayou or rivulet of point Remu, from whence, on that side, commences the Cherokee line. Here the hills again approach in gentle declivities, presenting beds of black slaty siliceous rock (grauwacke slate), inclined about 60° south-east. Both banks of the river in this distance are one continued line of farms. Some of the cabins are well situated on agreeable rising grounds; but the nearer, I perceive, the land is to the level of inundation, the greater is its fertility. The highest grounds are thin and sandy, so much so, that occasionally the Cactus or prickly-pear makes its appearance.

3d.] Still opposite point Remu. On this side of the river, where Mr. Ellis now resides, an agreeable site for a town offers, but the landing is bad. A few

miles back there are not less than 14 families scattered over the alluvial land.   There were also a number
of families settled along the banks of the Remu. Adjoining Mr. Ellis's there was a small sandy prairie,
over which I found Cactus's and the *Plantago gna-
phaloïdes* abundantly scattered.   I am informed that
there are considerable quantities of this poor and sandy land, though not in any one place very extensive,
and immediately surrounded with richer lands which
have been, and are yet skirted by the overflow. With
slight banking, these lands, not too deeply submerged,
will one day be considered the best for all kinds of
produce, but more particularly maize and rice.

4th.] A storm of wind sprang up during the night
from the south-west, and continued so as to retard us,
after proceeding with difficulty about six miles, in
which distance we arrived at the house of Mr. Tucker,
situated at the base of a lofty ridge of broken hills,
not less than 6 or 700 feet high, presenting an alternation of terraces and cliffs, and continuing in a north-
west direction nearly the same height for about eight
miles.   This range is known by the same name as
that of the contiguous rivulet, the Little John, some
Frenchman probably who first discovered it.   At the
south-east end I found the ascent very steep, and
which, like most considerable chains, was at this extremity the highest and most precipitous.   From the
summit a vast wilderness presented itself covered with
trees, and chequered with ranges of mountains, which
appeared to augment and converge towards the north-
west.   To the east a considerable plain stretches out,
almost uninterrupted by elevations.   From the south-
west I could enumerate four distinct chains of mountains, of which the furthest, about 40 miles distant,
presented in several places lofty blue peaks, much
higher than any of the intermediate and less broken
ridges.   I thought that this ridge tended somewhat
towards the Mamelle, whose summit at this distance

was quite distinct, though, at the lowest estimate, 40 miles distant. To the north-east the hills traverse the river, and are in this quarter also of great elevation, affording sources to some of the streams of White river, and to others which empty into the Arkansa. Over the vast plain immediately below me, appeared here and there belts of cypress, conspicuous by their brown tops and horizontal branches; they seem to occupy lagoons and swamps, at some remote period formed by the river. As it regards their structure, the lower level of the hills was slaty, the tabular summits a massive, fine-grained sandstone, containing nodules of iron ore. In one place I also saw one of those gigantic tessellated zoophytic impressions,* which indicate the existence of coal. The dip of the sandstone is inconsiderable, and to the north-west. Towards the southern extremity of the ridge which I ascended, there are several enormous masses of rock so nicely balanced as almost to appear the work of art; one of them, like the druidical monuments of England, rocked backwards and forwards on the slightest touch. On the shelvings of this extremity of the mountain, I found a new species of *Anemone*.

As we proceeded in the boat, towards the level of the river, and about a mile below the entrance of the Petit John, we could perceive a slaty and partly horizontal bed of matter, in which there were distinct indications of coal.

5th.] We passed the outlet of the Petit John, a rivulet about 200 miles long, deriving its source with the Pottoe and other streams in the Mazern mountains. Here the hills turn off abruptly to the south, and for four or five miles border the rivulet, which, for some distance, keeping a course not very far from the Arkansa, approaches within 10 miles to the south-east of the Dardanelle settlement. At the distance of

* A Strobilaria, more commonly considered as a species of Phytolite.

about five miles from the first Cherokee village, called
the Galley, Mr. D. and myself proceeded to it by
land.   The first two or three miles presented elevated
and rich alluvial lands, but in one or two directions
bordered by the back-water.   At length we arrived at
the Galley hills, a series of low and agreeable acclivities well suited for building.   Here the Cherokees
had a settlement of about a dozen families, who, in
the construction and furniture of their houses, and in
the management of their farms, imitate the whites,
and appeared to be progressing towards civilization,
were it not for their baneful attachment to whiskey.
Towards the level of the river a darkish bed of slate-
clay appeared, having a dip of not more than 10 to
15°; beneath which occurred a slaty sandstone, containing a little mica, and somewhat darkened apparently by bitumen.   It likewise abounded with organic reliquiæ, among which were something like large
alcyonites, sometimes the thickness of a finger, but
flexuous instead of rigid, and collected together in
considerable quantities; also, a moniliform fossil allied to the Icthyosarcolite of Desmarest, though not
very distinctly, being equally flexuous with the above,
and fragments resembling some species of turrilites,
but no shells of any other description, besides these,
were visible.

The insects which injure the morel cherry-trees so
much in Pennsylvania, I perceive, here occasionally
act in the same way upon the branches of the wild
cherry, (*Prunus virginiana*).

6th.] This morning the river appeared rapidly rising to its former elevation, being nearly bank full, almost a mile in width, and but little short of the Mississippi in magnitude.   The current was now probably four or five miles in the hour, and so difficult to
stem, that after the most laborious exertions since
day-light, we were still in the evening five miles below
the Dardanelle, having made only about 10 miles

from the Galley. We have had the low ridge, which
originated this fanciful name, in sight nearly the whole
day. On the same side of the river, but more distant,
a magnificent empurpled mountain occupies the horizon, apparently not less than 1000 feet high, forming
a long ridge or table, and abrupt at its southern extremity. From its peculiar form it had received the
name of the Magazine or Barn by the French hunters.
It strongly resembles the English mountain in the
north of Yorkshire, called Pendle-hill, familiar to me
from infancy, and by which all the good wives in the
surrounding country could foretel the weather better
than by the almanac.

Along either bank the lands are generally elevated
and fertile, and pretty thickly scattered with the cabins
and farms of the Cherokees, this being the land allotted to them by congress, in exchange for others in
the Mississippi Territory, where the principal part of
the nation still remain.

I was considerably disappointed in learning that
Mr. D. had relinquished the idea of proceeding to the
garrison, with whom I had entertained the hope of
continuing my passage, without interruption or additional delay.

7th.] Both banks of the river, as we proceeded, were
lined with the houses and farms of the Cherokees, and
though their dress was a mixture of indigenous and
European taste, yet in their houses, which are decently
furnished, and in their farms, which were well fenced
and stocked with cattle, we perceive a happy approach towards civilization. Their numerous families, also, well fed and clothed, argue a propitious
progress in their population. Their superior industry, either as hunters or farmers, proves the value of
property among them, and they are no longer strangers
to avarice, and the distinctions created by wealth;
some of them are possessed of property to the amount
of many thousands of dollars, have houses handsomely

and conveniently furnished, and their tables spread
with our dainties and luxuries.

They say, that their language is perfectly distinct
from that of every other spoken by the aborigines.*
Yet the Delawares, according to Mr. Heckewelder,
considered them as their descendants.

The following notice of them occurs in La Vega's
history of the incursion of Ferdinand de Soto, as early
as the year 1541. Seven days' journey from Cutifa-
chiqui, which is stated to be 430 Spanish leagues, or
860 miles from the bay of Apalache, and in a direction of from south-west to north-east, De Soto arrived in a province called Chalaque (evidently the
same people now called Cherokees, as they call themselves Chalakee). The country they then occupied
was said to be sterile, and affording but little maize,
that they fed upon spontaneous roots and herbs, which
they sought in the wilds, and upon the animals of the
forest, hunted with bows and arrows. In their manners they were gentle, and went habitually naked.
Their chief sent as a present to De Soto a couple of
deer skins, and their country abounded with wild
hens (probably the Prairie hen, *Tetrao cupido*). In
one town they made him a present of 700 of these
birds, and he experienced the like liberality in several
other of their towns.†

They were acquainted with this country prior to
their removal, but never laid any claim to it. It was
merely the resort of their renegadoes and wandering
hunters. The number who have now emigrated
hither are about 1500. The unsettled limit of their
claim in this country, has been the means of producing some dissatisfaction, and exciting their jealousy

---

* Charlevoix also remarks, "I cannot find out to what language the
Cherokees belong, a pretty numerous people, who inhabit the vast
meadows between the lake Erie, and the Mississippi," and adds, that
the Iroquois make war with them. Hist. Journal, p. 115, London Ed.
† Purchas's Pilgrims, vol. IV. p. 1539.

against the agents of government. One of their principal chiefs had said, that rather than suffer any embarrassment and uncertainty, he would proceed across Red river, and petition land from the Spaniards. The Cherokees, with their present civilized habits, industry, and augmenting population, would prove a dangerous enemy to the frontiers of the Arkansa Territory. As they have explicitly given up the lands which they possessed in the Mississippi Territory, in exchange for those which they have chosen here, there can be no reason why they should not immediately be confirmed, so as to preclude the visits of land speculators, which excite their jealousy. A serious misunderstanding will probably arise at their ejectment from the south side of the river, which has, I believe, been concluded on by the government. Although the power of the natives is now despised, who can at this time tell, what may grow out of this nation of the aborigines, who, by wisely embracing the habits and industry of the Anglo-Americans, may in time increase, and become a powerful and independent nation, subject by habit to a monarchial form of government.

We find mention, as already remarked, of the Cherokees (under the name of Chalaque) by Garcilasso de la Vega, who found them living near the Apalachian mountains, and speaks in contempt of their poverty and population. At this time, however, they amount to between 12 and 13,000 souls, and are in a promising way of advancing beyond all the other aborigines in strength and population. From examining the oldest histories and maps, it appears that a portion of this nation also occupied the sea-coast of South Carolina, where, according to a tradition still extant, they first saw the white people approach in ships, near to the present site of the city of Charlestown. They requested, say they, a small portion of land, which was readily granted, but at length en-

croached upon us, until we had to cross the mountains, and now even the banks of the Mississippi.

Arriving in the afternoon at Mr. Raphael's, who
keeps a store for the supply of the Cherokees, I hastened to examine the neighbouring ridge of rocks,
which originated the name of the Dardanelle, or as it
is here more commonly called Derdanai, both by the
French and Americans. The fires which commonly
take place among the dry herbage, and which had but
recently been in action, prevented me from making
any botanical collections, and I amused myself by ascending the ridge, which, at the first approach, appeared to be inaccessible. At length I gained the
summit, which, at the highest point on the bank of
the river, might be about 300 feet. The rock was a
massive sandstone, with the laminæ elevated towards
the south-east, at an inclination of near 60°, and, in
many places intricately traversed with seams of ferruginous matter, presenting, by their numerous intersec-
tions, an almost tessellated or retiform appearance.
In some specimens, the interstices were perfectly
rhomboidal, and separated into rhombic fragments.
Several enormous and romantic blocks were scattered
along the margin of the river, and on some of them
small trees were growing. From the summit opened
another sublime view of the surrounding country.
Again to the south and south-west, I could distinguish three of the four chains of mountains, which
were visible from the high hills of the Petit John, and
still, to my surprise, distinctly appeared the Mamelle,
though, by water, near upon 100 miles distant, and
not less than 60 by land, which would appear to argue
an elevation more considerable than that which I had
at first imagined. The Magazine mountain to the west,
though, at first, apparently so near, is not less than 10
miles distant, looking, if any thing, more considerably
elevated than the Mamelle, and probably not less than
1200 feet high. In this point of view, it appears

isolated, gradually descending into the plain, and accumulating in magnitude to the north-west; it here
descends rather more abruptly, though the highest
point is still to the south, where it appears to rise in
broken fasçades unconnectedly with the auxiliary
ridge.

8th.] From the Cherokees I understood that there
still exists some portion of the Natchez, who live with
the Chactaws, near Mobile river. It would be interesting to learn, what affinities their language possesses
with that of the existing nations. The Chetimachas
of bayou Placquimine, said by Du Pratz to speak
the same language, and to be a branch of the same
people, might also afford some information concerning the Natchez and their connections.

In the evening, we crossed to the right-hand cliff
of the Dardanelle, where Mr. D. again renewed his
trade with the Indians and their retailers. I embraced
this opportunity to make one of my usual rambles,
and found an extraordinary difference in the progress
of vegetation here, exposed to the south and sheltered from the north-western wind. Proceeding leisure-
ly towards the summit of the hill, I was amused by
the gentle murmurs of a rill of pellucid water, which
broke from rock to rock. The acclivity, through a
scanty thicket, rather than the usual sombre forest,
was already adorned with violets, and occasional clusters of the parti-coloured Collinsia. The groves and
thickets were whitened with the blossoms of the
Dogwood (Cornus florida). The lugubrious vociferations of the whip-poor-will; the croaking frogs,
chirping crickets, and whoops and halloos of the Indians, broke not disagreeably the silence of a calm
and fine evening, in which the thermometer still remained at 70°; and though the scene was not finished in the usual style of rural landscape, yet to me it
was peculiarly agreeable, when contrasted with the
dull monotony of a gloomy and interminable forest,

whose solitude had scarcely ever been cheered by the voices or habitations of men.

9th.] In the forenoon, I proceeded to Mr. Webber's, along the hills of the Dardanelle, which border the right bank of the river, opposite to which, a contiguous ridge and similar cliffs also appear, forming, as it were, a wide chasm traversed by the river. The approach of these hills to either bank, like vast portals, probably originated the name of this place. Walking along the margin of the continued precipice which bordered the river, I observed a brownish animal quickly retreating into its burrow, which in size appeared to be little short of that of a mole. On rolling away a fragment of rock, I succeeded in discovering that the object of my pursuit was an enormous spider, no less than four inches from the extremity of one foot to that of the other, and two inches from head to tail, covered with long brown hair; the eyes six in number and minute, the mouth not discoverable, but in the place of jaws, as in the Monoculi, two of the six pair of feet, of a strong cartilaginous texture, very short and retracted together, each terminated by a simple hooked claw, and internally lined with a row of minute teeth for mastication. In fact, it entirely resembled those gigantic tropical spiders, which we see exhibited in museums.

The rocks, like many others which we had now seen, are still arenilitic, and apparently destitute of organic remains. From the enormous dislocated masses and gaping chasms which here border the precipice, I am strongly inclined to believe, that this ridge had, at some period, been convulsed by an earthquake.

In the course of my inquiries concerning minerals, I was told of the existence of a silver mine, somewhere along the banks of White river, but though the opinion is a very prevalent one, it is necessary to receive it with caution. Fragments of pyrites, as usual, have been shown to me for precious ores, and the true statement of their value, so contrary to san-guine expectation, is often treated as an imposition to conceal their importance.

Mr. Walter Webber, a metif, who acts as an Indian trader, is also a chief of the nation, and lives in ease and affluence, possessing a decently furnished and well provided house, several negro slaves, a large, well clear-ed, and well fenced farm; and both himself and his nephew read, write, and speak English. Yesterday, while passing along the bank of the river, I observed with pleasure the fine farms and comfortable cabins occupied by the Indians, and found them very busily employed felling trees, and clearing their grounds preparatory to the seed-time. The failure, however, of last year's crops, in consequence of the dry weath-er, was severely felt, and more particularly in conse-quence of the arrival among them of many ill-provid-ed families of emigrants from the old nation.

In the evening, the brother of their late principal chief Tallantusky, arrived here, accompanied by his wife and two or three other Indians. He last year took leave of the old nation in the Mississippi territo-ry, and embarked with the emigrants, who are yet far from forming a majority of the nation. Being a half Indian, and dressed as a white man, I should scarcely have distinguished him from an American, except by his language. He was very plain, prudent, and unassuming in his dress and manners; a Franklin amongst his countrymen, and affectionately called the " beloved" father. Sensible to the wants of those who had accompanied him in his emigration, he had confidently expected a supply of flour and salt from Mr. Drope, all of which articles had, however, been sold below, excepting a small quantity reserved for the chief himself. He could have sent, he said, some of his people down to the mouth of the river, to pur-chase maize and flour, but that it would interrupt them

17

in preparing their fields for the ensuing crop. Mr.
D., who had in the Mississippi territory become acquainted with Jolly, the chief, tells me that his word
was inviolable, and that his generosity knew no
bounds, but the limitation of his means.

11th.] Returning from my rambles to-day, chiefly
in quest of insects, I picked off my skin and clothes
more than 50 ticks *(Acarus sanguisugas)*, which are
here more abundant and troublesome than in any
other part of America in which I have yet been.
Many of the same kinds of insects, common to the
banks of the Missouri, and, indeed, to most part of
the United States, are also found in this territory.

From the hills in the vicinity of Mr. Webber's, I
obtained a fine view of the Magazine mountain, and
now found that it was connected with a range of
others, proceeding for many miles a little to the north
of west. The side which here presents itself, appeared almost inaccessibly precipitous.

15th.] This afternoon, I had again the pleasure of
seeing the brother of the late governor Lewis, now
Cherokee agent, whom I had first met with at fort
Mandan, on the Missouri. From him I learn, that
the progress of civilization among the Cherokees, is
comparatively modern; that Nancy Ward, called by
way of eminence and esteeem " the beloved," first
introduced among them the domesticated cow. From
her have sprung several men of distinction in the nation, by whose influence and example the condition
of their Indian brethren has been ameliorated. Her
advice and council borders on supreme, her interference is allowed to be decisive even in affairs of life
and death.

From the civilized Cherokees, with whom alone I
could conveniently hold converse, I found it extremely difficult to acquire any knowledge, either of the
traditions, opinions, or ancient customs of their nation. The humiliating details of former poverty,

P. 150.

ignorance, and superstition, tended to wound the feelings of those, who, besides the advantages, had also imbibed the pride and luxury of Europe. If the Cherokees had only discarded their superstitions, and retained their social virtues, besides acquiring habits of industry, we might indeed congratulate them on the change of their condition; but, unfortunately, with the superior intelligence, conveniences, and luxuries of civilization, have also been acquired that selfish attachment to property, that love of riches, which, though not really intrinsic, have still the power to purchase sinister interest, and separate the condition of men, and hence arises that accumulation of laws and punishments, from which the patriarchal state of those we call savages was so happily exempt. No legal snares were laid for the heedless; no gallows erected for the guilty; no contest arose for wealth or power. Every tribe was but a single family; their aged chief and his venerable associates were as fathers, governors, and advisers. Their young men considered themselves as brothers. No one was rich while the others were poor; and they considered nothing of value that was not essentially useful. As their frugal wants were almost spontaneously supplied, they were strangers alike to poverty and affluence; they boasted not of possessions; and were habitually hospitable to strangers. Scarcely sensible of want, they were alive to friendship and undissembled passions. Their pride, confined to personal excellence, was always checked by the emulation of superior worth, sanctioned and acknowledged by the approbation of the aged.

Almost unrestrained by artifice or moral education, we should, perhaps, expect the man of nature to become the prey of passion, like the irrational creation. Yet so nicely balanced, in every situation, is the proportion of good and evil allotted to humanity, that one stage of society has but little advantage over an.

other.   Nature is not a cruel demon, nor delights in
the accomplishment of destruction.   Those who are
fed by her frugal bounties are but seldom hurried into
excess; indeed, the nations of America were stigmatized with apathy, so great was their command of the
social passions, and their magnanimity under suffering.   But the dire hatred which they bore their enemies, was a lasting proof of the strength of their affections, and mutual attachment.   They felt for each
other as members of the same family, as sons of the
same father.; a band of brothers mutually bound to
defend and revenge the cause of each other, by a just
and undeviating system of retaliation.

   Their affection for those, whom time or casualty
removed from the social circle, was as great and sincere, as extravagant demonstration could possibly declare.   Among the Cherokees and others, the dead
were not only accompanied by the choicest things
which they had valued in life, but even, if a chief or
father, interred in the house which had been his habitation, and which was thenceforth devoted to ruin and
desolation.   So awful even was the inanimate body
then considered, that all who had immediately attended the interment, or touched the corpse, refrained
from the company of their wives and families, for the
space of seven days and nights.

   In no part of North America have we ever met with
that kind of irrational adoration called idolatry.   All
the natives acknowledged the existence of a great,
good, and indivisible Spirit, the author of all created
being.   Believing also in the immortality of the soul,
and in the existence of invisible agencies, they were
often subjected to superstitious fears, and the observance of omens and dreams, the workings of per-
turbed fancy.   By these imaginary admonitions, they
sometimes suffered themselves to be controlled in their
most important undertakings, relinquishing every

thing which was accidentally attended by any inaus-
picious presage of misfortune.

As among the Asiatics, and other imperfectly civilized nations, the condition of the female sex bordered upon degradation. Considered rather as objects
of pleasure and necessity, than as rational companions,
several of them often lived together in the house of
the same husband. However custom might have
tolerated this habit, we are happy to find that civilization tends to its abolition. Polygamy among the
Cherokees, without any legal restraint, will, in time,
be spontaneously abandoned, as their conjugal attachment appears to be strong and sincere.

Marriage among the Cherokees, as with most of
the natives, was formerly consummated with very
little ceremony. When a young man became enam-
oured, it was the custom modestly to declare his desire to marry through the medium of some female
relative, who exclusively conferred with the mother,
the father never interfering. If the mother agreed,
and thought well of the proposal, it was immediately
made known. If not, she put off making a direct
answer by a reference to her brother or eldest son.
Consent being obtained of the mother, the bride-
groom without much further conference with the
bride, was then told where she lay, and thencefor-
ward admitted to her bed.

From some cause or other, it appears, that the women of the Cherokees frequently made use of means
to promote abortion, which at length became so
alarming, as to occasion a resort to punishment by
whipping.

In all stages of society regulations have existed,
either as controling customs, or written laws, whereby
the conduct of men with each other was limited and
restrained.   A system of equity was established, more
or less strictly according with justice, as influenced
by exterior circumstances ; thus life was claimed for

life, and objects wrested from the weak or unsus-
pecting, restored by the interference of moral power
vested in superiors and rulers.   Among the Cherokees and other Indians of North America, the conviction of natural justice went so far as frequently to
draw no distinction of punishment betwixt man-
slaughter and murder.   Governed also by the idea of
a general fraternity existing throughout a tribe of people, the brother of a murderer, or even his nearest relative was not secure from the fatal avenger, in the
absence of the principal.   In consequence of this, it
sometimes happened that the brother became the exe-
cutioner of his brother or nearest relative, who had
committed a murder, in order to save himself from
vengeance.   He who had taken away the life of another, either by malice or accident, was also occasionally suffered to redeem it, by obtaining, and presenting
to the injured party, a scalp or a prisoner of the enemy,
as they were satisfied in any way to obtain life for life.

An institution, I believe unparallelled in the policy
of the northern natives, except among the Cherokees
and Creeks (and which has been quoted by Mr. Adair
in order to prove an affinity with the Jews), was the
existence of a town of refuge, inhabited by the supreme chief, in which no blood was suffered to be
shed, and into which those who had committed man-
slaughter and other crimes were suffered to enter on
excusing themselves or professing contrition.

With the inequality of fortune which civilization
has introduced among the Cherokees, we find also a
severity in their legal punishments, to which they
were formerly strangers.   Out of their salaries now
received from government, they appropriate a certain
sum towards the support of a police, whose duty it is
to punish those who are guilty of crimes against the
public.   A man who has for the first time been con-
victed of horse-stealing, receives a punishment of 100
lashes, and for the second offence 200, thus increasing

the punishment for every additional offence. For stealing a cow 50 lashes were inflicted, and so on, in proportion to the value of the property stolen.

Mr. John Rogers, a very respectable and civilized Cherokee, told me that one of the regulators happening to have a relation who had been repeatedly guilty of theft, and finding him incorrigible, he destroyed his eye-sight with a penknife, saying, " as long as you can see you will steal, I will therefore prevent your thefts by the destruction of your sight." Dissatisfied with this system of punishment, many of the poor renegadoes fled from the bosom of the Cherokee nation, and came to the banks of the Arkansa and Red river. The same punishment for theft will now, however, probably be established also in this territory.

The former preparation of the warrior, among the Cherokees, was more calculated to inspire fortitude under suffering than courage in the field. The chief was ever attentive to the admonition of dreams and omens. They sung the songs of war, and imposed upon themselves the most rigid fasts and mortifying ablutions, at all seasons of the year, in order to obtain a favourable omen for their departure. Day after day these privations and voluntary sufferings were continued with fearful austerity, and those who might express a wish for relaxation were desired to leave the society.

The arrival of the Cherokees in this country did not fail, as might have been foreseen, to excite the jealousy of the Osages, within whose former territory they had now taken up their residence. Major Lovely, the first agent appointed to reside among the Cherokees of the Arkansa, on his arrival held a council with the Osages at the falls of the Verdigris, and about 60 miles distant from their village. Some quarrel, however, about two years ago arising between the two na-

tions, the Osages way-layed 12 or 14 of the Cherokees and killed them.   On this occasion, the Cherokees collected together in considerable numbers, and
ascended the river to take revenge upon the Osages,
who fled at their approach, losing about 10 of their
men, who either fell in the retreat, or becoming
prisoners, were reserved for a more cruel destiny.
The Cherokees, now forgetting the claims of civilization, fell upon the old and decrepid, upon the women
and innocent children, and by their own account destroyed not less than 90 individuals! and carried away
a number of prisoners.   A white man who accompanied them (named Chisholm), with a diabolical
cruelty that ought to have been punished with death,
dashed out the brains of a helpless infant, torn from
the arms of its butchered mother! Satiated with a horrid vengeance, the Cherokees returned with exultation
to bear the tidings of their own infamy and atrocity.

It appears, to me, to have been the duty of the su-
perintendent of Indian affairs to have apprehended that
white man, and delivered him over to the government
for trial and punishment.   Without some interference
of this kind, and indeed a cognizance of the conduct
of every white man found permanently dwelling
among the Indians, it will not be possible for a traveller or a merchant to go amongst these people without
incurring the greatest personal risk, as their revenge
is but too often indiscriminate in its object; neither
can the security of the frontier settlements ever be
rendered certain, until these wanton and unprovoked
cruelties of the whites, and their piratical wars, be prevented.

Two or three families of the Delawares are now
living with the Cherokees, who appeared to be very
poor, and addicted to intoxication.   Another remnant
of these unfortunate people, once so considerable, is also
about to be transferred from the state of Ohio to the

banks of the Arkansa, where, it is to be hoped, they will enjoy amidst domestic tranquillity the superior advantages of civilization.

17th.] My rambles to day were rewarded with the discovery of a new genus, of the class Tetradynamia or Cruciferæ, allied to *Ricotia* and *Lunaria*. In the evening I visited Mr. Rollins, the agent for Indian trade, who treated me with politeness and hospitality.

CHAPTER VIII.

Pass several inconsiderable rivulets, and obtain sight of the Tomahawk mountain and the Gascon hills—Mulberry creek—that of Vache Grasse.—Lee's creek—prairies—Sugarloaf mountain.—Arrive at the garrison of Belle Point—a change in the vegetation—The Maclura or Bow-wood—The garrison—Cedar prairie—Rare plants.

20th.] This morning I left Mr. Webber's, in a perogue with two French boatmen, in order to proceed to the garrison, about 120 miles distant by water. We proceeded nearly to Charbonniere creek, 24 miles from the place of departure. Ten miles from Webber's we passed the outlet of Piney creek, so called from the pine-hills by which it is bordered. Eight miles further we came to Rocky creek, opposite to the outlet of which, a ledge of rocks nearly traverses the Arkansa, and presents a considerable obstruction in the navigation at a low stage of water. The current even at this time broke with a considerable noise.

21st.] About six miles above Rocky creek we passed the Charbonniere, so called from the occurrence of coal in its vicinity; we also observed the outlet of Spadric creek, on the borders of which there

18

are considerable tracts of fertile land, well supplied with springs, and occupied by the Cherokees.
The rocks which occasionally border the river, of
very inconsiderable elevation, are composed of slaty
sandstone, dipping about 25°, sometimes towards the
north-west, and at others to the south-east, or in opposite directions, and also exhibiting indications of
coal. The Charbonniere rock, in particular, about
50 feet high, presents beds of a slaty sandstone, with
a dip of scarcely 20°, and inclined in opposite directions so as to form a basin, in which there are indications of coal. A lofty blue ridge appears to the south,
called by the French hunters the Cassetête or Tomahawk mountain, and about eight miles from hence
enters the creek of the same name, beyond which we
proceeded eight miles of a 12 mile bend, making a
journey of about 28 miles in the course of the day,
and encamped in view of another lofty ridge of mountains. We saw, as we proceeded, no less than 13
deer and a bear.

22d.] Four miles from Allmand creek the Cassetête
mountain appears very distinct, and somewhat resembles the Magazine; being a long ridge abrupt at either'
end. Another range also was visible at a considerable distance, called the Gascon hills. We were detained awhile by a thunder-storm, but proceeded, notwithstanding, about 30 miles, and encamped on an
island just below the outlet of Mulberry creek, on the
banks of which, before the arrival of the Cherokees,
there was a considerable settlement on a body of excellent land. It now constitutes the Cherokee line of
demarkation, and they made free to occupy the deserted cabins and improvements of the whites without
any compensation received either from them or the
government. The bend, which we continued this
morning, of 12 miles extent, is surrrounded on the
right hand side with an amphitheatre of lofty cliffs,
3 to 400 feet high, having a highly romantic and pic-

turesque appearance. Nearly continuing to Mulberry creek, a fine stretch of about eight miles opens to view, affording an ample prospect of the river; its rich alluvions were now clothed in youthful verdure, and backed in the distance by bluish and empurpled hills. The beauty of the scenery was also enlivened by the melody of innumerable birds, and the gentle humming of the wild bees, feeding on the early blooming willows,* which in the same manner line the picturesque banks of the Ohio. The Arkansa, in its general appearance throughout this day's voyage, bears, indeed, a considerable resemblance to that river. It is equally diversified with islands, and obstructed in its course by gravelly rapids; two of them which we passed today, could not have a collective fall of less than 10 or 12 feet each.

The sandstone beds still present very little dip, and by contrary inclinations produce the appearance of basins or circumscribed vallies.

23d.] Two miles above Mulberry creek we passed two islands nearly opposite to each other, and a settlement of three or four families situated along the left bank of the river, on a handsome rising ground, flanked by a continued ridge of low hills. The dawn of morning was again ushered in by the songs of thousands of birds, re-echoing through the woods, and seeking shelter from the extensive plains, which every where now border the alluvion.

We proceeded about 32 miles, and experienced a scorching sun from noon till night, when at length the sky became obscured by clouds portentous of thunder. My thermometer when exposed to the sun rose to 100°. Nearly opposite Vache Grasse creek we passed a rapid, over which there is scarcely more than 12 inches water, in the lowest stage. No hills now appear on either hand, and a little distance in the prairie,

---

* *Salix caroliniana.*

near Vache Grasse, stands the last habitation of the
whites to be met with on the banks of the Arkansa,
except those of the garrison.

Not far from Lee's creek, Perpillon of the French
hunters,* a low ridge again comes up to the border
of the river, in which is discoverable the first calcareous
rock on ascending the Arkansa. From hence also
the prairies or grassy plains begin to be prevalent,
and the trees to decrease in number and magnitude.
Contiguous to our encampment commenced a prairie
of seven miles in length, and continuing within a mile
of the garrison. The river, now presenting long and
romantic views, was almost exclusively bordered with
groves of cotton-wood, at this season extremely beautiful, resembling so many vistas clad in the softest and
most vivid verdure, and crowded with innumerable
birds, but of species common to the rest of the United
States.

24th.] This morning we passed the hills of Lee's
creek, which for a short distance border the Arkansa ;
and about noon arrived at the garrison, which comes
into view at the distance of about four miles, agreeably
terminating a stretch of the river. Rising, as it were,
out of the alluvial forest, is seen from hence, at the
distance of 35 miles, a conic mountain nearly as blue
as the sky, and known by the French hunters under
the name of Point de Sucre, or the sugar loaf.

I met with politeness from major Bradford the
commander of the garrison, but was disagreeably surprised to be given to understand, that I could not have
permission to proceed any higher up the river without
a special credential from the secretary of state, autho-
rizing me to hold that intercourse with the natives,
which I might deem necessary in further pursuing
my journey. It appeared to me, however, sufficiently
obvious, that the governor of the territory must be

* So named after some Frenchman, and not Papillon, as called by
Pike.

empowered to permit an intercourse, civil and commercial, with the Indians, and liberty to travel through their country by their concurrence. And, indeed, all difficulty was removed by a reference to the recent regulations, which empowered the commanders of the garrisons optionally to permit such intercourse ; and I am happy to add, that this measure, which referred me to the hospitality of the major, was, apparently, as gratifying to him as to myself.

At the benevolent request of the commander, and agreeably to my intentions of exploring the natural history of the territory, I resolved to spend a few weeks at the garrison, and make it the depot of my collections. It is with a satisfaction, clouded by melancholy, that I now call to mind the agreeable hours I spent at this station, while accompanied by the friendly aid and kind participation of Dr. Russel, whose memory I have faintly endeavoured to commemorate in the specific name of a beautiful species of *Monarda*.* But relentless death, whose ever-withering hand delights to pluck the fairest flowers, added, in the fleeting space of a few short days, another early trophy to his mortal garland ; and Russel, the only hope of a fond and widowed mother, the last of his name and family, now sleeps obscurely in unhallowed earth ! Gentle Reader, forgive this tribute of sympathy to the recollection of one, whom fully to know was surely to esteem, as a gentleman, an accomplished scholar, and a sincere admirer of the simple beauties of the field of nature.

* * * *

27th.] Yesterday I took a walk of about five miles up the banks of the Pottoe, and found my labour well repayed by the discovery of several new or undescribed plants. In this direction the surface of the ground is gently broken or undulated, and thinly scat-

---

* *Monarda russeliana.*

tered with trees, resembling almost in this respect a
cultivated park. The whole expanse of forest, hill,
and dale, was now richly enamelled with a profusion
of beautiful and curious flowers; among the most
conspicuous was the charming Daisy of America,*
of a delicate lilac colour, and altogether corresponding
in general aspect with the European species; intermingled, appears a new species of *Collinsia*, a large-
flowered *Tradescantia*, various species of *Phlox*, the
Verbena aubletia, and the esculent *Scilla*. From a
low hill, the neighbouring prairie appeared circumscribed by forests, but the mountains of the Pottoe
were not visible. The soil, even throughout the uplands, appeared nearly as fertile as the alluvions, and
affords a most productive pasture to the cattle.

On the 28th, a slow rise in the river was perceptible, produced by the Canadian, or similar branches,
and communicating a chocolate-red colour to the
stream.

In the course of the day, I walked over the hills
bordering the Pottoe, about six miles, in order to see
some trees of the yellow-wood *(Maclura)*, but they
were scarcely yet in leaf, and showed no indications
of producing bloom. Some of them were as much
as 12 inches in diameter, with a crooked and spreading trunk, 50 or 60 feet high. Its wood dies yellow,
and scarcely differs from the Fustick of the West
Indies. From appearances, those few insulated trees
of the Pottoe, are on the utmost limit of their northern
range, and, though old and decayed, do not appear to
be succeeded by others, or to produce any perfect
fruit. The day was so warm, that at 9 o'clock in the
evening, the thermometer still stood at 75°.

The soil, wherever there is the slightest depression,
is of a superior quality, and thickly covered with vegetable earth. The trees appear scattered as if plant-

* *Bellis integrifolia.*

ed by art, affording an unobstructed range for the hunter, equal to that of a planted park.

On the 29th, I took an agreeable walk into the adjoining prairie, which is about two miles wide and seven long. I found it equally undulated with the surrounding woodland, and could perceive no reason for the absence of trees, except the annual conflagration. A ridge of considerable elevation divides it about the centre, from whence the hills of the Pottoe, the Cavaniol, and the Sugar-loaf, at the distance of about 30 miles, appear partly enveloped in the mists of the horizon. Like an immense meadow, the expanse was now covered with a luxuriant herbage, and beautifully decorated with flowers, amongst which I was pleased to see the Painted Cup* of the eastern states, accompanied by occasional clusters of a white flowered *Dodecatheon* or American primrose. The numerous rounded elevations which chequer this verdant plain, are so many partial attempts at shrubby and arborescent vegetation, which nature has repeatedly made, and which have only been subdued by the reiterated operation of annual burning, employed by the natives, for the purpose of hunting with more facility, and of affording a tender pasturage for the game.

May 1st.] The river still continued rising, and also red and turbid from an admixture of the clay of the salt formation.

The garrison, consisting of two block-houses, and lines of cabins or barracks for the accommodation of 70 men whom it contains, is agreeably situated at the junction of the Pottoe, on a rising ground of about 50 feet elevation, and surrounded by alluvial and uplands of unusual fertility. The view is more commanding and picturesque, than any other spot of equal elevation on the banks of the Arkansa. The meanders of the river to the eastward, backed by the hills

---

* *Euchroma coccinea (Bartsia coccinea.* LIN.)

of Lee's creek, are visible for more than six miles.
The basis of the fort is a dark-coloured slaty micaceous sandstone, the lamina of which, nearly horizontal,
and occasionally traversed by calcareous illinitions, are
about four to six inches in thickness, and denudated
for some hundreds of yards by the washing of the
current, which, in an elevated stage, roars and foams
with great velocity.   About three or four miles up
the Pottoe, this rock is underlayed by a bituminous
slate-clay, indicative of coal, beneath which, no doubt,
would be found calcareous rock; neither this nor the
sandstone, however, present any organic remains.

3d.] To-day, accompanied by Doctor Russel,
and another gentleman of the fort, I rode to Cedar
prairie, lying about 10 miles south-east of the garrison, and presenting an irregular or undulating surface.   I here found a second species of that interesting plant, which my venerable friend, William Bartram,
called *Ixia cœlestina;* * the flowers of this species
are also of a beautiful blue, and white at the base.
The whole plain was, in places, enlivened with the
Sysirinchium anceps, producing flowers of an uncommon magnitude; amidst this assemblage it was not
easy to lose sight of the azure larkspur,† whose flowers are of the brightest ultramarine; in the depressions also grew the ochroleucous *Baptisia‡*, loaded
with papilionaceous flowers, nearly as large as those
of the garden pea.

From this prairie, and more particularly from a hill
which partly traverses it, the mountains of the Pottoe
appeared quite distinct, the Sugar-loaf on the east,
and the Cavaniol, about three miles apart, on the west
side of the river; the latter is to all appearance much
the highest, and presents a tabular summit.   The extensive and verdant meadow, in every direction appeared picturesquely bounded by woody hills of different degrees of elevation and distance, and lacked

---

* *Nemastylis cœlestina.*   † *Delphinium azureum.*   ‡ *Baptisia leucophæa.*

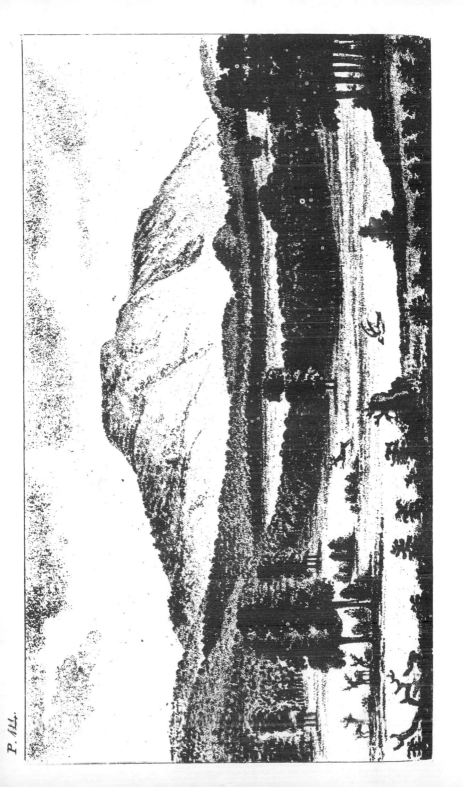

nothing but human occupation to reclaim it from barren solitude, and cast over it the air of rural cheerfulness and abundance.

7th.] The Pottoe and the Arkansa were now at their utmost elevation, and their waters of a pale or milky colour, in consequence of being swelled by the northern streams. The sand-bars and beaches were entirely submerged, and the river still also continued augmenting on the 8th.

On the 9th, I again rode out to Cedar prairie, accompanied by the Doctor, and one of the soldiers, whose intention was to hunt. Several deer were discovered, but all too shy to be approached. We spent the night about the centre of the first portion of the prairie, which is divided into two parts by the intersection of a small wooded rivulet; and though the evening was mild and delightfully tranquil, the swarms of musquetoes, augmented since the recent freshet, would not permit us to sleep.

It is truly remarkable how greatly the sound of objects, becomes absorbed in these extensive woodless plains. No echo answers the voice, and its tones die away in boundless and enfeebled undulations. Even game will sometimes remain undispersed at the report of the gun. Encamping near a small brook, we were favoured by the usual music of frogs, and among them heard a species which almost exactly imitated the lowing of a calf. Just as night commenced, the cheerless howling of a distant wolf accosted our ears amidst the tranquil solitude, and the whole night we were serenaded with the vociferations of the two species of whip-poor-will.

The dawn of a cloudy day, after to us a wakeful night, was ushered in by the melodious chorus of many thousands of birds, agreeably dispersing the solemnity of the ambiguous twilight.

Amongst other objects of nature, my attention was momentarily arrested by the curious appearance of

19

certain conic hillocks, about three feet high, generally situated in denudated places, and covered over with minute pebbles; these on closer examination proved to be the habitations of swarms of large red ants, who entered and came out by one or two common apertures.

On the wooded margin of the prairie, the doctor and myself were gratified by the discovery of a very elegant plant, which constitutes a new genus allied reciprocally to *Phacelia* and *Hydrophyllum.**

CHAPTER IX.

Journey to Red river—Prairies and mountains of the Pottoe—Pass the dividing ridge—Kiamesha river —Arrival on the banks of Red river—The murder of a Cherokee; attempts to obtain redress— Wild horses—Character, geological structure, and rare vegetable productions of the prairies—Return to the garrison at Belle Point.

May 16th.] This morning I left Fort Smith with major Bradford and a company of soldiers, in order to proceed across the wilderness, to the confluence of the Kiamesha and Red river. The object of the major was to execute the orders of government, by removing all the resident whites out of the territory of the Osages; the Kiamesha river being now chosen as the line of demarkation.

On this route we again proceeded through Cedar prairie, and, after traversing two tiresome ridges of sandstone hills, scattered with oaks and pines, we encamped in the evening near to the base of the Sugar-loaf mountain, having travelled about 25 miles in

---

* I have given it the trivial name of *Nemophila*, as, in this country, it now constituted the prevailing ornament of the shady woods.

a south-west direction. After passing the two ridges and crossing two brooks, one of them called James' Fork, we kept westwardly towards the banks of the Pottoe, and found the whole country a prairie, full of luxuriant grass about knee high, in which we surprised herds of fleeting deer, feeding as by stealth.

The Cavaniol, now clear of mist, appeared sufficiently near to afford some more adequate idea of its form and character. A prominent point which appears on its summit, is, I am told by the Cherokees who accompanied us, a mound of loose stones, thrown up either as a funeral pile or a beacon by the aborigines. The natives and hunters assert that subterraneous rumblings have been heard in this mountain. The Sugar-loaf, covered to its summit with trees and shrubs, is composed of sandstone, and appears now accompanied by three others less elevated conic eminences, all mutually connected at the base by saliant ridges. From what I perceive, I am inclined to consider the Cavaniol as a continuation of the same chain, proceeding west by north. From the garrison to the encampment of this evening, indications of coal are sufficiently obvious in the bituminous shale and carbonaceous reliquiæ.

17th.] The day was delightfully clear and warm, and the whole aspect of nature appeared peculiarly charming. In the morning our party fell in with a favourite amusement, in the pursuit of two bears, harmlessly feeding in the prairies, which, being very fat, were soon overtaken and killed. We proceeded about 20 miles; towards evening passing the Pottoe, which was quite fordable, notwithstanding the late fresh. Our course was principally south-south-west, and this evening, after crossing the Pottoe, more westwardly. We were again in full view of the two picturesque mountains, the Cavaniol and Point Sucre; the latter yet appeared somewhat conic, and scantily wooded, but covered with thickets like the Alleghany mountains. Our route was continued through prairies, occasionally divided by sombre belts of timber, which serve to mark the course of the rivulets. These vast plains, beautiful almost as the fancied Elysium, were now enamelled with innumerable flowers, among the most splendid of which were the azure Larkspur, gilded Coreopsides, Rudbeckias, fragrant Phloxes, and the purple Psilotria. Serene and charming as the blissful regions of fancy, nothing here appeared to exist but what contributes to harmony.

18th.] To-day, in a journey of about 25 miles, we passed several very rocky pine ridges, but over which a loaded wagon had been dragged as far as the Kiamesha, accompanied by a family of emigrants, who had been obliged to remove from the settlement of Mulberry creek, on the arrival of the Cherokees. At breakfast time, we were regaled with the wild honey of the country, taken from a tree which the guide had discovered for us. Our course was still to the south of south-west, in which direction we twice crossed the meanders of a branch of the Pottoe, called Fourche Malin. About 2 o'clock we passed the dividing ridge of the Pottoe and Kiamesha, nearly the height of the Alleghany in Pennsylvania, very rocky, and thinly scattered with pines and oaks; the rock sandstone, and destitute of organic remains. This ridge forms part of the principal chain called Mazern mountains by Darby. In the rivulets and ravines I was gratified by the discovery of a new shrubby plant allied to the genus Phyllanthus. After crossing the mountain, we proceeded, at first, a little east of south, to clear the subsidiary ridges, afterwards westwardly, the mountains passing north-west; we then came upon an extensive prairie cove considerably diversified with hills and groves of trees. To the west continued a proximate chain of piney hills, with remarkable serrated summits, known by the familiar name of the Potatoe hills, and to the north-west backed by a more distant and more lofty chain equally piney. On the summit of the dividing ridge, we observed a pile of stones in the bison path that we travelled, which, I was informed, had been thrown up as a monument by the Osages when they were going to war, each warrior casting a stone upon the pile. Discovering herds of Bison in the prairie, the soldiers immediately commenced the chase, and the bulls, now lean and agile, galloped along the plain with prodigious swiftness, like so many huge lions. The pendent beard, large head hid in bushy locks, with the rest of the body nearly divested of hair, give a peculiar and characteristic grace to this animal when in motion. We discovered them in a state of repose, and could perceive the places where they had been gratifying themselves by wallowing or rolling in the dust. The bison, entirely distinct from the buffalo of Europe, notwithstanding the surmises of Doctor Robertson, can scarcely be domesticated. The male, infuriate and jealous in his amours, gores every thing which falls in his way, and becomes totally unmanageable.

Perhaps no animal employs a greater diversity of diet than the bear; the common American species feeds upon fruits, honey, wasps, and bees; they will turn over large logs in quest of other insects, and are also destructive to pigs and fawns, by which means the hunters, imitating the bleat of the latter, will sometimes decoy them within gun-shot.

Panthers are said to be abundant in the woods of Red river, nor are they uncommon on the banks of the Arkansa. A somewhat curious anecdote of one of these animals was related to me by our guide. A party of hunters in the morning missed one of their dogs from the encampment, and after a fruitless search were proceeding on their route, when one of the other dogs obtaining a scent, discovered to the hunters, dead beneath a tree, the dog which had strayed, together with a deer and a wolf in the same condition.

It appeared, that the panther having killed a deer, and eat his fill, got into a tree to watch the remainder, and had, in his own defence, successively fallen upon the wolf and the dog as intruders on his provision.

19th.] This morning we set out late in conse-quence of the rain, which had continued throughout the night. We proceeded a little west of south, along the hills and prairies which divide the three principal branches of the Kiamesha, skirting the south side of the bare serrated hills already noticed scattered with pine and post-oak, in order to shorten the distance which we should have been obliged to make by keep-ing more into the level prairies. In this course we passed a number of little rivulets or torrents with rocky beds. The hills abounded with a kind of slaty petrosilex, which, as well as the slate-clay with which it alternates, appears destitute of organic remains. Some of the fragments were greenish, and appeared to be of the same character with the hone-slate of the Washita. At the junction of its three branches, the Kia-mesha is hemmed in by very lofty ridges, partly co-vered with pine and oak. On one of the most conspicu-ous summits we had observed, for many miles, a beacon of the Osages, being a solitary tree fantasti-cally trimmed like a broom. Our path now became difficult and obstructed by fallen rocks ; that which we had pursued in the earlier part of the day was one of those, which, from time immemorial, had been trod-den out by the bison. We still continued in a south-south-west direction, along the rocky valley of the Kiamesha, which this evening we crossed. The wooded hills prevailed on either hand without any prospect of termination, and strongly resemble the mountains of the Blue ridge, at Harper's Ferry, in Virginia.

20th.] This morning we proceeded four or five miles before breakfast through a pathless thicket, equal in difficulty to any in the Alleghany mountains. The

hills now approached the river in cliffs and inaccessible acclivities, and we concluded to leave the impassable windings of the river by the first gap of the
mountain.   Having now left the almost impenetrable
barriers of the river, we proceeded along a blind bison trace, but at length descended into a rocky ra-
vine, scarcely passable for goats, but which at length
we cleared, after being some hours dispersed from
each other, and came again into hilly open woods,
near the head of Field's cove and creek, deriving its
name from an outlaw who here sought refuge from
justice.   This cove was a kind of hilly prairie land
interspersed with small plains, presenting rocky terraces where most elevated, and covered with herbage.
Lofty wooded hills, scarcely inferior to those of the
river, hemmed in this cove on either hand.   I am informed that the sources of all the rivers in this part
of the Arkansa territory, however closely locked betwixt mountains, present extensive prairies or plains,
where they divaricate to their sources.

Our course was a little west of south, and the distance we travelled probably 20 miles.   We calculated
upon arriving at Red river on the succeeding evening,
being somewhere about 30 miles distant.   The woods
were now disgustingly infested with ticks, though
free from musquetoes.

21st.] We continued about five miles over dreary
and rocky pine hills, without the good fortune of a
bison trace, when, after taking a frugal breakfast, our
hunters again surprised a herd of Bison lying down,
but which were quickly roused into an active gallop.
Deer were uncommonly abundant, and scarcely timid,
or conscious of the aim of their destroyers.   At length
getting rid of the pine hills, we proceeded through a
shrubby prairie, but, by continuing too much to the
westward, again came inadvertently to the Kiamesha,
and were obliged to leave it some miles directly behind us, in order to keep clear of the swampy allu-

vions and ponds by which it was bordered. We now continued south-east, about 20 miles, over hilly woods covered with dwarfish post and black oaks, which having been burnt were extremely difficult to penetrate, lashing and tearing every thing with which they came in contact; we had also to encounter the additional embarrassment of ponds and wet prairies.

The rock was still sandstone, containing appearances indicative of coal. For the last two days I was busily employed in collecting new and curious plants, which continually presented themselves.

22d.] This morning we kept two or three miles to the south-east, and on turning to the south, had the good fortune to enter upon a beaten path, recognised by our guide, which, in the distance of about three miles, brought us to Mr. Styles's, were we had the gratification of obtaining milk and butter for breakfast. This was the emigrant whose traces we had discovered, and who had encountered the Mazern mountains with a loaded wagon, women, and children, among whom was the mother of his wife, blind, and 90 years of age! Mr. Styles had chosen the margin of the prairie for his residence, at a short distance from whence commences the usual bushy hills. After breakfast we continued our route, parallel with Red river, over an extensive prairie to the confluence of the Kiamesha. The people appeared but ill prepared for the unpleasant official intelligence of their ejectment. Some who had cleared considerable farms were thus unexpectedly thrust out into the inhospitable wilderness. I could not but sympathise with their complaints, notwithstanding the justice and propriety of the requisition. Would it had always been the liberal policy of the Europeans to act with becoming justice, and to reciprocate the law of nations with the unfortunate natives!

A flagrant act of injustice to the Indians now, however, came to our knowledge. It was, no doubt, the hopes of employing the present opportunity of gaining redress, which had instigated the journey of the two civilized Cherokees (Messrs. Rodgers), who had accompanied us ; one of whom acted as the state interpreter. The information which we obtained concerning this affair gives it almost an incredible air of atrocity. It appears, that about three months ago, one of the Cherokees, returning from hunting in this quarter, saw some horses in the possession of two brothers named Gibbs, which he recognised to have belonged to Monsieur Vaugin, of the Arkansa, and which had been stolen by these renegadoes. For fear he should convict them of the theft, they treacherously took an opportunity of way-laying the Indian, and shot him dead with a rifle. The same two brothers, this very evening, inadvertently passed by our camp, but in the absence of the major and the Cherokees, and though our circumstantial knowledge of this horrid fact was purely accidental, yet such is the self-condemning nature of guilt, that no sooner had they learnt who we were, than they rushed into the adjoining cane-brake, and effected their escape into the neighbouring province of Texas. A party, indeed, went out instantly in pursuit of them, but were obliged to return in consequence of the darkness of the night, and the extreme difficulty of the way. Orders for their apprehension were left with the magistrate of the district, accompanied by a reward from the Cherokees. They returned after an absence of three weeks, when an attempt was made to bring them to justice by two hunters armed with rifles ; and one of the brothers, who had not actually committed the murder, in the act of warning the other, was shot dead by one of the hunters, whom he had formerly injured in the most indelicate manner. With this revenge, though not sufficiently discriminate, I afterwards learnt, that the Cherokees had expressed themselves satisfied, as it accorded probably with their own ideas of diverging retaliation.

20

The change of soil in the great Prairie of Red river now appeared obvious. It was here that I saw the first calcareous rock charged with shells, &c. since my departure from the banks of the Ohio. Nothing could at this season exceed the beauty of these plains, enamelled with such an uncommon variety of flowers of vivid tints, possessing all the brilliancy of tropical productions.

After passing through a swamp, we crossed the Kiamesha in boats, and swam our horses. Five or six miles from Styles's we, at length, obtained sight of Red river, appearing here scarcely more than 100 yards wide, passing to the south-east, with the water very red and turbid. I was told that the river was here 1100 miles from its confluence by the meanders, or 900 above Natchitoches.

Here, for the first time, I saw the *Maclura* (or Bow wood) in abundance, but almost a month past flowering, at least with the staminiferous plant.

We found in this country two poisonous species of Coluber, or common snake, one of them very small, and finely marbled with vivid colours. The other frequents waters, and is called the water-mockasin, and poisonous black-snake; it is nearly black, two or three feet long, and thick in proportion, the head triangular and compressed at the sides. Both of them were furnished with the mortal fangs.

24th.] To day we continued to the Horse-prairie, 15 miles above the mouth of the Kiamesha. In our way we proceeded for about three miles through the fertile alluvion of Red river to Mr. Varner's, where we breakfasted, and at length arriving at our destination on the banks of Red river, we remained there the whole of the following day. This prairie derives its name from the herds of wild horses, which till lately frequented it, and of which we saw a small gang on our return. It is very extensive, but flat, and in some places swampy. In these depressions we saw whole acres of the *Crinum americanum* of the West Indies, besides extensive glaucous fields of a large leaved and new species of *Rudbeckia*. The *Sus tajassu* or Mexican hog, is not uncommon some distance higher up Red river. A great part of the skin of one of these animals was shown me by Mr. Varner ; so that we need not go to Mexico, in order to account for the head of this animal which was found in one of the saltpetre caves of Kentucky. That a continual intercourse was also kept up by the natives of the east and west sides of the Mississippi, is evident from the authority of Du Pratz, who tells us that the Mobilian or Chicasaw language was even spoken by the natives of Red river.

On the banks of Red river, nearly on a level with the water, as it appeared at the present depression, I noticed a dark greenish-grey sandstone, resembling trap, and occasionally interspersed with pebbles of agate, jasper, and chalcedony ; the cement of this curious conglomerate proved to be calcareous spar.

26th.] To-day we prepared to return by the route which we had come. Knowing that we should arrive early at Mr. Styles's, and spend the remainder of the day there, I delayed about two hours behind the party, for the purpose of collecting some of the new and curious plants interspersed over these enchanting prairies. It was not, however, my fortune ever again to overtake the party. Deceived by the continued traces of two strangers who had accompanied us, I passed the place of rendezvous, and was, in fact, so much engaged as to travel along no less than seven miles below Mr. Styles's, which I ascertaind by enquiring at another house, to which accident had directed me. Night began to approach, and I had proceeded but about three miles on my return when the sun set. By pursuing a new path which now opened, I had the good fortune to arrive at the house of Mr. Davis, contiguous to Gates's creek, which I had crossed.   Here I was kindly requested to remain for the night, as the path from hence was even difficult to trace by day-light.   Four guns were fired at major Bradford's camp as signals to me, which were answered by Mr. Davis, but unfortunately they were never heard.

27th.] It was scarcely day-break when I arose, impatient to join my companions; but now my horse was not to be found, and it was not until we had made two or three unsuccessful searches, that he was at length discovered two miles on the path I had yesterday travelled.   By this time it was near eight o'clock, and nine when I arrived at the major's camp, where I found they had departed about half an hour. It is unnecessary to pourtray my apprehensions on this occasion; not a moment was to be lost, and I offered one of Mr. Styles's sons two dollars to accompany me for a few hours to find their trace, and, if possible, to overtake them.   We travelled as fast as possible for about 10 miles through a horrid brake of scrubby oaks, but all to no purpose, and, after firing a gun, which was neither heard nor answered, we returned again, as I dared not to venture alone and unprepared through such a difficult and mountainous wilderness.   My botanical acquisitions in the prairies, proved, however, so interesting as almost to make me forget my situation, cast away as I was amidst the refuse of society, without money and without acquaintance; for calculating upon nothing more certain than an immediate return, I was consequently unprovided with every means of subsistence.

I was informed by the hunters, that these prairies, partially divided by groves and strips of timber, bordering the water courses, continued with little interruption to the hot springs of the Washita, to which, from hence, there is a plain and direct road.   The surface of these woodless expanses was gently undulated, and thickly covered with grass knee high, even to the summits of the hills, offering an almost inexhaustible range to cattle. The flowers, which beautify them at this season of nature's vigour, communicated all the appearance of a magnificent garden, fantastically decked with innumerable flowers of the most splendid hues. The soil appears to be universally calcareous, with the limestone nearly white and full of shells, among which there was abundance of a small species of gryphite, and in the more compact beds some species of terebratulites. This calcareous rock, different from the mountain limestone, often contains uncemented or loose shells immersed in beds of friable clay, and is more analogous to that of South Carolina and Georgia, than that of St. Louis and the Ohio.

Along the further edge of the prairie, relative to Red river, there were, in the distance of 10 miles, five or six families settled, or rather encamped, upon the lands of the United States, which have not yet been surveyed or offered for sale.

June 1st.—5th.] I still remained at the house of Mr. Styles, without any very obvious prospect of regaining fort Smith. On the 4th I walked over the adjoining prairie to a more considerable hill than any which I had yet visited, near Red river. Its northwestern declivity was thinly wooded; here I found the limestone more compact than usual, containing also smaller shells, but still presenting scarcely any perceptible dip. The summit was scattered with coarse quartzy and petrosiliceous pebbles, originating from the disintegration of a ferruginous conglomerate, of which large masses still lay on the surface compact. A similar overlay, though much more abundant and continuous, occurs over the calcareous rock of South Carolina and Georgia.

The singular appearance of these vast meadows, now so profusely decorated with flowers, as seen from a distance, can scarcely be described. Several large circumscribed tracts were perfectly gilded with millions of the flowers of *Rudbeckia amplexicaulis*, bordered by other irregular snow-white fields of a new species of *Coriandrum*. The principal grasses which prevail are *Kœleria cristata* of Europe, *Phalaris canariensis* (Canary bird-seed), *Tripsacum dactyloides*, which is most greedily sought after by the horses, *Elymus virginicus* (sometimes called wild rye), a new *Rotbolia*, one or two species of *Stipa* and *Aristida*, with the *Agrostis arachnoides* of Mr. Elliott, and two species of *Atheropogon*. The common Milfoil, and sorrel *(Rumex acetocella)*, are as prevalent, at least the former, as in Europe. In these plains there also grew a large species of *Centaurea*, scarcely distinct from *C. austriaca;* and along the margin of all the rivulets we met with abundance of the Bow-wood *(Maclura aurantiaca)*, here familiarly employed as a yellow dye, very similar to fustic.

6th.] To-day I went five or six miles to collect specimens of the *Centaurea*, which, as being the only species of this numerous genus indigenous to America, had excited my curiosity. All the lesser brooks and neighbouring springs were now already dried up, and the arid places appeared quite scorched with the heat. Still there prevailed throughout these prairies, as over the sea, a refreshing breeze, which continued for the greatest part of the day. The swarms of musquitoes, which prove so troublesome along the banks of the Mississippi and the Missouri are here almost unknown, and never met with except on the immediate alluvial borders of the rivulets.

In my solitary, but amusing rambles over these delightful prairies, I now, for the first time in my life, notwithstanding my long residence and peregrinations in North America, hearkened to the inimitable notes of the mocking-bird *(Turdus polyglottus)*. After amusing itself in ludicrous imitations of other birds,

perched on the topmost bough of a spreading elm, it
at length broke forth into a strain of melody the most
wild, varied, and pathetic, that ever I had heard from
any thing less than human. In the midst of these
enchanting strains, which gradually increased to loud-
ness, it oftentimes flew upwards from the topmost
twig, continuing its note as if overpowered by the
sublimest ecstasy.

On the 8th I went down to the Red river settlement, to inquire concerning some company, which I
had heard of, on my returning route to the Arkansa;
and, on conferring together, we concluded to take our
departure on Sunday next, a day generally chosen by
these hunters and voyagers on which to commence their
journeys. In our way to this settlement we crossed
Gates's and Lemon's creek and another smaller brook.
The width of the prairie to the banks of Red river
might be about five miles, and the contracted alluvial
lands, which by the crops of corn and cotton appeared
to be exceedingly fertile, were nearly inhabited to
their full extent. The wheat planted here produced
about 80 bushels to the acre, for which some of the
inhabitants had now the conscience to demand three
dollars and a half per bushel, in consequence of the
scarcity of last season. Along the borders of this
part of Red river a chain of low hills appears, on which
I observed large dislocated masses of a ferruginous
conglomerate, inclined towards the river, and incumbent on the usual calcareous rock.

These people, as well as the generality of those who,
till lately, inhabited the banks of the Arkansa, bear
the worst moral character imaginable, being many of
them renegadoes from justice, and such as have forfeited the esteem of civilized society. When a further flight from justice became necessary, they passed
over into the Spanish territory, towards St. Antonio,
where it appears encouragement was given to all sorts
of refugees. From these people we frequently heard

disrespectful murmurs against the government of the United States.   There is, indeed, an universal 'complaint of showing unnecessary and ill-timed favours to the Indians.   It is true that the Osages and Cherokees have been permitted, almost without molestation, to rob the people on this river, not only of their horses and cattle, but even occasionally of their household furniture.   It does not appear from experiment, that the expensive forts, now established and still extending, possess any beneficial influence over the savages which could not be answered by the interference of the territorial government.

It is now also the intention of the United States government, to bring together, as much as possible, the savages beyond the frontier, and thus to render them, in all probability, belligerent to each other, and to the civilized settlements which they border.   To strengthen the hands of an enemy by conceding to them positions favourable to their designs, must certainly be far removed from prudence and good policy. To have left the aborigines on their ancient sites, rendered venerable by the endearments and attachments of patriotism, and surrounded by a condensed population of the whites, must either have held out to them the necessity of adopting civilization, or at all events have most effectually checked them from committing depredations.   Bridled by this restraint, there would have been no necessity for establishing among them an expensive military agency, and coercing them by terror.

14th.] According to our appointment, my traveling companions called upon me, and, although about the middle of a Sunday afternoon, it was not possible to persuade them to wait for Monday morning.   So, without almost any supply of provision, I was obliged to take a hasty departure from my kind host and family, who, knowing from the first my destitute situation, separated from pecuniary resources, could scarcely be prevailed upon to accept the trifling pittance which I accidentally possessed. I shall always remember, with feelings of gratitude, the sincere kindness and unfeigned hospitality, which I so seasonably experienced from these poor and honest people, when left in the midst of the wilderness.

The evening was pleasant, and, after proceeding about eight miles through oak thickets in a path of the hunters, we reposed without further trouble by a brook, beneath the shade of the forest, and under the serene canopy of a cloudless sky.

15th.] My companions, three in number, appeared to be men of diligence and industry, and were up by break of day. The object of their journey was the recovery of horses stolen from them by the Cherokees. After proceeding about six miles from the place of departure, the trace or path could no longer easily be followed, as we now began to enter upon the pine hills scattered with loose rocks. Our first object was to have entered Field's cove ; we got, however, too far to the east, and crossed a considerable brook of the Kiamesha. All ignorant of the country, except myself, we had taken the precaution to mark down the reported bearings and distances, from the information of Mr. Styles. Our proper course was now north-north-east, but the man who took the lead, embarrassed by the accumulation of the mountains, which appeared in succeeding ridges for 40 miles before us, and too confidently considering the proposed route impracticable, kept towards the west in direct opposition to our proper course, so that on the 16th, about noon, we obtained sight of Field's cove, which we ought now to have left, and crossing the Kiamesha, much too low down, found it running nearly due west, and very low. Our labour and distance was thus doubled, and we passed and repassed several terrific ridges, over which our horses could scarcely keep their feet, and which were,

21

besides, so overgrown with bushes and trees half-
burnt, with ragged limbs, that every thing about us,
not of leather, was lashed and torn to pieces. We
now relinquished the mountains, and kept up along
the banks of the Kiamesha, by a bison path, frequently crossing the river, which was almost uniformly
bordered by mountains or inaccessible cliffs. Having
killed a fat bison bull, we encamped at an early hour
in a small prairie, in order to jerk or dry some of the
beef for our future subsistence, it being now all the
provision on which we had to depend.

All the rock we saw since our departure from Mr.
Styles', consisted of a fine-grained sandstone, with no
inconsiderable dip, and, as far as visible, destitute of
organic remains.

In a lake, about a mile from the Kiamesha, where
we crossed it at noon, grew the *Pontederia cordata,
Nymphæa advena, Brassenia peltata,* and *Myrio-
phyllum verticillatum,* all of them plants which I had
not before seen in the territory, and which I have
found chiefly confined to the limits of tide water. In
a northern bend of the Kiamesha, about 30 miles
from its mouth, I am informed, there exists a very
copious salt spring.

17th.] We still continued up the Kiamesha, over
pine hills, and through a succession of horrid, laby-
rinthine thickets and cane-brakes, meeting, to our disappointment, very little prairie. At length, we arrived at the three main branches of the river: Jack's
creek to the south, Kiamesha to the east, and a third
rivulet to the north. To the entrance of Jack's fork,
as it is called, the Kiamesha continues hemmed in
with lofty pine hills. From hence the mountains di-
verge; the highest chain still continuing on one side
to border the main stream, while, to the north, we
came in sight of the " Potatoe hills." In this extensive cove, covered with grass, and mostly a prairie of
undulated surface, I had the satisfaction to find, as I

had also done at noon, the *Ixia cœlestina* of my venerable friend, Wm. Bartram. Instead of sandstone, we now found a predominance of slaty petrosiliceous rock breaking in rhombic fragments, nearly of the same nature as the hone-slate of the Washita, and alike destitute of organic reliquiæ.

18th.] We continued across the great cove of the Kiamesha, towards the dividing ridge of mountains which separates the waters of the Arkansa and Red river, and which had been visible to us on the very day after our departure. We now kept a course rather too much south of east, and encamped on the banks of a creek that appeared to issue from a conspicuous gap in the mountains. The prairie, though in many places open and hilly, was still divided by small torrents, now generally dry, and lined with thickets, laced with thorns and green briers. Towards the middle of this fertile cove. we passed over a large tract formed like a lake, and, except a southern outlet towards the Kiamesha, surrounded with low hills. In one of these rich alluvial bottoms, we saw abundance of tumuli. On the hills of the prairies of Red river, I also saw them of stone, and containing, according to custom, fragments of earthen pots. All the hills in this cove, which abound with pine, present slaty rocks of the petrosilex already mentioned, apparently forming partial beds, alternating with a soft slaty or shale rock, which occasionally exhibits balls of argillaceous iron ore, and the fibrous mineral production which has been called cone coralloid.*

To-day we came very near losing our horses, for, while reposing at noon, though as usual hobbled, the torments of the large flies which appear at this time of the day and in the evening, became so extreme, as to excite them to run away, and with some difficulty we traced them for five or six miles, through woods and prairies, to the banks of the Kiamesha, into which

* See Martyn's Petrificata Derbyensia, Tab. 27. fig. 4.

they had rushed for alleviation. We here also found, by the bell, a horse which had been lost by some hunters. In consequence of this unexpected delay, we did not proceed more than about 20 miles.

19th.] We continued across the cove towards the the mountains, and began the ascent, but totally missing the gap, arrived at length, with much difficulty, upon one of the highest summits of the dividing ridge. Towards the Pottoe, the descent was altogether impracticable : for miles we could perceive nothing but one continued precipice of the most frightful elevation. After proceeding, however, with difficulty for about three miles along the summit of the mountain, high as any part of the Blue ridge, through thickets of dwarf oaks *(Quercus chinquapin, Q. montana,* and *Q. alba),* none of them scarcely exceeding the height of a man ; we began the descent, which we still found extremely steep and broken, and, after toiling four or five hours in the mountains, had, at last, the unexpected satisfaction of entering upon, and pursuing the wagon trace, so recently trod by the major's party. We now clearly saw, a little to the north-west, the right gap of the mountain which we ought to have sought.

In the course of the afternoon, we passed over three pine ridges, and two creeks, and then re-entering the prairie, proceeded before night about ten miles from the mountain, which, as well as the lesser ridges, consisted of sandstone.

20th] This morning we passed the Pottoe, and proceeded along the trace, some distance beyond the Sugar-loaf mountain. The prairies were now horribly infested with cleg flies, which tormented and stimulated our horses into a perpetual gallop. In the evening, we encamped in the valley of the third oak ridge that separated us from Cedar prairie.

21st.] Passing the fourth ridge, I again entered Cedar prairie, and before noon arrived at the garrison, where I had been long expected, and was very cordially welcomed by the Doctor and the Major.

To the end of the month, I now remained at the garrison.

CHAPTER X.

Continue my voyage up the Arkansa—Geological remarks—Pass several lesser rivulets, and the outlet of the Canadian and the Illinois—Salt springs—Obstructions in the navigation—Indications of coal—Pass Grand river, and enter the Verdigris.

July 6th.] Having obtained accommodation in the boat of Mr. Bougie, agent for Mr. Drope, I left the garrison in order to proceed to the trading establishment, at the confluence of the Verdigris, by the course of the river about 130 miles distant. The day being very warm we did not proceed more than 10 miles, having delayed our departure until near noon. Eight miles from the garrison we had another conspicuous view of the Cavaniol.

Among three or four other new plants afforded me by examining the sand-beaches, was a *Portulaca*, apparently the same with *P. pilosa* of the West Indies; its taste was almost as disagreeably bitter as the succulent *Stapelias* of Africa. On these sand-flats we also saw abundance of deer, brought to the river in search of water, as well as to escape the goading of insects; and it is customary for them to remain for hours licking the saline efflorescences which are deposited upon the alluvial clay. We encamped four miles below Skin bayou, and our party amused themselves by searching for turtle's eggs, which the females deposit in the sand at the depth of about eight or ten inches, and then abandon their hatching to the genial heat of the sun. They are spherical, covered with a flexible skin, and considered wholesome food.

7th.] The river land on both sides appears to be of a good quality, and generally elevated above inundation. The depression of the forest also begins to be obvious. About half a league below Skin bayou occur low cliffs of dark-coloured grauwacke slate, resembing sand-stone, which continue for about a mile along the right hand bank. The rock is entirely similar to that of the garrison (or Belle Point, as the situation is called), equally horizontal, and probably underlaid by coal. The under stratum was singularly undulated in short and broken waves, while the upper was almost perfectly horizontal. Not far from the place of our encampment, on the left, we passed the Swallow (or Hirundel) rocks, a projecting cliff, about 150 feet high, adorned with bushes of cedar, in the centre of which there appears to be an entrance into a cavern, and several other fretted excavations scattered over with clusters of martin nests. The rock consists of two beds; the upper a lighter coloured ferruginous and laminated sand-stone, excavated with appearances similar to nitre caves; the lowest bed, with a more considerable dip (about 10° to the south-east), consists of thinner greenish grey lamina, containing a little mica, and exhibiting the usual zoophytic carbonaceous impressions, indicative of coal. The river bars now abound in gravel, which is principally petrosiliceous. After passing Cajou creek, on the left, about two miles, we encamped near a bar, to avoid the visits of the musquetoes, our progress to-day being about 24 miles.

8th.] Four miles further we again obtained a view of Point de Sucre and the Cavaniol. On Sambo island, about 12 miles from our departure this morning, we stopped to dine; and here on a bar of gravel I found a new species of the Mexican genus *Stevia,* and never saw it afterwards in any other locality. To the taste it was quite as bitter as many of the *Eupatoria*. This plant, and the *Portulaca* already mentioned, appear to have been recently, and almost accidentally, disseminated from the interior. The cane still continues abundant, and the alluvial lands are extensive and fertile, with a basis of sand-stone, which two miles below appears in the same dark and ferruginous rocky mass as near Skin bayou. On some of our party going out a hunting, we concluded to spend the remainder of the day on the island.

9th.] This morning we crossed the river to the mouth of Sambo creek, and went out into the neighbouring prairie to hunt for bison ; but after walking about nine miles, going and returning, were not fortunate enough to find any game. The grass was now so loaded with honey dew as to give our mocasins and pantaloons the appearance of being soaked in oil, seeming totally inexplicable as the produce of aphides, and rather attributable to some vitiation in the proper juices of the plant, taking place apparently at the ultimate period of vegetative vigour, and being more or less copious in proportion to the prevailing degree of heat. The cane brake which we here crossed by a hunting path, was about half a league wide, and flanked by low hills, whose declivities gently subside into the adjoining prairie, of about 20 miles in circuit, and five in width. Here the Cavaniol and Sugar-loaf mountains appeared, at least the latter, not more than 15 or 18 miles distant, towards the south-east. We proceeded about five miles above the creek, and spent the night on the margin of a sand bar, according to our usual custom, to avoid the musquetoes.

10th.] I went out this morning on the second bar we arrived at, which continued uninterruptedly for about five miles ; we found a few Chicasaw plumbs, with natural orchards of which every beach abounds, but this year, in consequence of the late frosts, they were generally destitute of fruit. The current of the

Arkansa was here unusually rapid ; on the right hand side the water was clear, but on the left, red and muddy. The clear water issued from the Illinois river, to which we were now contiguous. Among the scattered boulders and gravel of the bar, there were fragments of limestone and petrosilex, containing organic remains, also pebbles of chalcedony ; we likewise saw specimens of coal, accompanied by the usual carbonaceous, tessellated vegetable, or zoophitic remains. One of the masses of chalcedony contained chrystalline illinitions of coal.—About breakfast time, we passed the mouth of the rivulet or brook, called by the French Salaiseau, from some hunters having here killed a quantity of bison, and salted the beef for traffic. Major Bradford, who explored this stream, informed me, that the uplands as well as the prairies along this creek, were uncommonly fertile, and well watered by springs, and that the upper side of the creek presents a calcareous soil. Here, for the first time, near the Arkansa, we meet with the hazel (*Corylus americana*), and the American raspberry (*Rubus occidentalis*). In consequence of the rapidity of the current, we only proceeded about 12 miles.

11th.] After ascending about six miles, we passed the outlet of the Canadian, 60 miles below the confluence of Grand river, or the Six Bull, a navigable river of considerable magnitude. Its main south branch sources with Red river, while another considerable body keeps a western course through the saline plains, where it becomes partially absorbed in the sands of the desert, but afterwards continues towards Santa Fe or the Del Norte. The Canadian, like Red river, always continues red and muddy, and is often impotably saline ; 100 miles from its mouth, its banks are said to abound with selenite, disseminated through beds of red clay. Above the confluence of this stream, the Arkansa, where deep, appears clear, green, and limpid. The alluvial lands now begin to be somewhat narrower, though neither hills nor cliffs approach the bank. This morning, however, we again observed a horizontal ledge of the grauwacke slate. About four miles above the Canadian, we passed the river Illinois on the right, a considerable stream of clear water, as are all the other rivers flowing into the Arkansa from the north. A few miles from its mouth, its banks present salt springs similar to those of Grand river, and scarcely less productive ; indeed, most of the streams on this side the Arkansa are said to afford springs of salt water which might be wrought with profit. On the south side, the salines commencing about the Canadian, occur in the red clay formation, forming as it were a belt which extends to the third Red fork, or saline rivulet of the Arkansa. The salines on the north, appear rather in connection with the coal formation, at least, they do not belong to the same series as those on the south side of the river.

This afternoon, two of the hunters went out and brought in the most part of the meat of a fat bison, whose track they had followed from the bar.

About four miles above the Illinois, we came to a cascade of two or three feet perpendicular fall. In endeavouring to pass it, our boat grounded upon the rocks, and we spent several hours in the fruitless attempt to pass them, but had at last to fall back, and attempt it again in the morning, which we then (on the 13th) effected by the assistance of the wind without much difficulty, by passing further into the shute. At this season, in which the water is far from being at its lowest ebb, no boats drawing more than from 12 to 18 inches water, could pass this rapid without lightening, and it appears to form one of the first obstacles of consequence in the navigation of the Arkansa.

The variety of trees which commonly form the North American forest, here begin very sensibly to

22

diminish. We now scarcely see any other than the smooth-barked cottonwood, the elm, box-elder *(Acer Negundo)*, curled maple *(Acer dasycarpon)*, and ash, all of them reduced in stature. From hence the forest begins to disappear before the pervading plain. To-day we were favoured with a fine south-east breeze, and sailed along with rapidity. Early in the afternon we passed Bougie's island, near to which, and in two other places, the hills, of about 300 feet elevation, approach the river; the rocks being still a slaty sandstone. Elk and deer now appeared common on the sand beaches, being obliged to come to the river for water, as the springs in the prairies are at this season nearly all dried up. We continued to pass several rapids, with the water curling over beds of gravel. According to the common estimate, we proceeded to-day 45 miles, and in the evening were only two leagues from our destination.

14th.] This morning we passed a low ledge of rocks on our left, apparently the usual dark-coloured slaty sandstone, and which has received the name of the Charbonniere, from the appearances of coal which it exhibits. On this side, the prairie approaches the immediate bank of the river, and presents a very unusual open prospect. We again passed three or four difficult rapids, within the short distance which remained to complete our present voyage, but presently after saw the outlet of Grand river (or the Six Bulls as it is called by the French hunters), and now entered the Verdigris, where M. Bougie and Mr. Prior had their trading houses. The water of both these rivers was quite pellucid; while that of the Arkansa was now whitish and muddy, from the partial influx and augmentation of some neigbouring streams.

CHAPTER XI.

Character of the surrounding country of the Verdi-
gris river—Remarks on the Osage Indians.

14th.] This morning, accompanied by Mr. Prior,
I walked over a portion of the alluvial land of the
Verdigris, the fertility of which was sufficiently obvious in the disagreeable and smothering luxuriance
of the tall weeds, with which it was overrun. This
neck of land, situated betwixt Grand river and the
Verdigris, is about two miles wide, free from inundation, and covered with larger trees than any other
I had seen since leaving Fort Smith. Among them
were lofty scarlet oaks, ash, and hackberry, and
whole acres of nettles *(Urtica divaricata)*, with whose
property of affording hemp, the French hunters and
settlers have been long acquainted. Contiguous to the
lower side of Grand river, there was a thick cane-
brake, more than two miles in width, backed by the
prairie, without the intervention of hills. As is common in large alluvions, so in this of the Verdigris, a
second terrace or more elevated bottom succeeds the
first, beyond which, occur thinly timbered hills. We
then enter upon the great western prairies, or grassy
plains, separated from each other by small rivulets,
exhibiting belts of trees along their margin. About
eight miles from the Arkansa, commences the great
Osage prairie, more than 60 miles in length, and, in
fact, succeeded by a continuation of woodless plains
to the banks of the Missouri. Mr. Prior informed
me, that in the first hills below, not far from the Arkansa, on the east side, and about six miles distant,
there is calcareous rock. On entering the prairie,
I was greatly disappointed to find no change in the
vegetation, and indeed, rather a diminution of species. The *Amorpha canescens*, which I had not here-

tofore seen, since leaving St. Louis and the Missouri, and a new species of *Helianthus*, however, instantly struck me as novel.

Leaving the path to the Osage village, we visited the rapids of the Verdigris, which are situated five miles above its embouchure. This obstruction is occasioned by a ledge of rocks, which traverse the river, now bare, except about three or four yards, over which the water foamed in a small cascade. The stream was quite pellucid, and along the ledge we saw great numbers of buffaloe fish, as well as gars *(Esox osseus)*, accompanied by several other smaller kinds. While viewing the surrounding objects, my attention was attracted to a beautiful green-striped lizard, resembling, except in the colour and larger size, the *Lacerta vittata*.

If the confluence of the Verdigris, Arkansa, and Grand rivers, shall ever become of importance as a settlement, which the great and irresistible tide of western emigration promises, a town will probably be founded here, at the junction of these streams; and this obstruction in the navigation of the Verdigris, as well as the rapids of Grand river, will afford good and convenient situations for mills, a matter of no small importance in the list of civilized comforts. From the Verdigris to St. Louis, there is an Osage trace, which reduces the distance of those two places to about 300 miles, and that also over a country scarcely obstructed by mountains. The low hills contiguous to the falls of this river, and on which there exist several aboriginal mounds, were chosen by the Cherokees and Osages to hold their council, and to form a treaty of reciprocal amity as neighbours. This first friendly interview with the Cherokees, was soon after broke through by jealousy, and accompanied on both sides with the most barbarous revenge. Scarcely any nation of Indians have encountered more enemies than the Osages; still they flatter themselves, by saying, that they are seated in the middle of the world, and, although surrounded by so many enemies, they have ever maintained their usual population, and their country. From conversations with the traders, it appeared, that they would not be unwilling to dispose of more of their lands, provided that the government of the United States would enter into a stipulation, not to settle it with the aborigines, whom they have now much greater reason to fear than the whites. The limit of their last cession proceeds in a northeast direction from the falls of the Verdigris, and enters the line which was run from Fire prairie, on the Missouri, to Frog bayou, about 60 miles from the Arkansa ; but, as it would appear, through a culpable oversight, the saline of Grand river was omitted, on the supply of which the whole territory so much depended for salt.

Limestone appears to exist along the banks of the Verdigris, not many miles above the falls, as large rolled fragments charged with shells were scattered along the shores. The slaty sandstone, also, which forms the falls, dipping about 10° to the north west, exhibits, in some of its beds, organic impressions, resembling a very serpentine caryophyllite, and traversed with calcareous sparry illinitions.

15th.] The first village of the Osages lies about 60 miles from the mouth of the Verdigris, and is said to contain 7 or 800 men and their families. About 60 miles further, on the Osage river, is situated the village of the chief called White Hair. The whole of the Osages are now, by governor Clarke, enumerated at about 8000 souls. At this time nearly the whole town, men and women, were engaged in their summer hunt, collecting bison tallow and meat. The principal chief is called by the French Clarmont, although his proper name is the Iron bird, a species of Eagle. The right of governing is commonly hereditary, but not always directed by primogeniture.

Tálai, the son of the last chief, being considered too young at the decease of his father, the rule was conferred on Clarmont, son of the chief of White Hair's village, on the Osage river, and his behaviour as regent for many years, secured to him the undivided controul of the village. Like most of the rulers among the aborigines, he neither affects nor supports any shadow of pomp or distinction beyond that of his office as supreme commander, and leader of the council. His influence is, however, so great as to be prudentially courted by all who would obtain any object with the village. He appeared to be shrewd and sagacious, and no way deficient in Indian bravery and cunning.

The Osages at this time entertained a considerable jealousy of the whites, in consequence of the emigration of the Cherokees to their frontiers; they considered it as a step of policy in the government to overawe them, and intended to act in concert with the establishment of the garrison. This consideration, as well as the power and wealth of the whites, which have been witnessed by their chiefs on their deputation to Washington, has, within these two years back, had a salutary tendency to restrain their pretensions. Still the white hunters and trappers are frequently insulted and chastised by them. And, on the other hand, we have surely no just reason to expect from the Indians an unstipulated licence to rob their country of that game, which is necessary to their convenience and subsistence.

From the Osage interpreter, of whom I made the inquiry, I learned, that, in common with many other Indians, as might be supposed from their wandering habits and exposure to the elements, they are not unacquainted with some peculiar characters and configurations of the stars. Habitual observation had taught them that the pole star remains stationary, and that all the others appear to revolve around it; they were ac-

quainted with the Pleiades, for which they had a peculiar name, and remarked the three stars of Orion's
belt. The planet Venus they recognised as the Lu-
cifer or harbinger of day ; and, as well as the Europeans, they called the Galaxy the heavenly path or
celestial road. The filling and waning of the moon
regulated their minor periods of time, and the number of moons, accompanied by the concomitant phenomena of the seasons, pointed out the natural duration of the year.

The superstitions of the Osages differ but little
from those which have so often been described, as
practised by the other natives. The importance of
smoking, as a religious ceremony, is such as to be
often accompanied by invocations for every aid or
necessary of life. Before going out to war they raise
the pipe towards heaven or the sun,* and implore the
assistance of the Great Spirit to favour them in their
reprisals, in the stealing of horses, and the destruction
of their enemies, &c. &c. They are acquainted with
the value of wampum, know the destructive effects of
guns and gunpowder, and the fascinating, but delete-
rious qualities of spiritous liquors. Their minds
have not been deluded into a belief in sorcery, which,
from its supposed fatality, is by many of the eastern
Indians punished with death. At their festivals, as
among most of the other natives, the warriors recount
their actions of bravery, and number them by throwing
down a stick upon the ground for every exploit, or strik-
ing at a post fixed for the purpose. On such occasions,
they sometimes challenge each other with a mutual emulation, to recount a like number of warlike deeds. Yet
this ostentation is rarely suffered to degenerate into insult or envious combat; vulgarity is unknown amongst

---

* The Naudowessies, and, as we are told by La Hontan, the Hurons,
smoked to the sun and the four cardinal points of the compass, which,
according to Sir William Jones, is the characteristic ritual of the Tartars.

the aborigines of America; and the crest-fallen warrior, superceded by a competitor, only seeks an equal
share of honour in the claims of patriotism, in the
wars of his nation.

After scalping, the greatest feat of the Indian warrior is the stealing of horses from the enemy, which
they effect with notorious dexterity. The bad effects,
which may easily be anticipated to arise from this thirst
for martial fame, is a perpetual and obstinate continuance of war upon the slightest pretext; to which
may also be added, their inability often, or unwilling-
ness to distinguish betwixt public and personal wrong.
Instead of punishing offenders against the peace, and
thus endeavouring to keep up a good understanding
with their neighbours, the friends of the incendiary,
who has hurried his nation into war, hearken perhaps
with indulgence to his misrepresentations, and thus
too often effectually prohibit the application of salutary punishment. In fact, the want of legal restraint,
and of an efficient government, in spite of all our admiration of patriarchal rule, have proved the ever
baneful means of aboriginal depopulation. It is this
anarchy which has so often prevented their common
union against the encroachment of foreigners, and deprived them, in a great degree, of the advantages and
comforts of public security and civilization. The
most tyrannical oligarchy, as we have seen in the example of the Mexicans, the Peruvians, and the Natchez, would have been less injurious in its effects on
their society, than this paternal form of government,
which, unfortunately, however natural and virtuous
in its principle, proves, by its lenity, insufficient to
check a vicious populace.

CHAPTER XII.

An excursion up Grand River to visit the Osage salt works—Geological observations—Return across the prairie ; its general appearance and phenomena.

17th.] To-day I proceeded with two young men in a canoe up Grand river, with an intention of visiting the salt works. We found the water of this stream very clear, and the channel little inferior in breadth to some parts of the Arkansa ; also full of rapids, and now so shallow as to admit of no vessel drawing more than 12 inches of water. The islands are very numerous and small, and the bars and bends, except by the predominance of gravel, resemble the Arkansa on a reduced scale. The gravel is entirely composed of lime-stone and chert. In the distance of about seven miles we found the first ridge terminating on the borders of the river to be calcareous. Below this, and about two or three miles from the mouth of the river, the usual dark-coloured slaty sandstone prevails. In the course of the day we killed several large buffaloe fish, which are very abundant in all the shallow and gravelly ripples, apparently a *Cyprinus*, and very palatable when fried in oil. The boney gar *(Esox osseus)*, and the large grey cat-fish, are also sufficiently common. We proceeded about 30 miles.

18th.] The morning was fine, and we embarked at sunrise. About eight o'clock we passed a bend called the Eagle's nest, a mile above which, and its island, a fascade of calcareous rock appears, inlaid with beds of whitish hornstone. While examining these cliffs, I recognised as new, a large shrub, and to my great surprise found it to be a simple-leaved *Rhus*, scarcely distinct from the *R. Cotinus* of the south of Europe and of our gardens. Hills and cliffs, but

23

partly hid in woods, were now of frequent occurrence
along the river bank. The neighbouring thickets
abounded with game, amongst which two bears made
their appearance. The gravel bars were almost
covered with *Amsonia salicifolia*, with which grew
also the *Sesbania macrocarpa* of Florida.

This evening I arrived at Mr. Slover's, two miles
below the saline. The farm which this hunter occupied was finely elevated and productive, and apparently well suited to the production of small grain.
Up to this place, which is said to be 50 miles from
the Arkansa, the cane continues to be abundant.
In this elevated alluvion I still observed the Coffee-
bean tree *(Gymnocladus canadensis)*, the over-cup
white oak *(Quercus macrocarpa)*, the pecan *(Carya
olivæformis)*, the common hickory, ash, elm; and below, in places near the margin of the river, the poplar-
leaved birch *(Betula populifolia)*.

Mr. S. informed me, that on the opposite side of
the river, and two miles from hence, another strong
salt spring breaks out through the incumbent gravel;
and that there are other productive springs 25 miles
above.

19th.] This morning, I walked with Mr. Slover to
see the salt works, now indeed lying idle, and nearly
deserted in consequence of the murder of Mr. Camp-
bel, by Erhart, his late partner, and two accomplices
in their employ. Melancholy as were the reflections
naturally arising from this horrid circumstance, I
could not but congratulate myself on having escaped, perhaps a similar fate. At the Cadron, I had
made application to Childer's, one of these remorse-
less villains, as a woodsman and hunter, to accompany me for hire, only about a month before he had shot
and barbarously scalped Mr. Campbell, for the purpose of obtaining his little property, and in spite of
the friendship which he had uniformly received from
the deceased.

But to return to the subject. We proceeded two miles, along the hilly and woody skirts of the river, and through the adjoining prairie to the saline, which appeared to be a gravelly, alluvial basin, of about an acre in extent, and destitute of all vegetation. A small fresh water brook, now scarcely running, passed through this area, and the salt water, quite pellucid, issued copiously to the surface in various directions. In one place it boiled up out of a focus of near six inches diameter, emiting fetid bubbles of sulphuretted hydrogen, which deposited a slight scum of sulphur. All the springs are more or less hepatic, which circumstance is attributable to a bed of bituminous and sulphuretted slate-clay, visible on the margin of the stream, and, probably, underlaid by coal, through which the water rises to the surface. In the adjoining heights, a coarse-grained sandstone occurs, answering the purpose of mill-stones ; the stream then contracts at the entrance of a ledge of slaty rocks, and, about half a mile from its immediate outlet, the water is perfectly fresh. The only well dug upon the premises for the salt water, was about five feet deep, and quarried through a bed of dark-coloured limestone, containing shells and nodules of black hornstone, similar to the chert of Derbyshire. This salt appears to be concomitant with a coaly or bituminous formation. No marine plants appear in this vicinity, as at Onondago, where we meet with the Salicornia of the sea marshes. When the works were in operation, 120 bushels of salt were manufactured in a week, and the water is said to be so strong, that after the second boiling, it became necessary to remove the lye. No mother water, or any thing almost but what is volatile, appears mixed with this salt, which is of the purest whiteness on the first boiling, and only takes about 80 gallons of water to produce a bushel. Hitherto these springs have been unaccompanied by any fossil remains of quadrupeds.

This forenoon I was disagreeably surprised by a slight attack of the intermittent fever, which was also beginning to make its appearance in the family of Mr. Slover. In the spring, they were likewise affected by the influenza, which prevailed in the Osage village, and induced several pulmonary consumptions. No medicines being at hand, as imprudently I had not calculated upon sickness, I took in the evening about a pint of a strong and very bitter decoction, of the *Eupatorium cuneifolium*, the *E. perfoliatum* or Bone-set, not being to be found in the neighbourhood. This dose, though very nauseous, did not prove sufficient to operate as an emetic, but acted as a diaphoretic and gentle laxative, and prevented the proximate return of the disease.

20th.] This morning I left Mr. Slover's, and proceeded, by compass, across the Great Osage plain, towards the mouth of the Verdigris. My course was south by west, the distance being about 30 miles. Twenty miles of this route was without any path, and through grass three feet deep, often entangled with brambles, and particularly with the tenacious "saw-brier" *(Schrankia horridula)*. The honey upon the grass, as at Sambo prairie, was so universally abundant, that my mockasins and pantaloons were soaked as with oil. Several insulated eminences, appearing almost artificial, served to diversify the cheerless uniformity of the extensive plain, still wrapt in primeval solitude. Not even a tree appeared, except along the brooks of Grand river and the Verdigris, which rivers, for 25 or 30 leagues, are not more than 12 to 15 miles apart. About a mile from the base of one of those prominent hills, insulated like an aboriginal mound, and towards which I was directed to proceed, passed the path to the Indian village, and the outlet of the Verdigris. It was evening when I arrived at this hill, which had been a prominent object in view, ever since my outset this morning. From its summit, the wide and verdant plain appeared visible for 40 miles. Proceeding about four miles from this eminence, much fatigued, I lay down to sleep in the prairie, under the clear canopy of heaven ;—but alone, and without the necessary comforts of either fire, food, or water. The crickets, grashoppers, catidids, and stocking-weavers, as they are familiarly called, kept up such a loud and shrill crepitation, as to prove extremely irksome, and almost stunning to the ears. Every tender leaved plant, whether bitter or sweet, by thousands of acres, were now entirely devoured by the locust grashoppers, which arose before me almost in clouds. I slept, however, in comfort, and was scarcely at all molested by musquetoes. The next day, after spending considerable time in botanizing, I arrived at the trading houses.

CHAPTER XIII.

Interviews with the Osages—Occasional observations on their manners and habits, &c.—Sickness in the encampment.

24th.] Last evening, as well as this morning, we we were waited upon by two of the Osage chiefs from the village, one of whom was Tá-lai, their hereditary ruler. Some of the inferior chiefs were begging tobacco, like earnest and genuine mendicants. It is to be regretted, that the man of nature should sink so low by intercourse with the civilized world, and by the acquisition of what were once to him merely artificial wants. Surrounded by a fertile country, the Indian, without ever being either rich or independent, finds it difficult to obtain subsistence, trespasses upon his neighbours, lives in insecurity, and in implacable enmity with those of his own race. A

stranger to our ideas of honour, he destroys his enemies by the meanest stratagems, and levels, in his revenge, all distinctions of age and sex.   Such is the
general character of the Osages, and such even that
of the Cherokees, after all their external approaches
towards civilization.

To give my Reader some idea of the laborious exertions which these people exercise to obtain a livelihood, I need only relate, that the Osages had now returned to their village from a tallow hunt, in which
they had travelled not less than 300 miles up the Arkansa, and had crossed the Saline plains, situated betwixt that river and the Canadian.   In this hunt, they
say, that 10 villages of themselves and friends (as the
Kansas, who speak nearly the same language) joined
for common safety.   They were, however, attacked -
by a small scout of the Pawnees, and lost one of their
young men who was much esteemed, and, as I myself witnessed, distractingly lamented by the father, of
whom he was the only son.   They say, the country
through which they passed is so destitute of timber,
that they had to carry along their tent poles, and to
make fire of the bison ordure.

The activity and agility of the Osages is scarcely
credible.   They not uncommonly walk from their
village to the trading houses, at the mouth of the
Verdigris, in one day, a distance of about 60 miles.

The Osages, in their private conversations, do not appear still to be on an amicable footing with the Cherokees.   One of their chiefs insisted on the hunting
boundary being established betwixt the two nations,
so that either party might be punished, by robbery
and plunder (or confiscation as we term it), who
should be found transgressing the limits assigned.
Aware of the strength of their enemies, they have
been led to seek the alliance of other Indians, and
have recently cultivated the friendship of the Outigamis (now called Sauks and Foxes) of the Missis-

sippi. In a recent council, held at the village of the Verdigris, these people were presented with 100 horses by the Osages. Sensible of this liberality, the Outigamis pledged themselves to prove their active allies, whenever necessity should dictate it to them. These gifts, however great, are not difficult to replace, as they now, this hunt, obtained more than 300 horses, which they had either caught wild, or stolen from the Pawnees, their enemies.

27th.] This morning, Clarmont, accompanied by some of the lesser chiefs, arrived from the lower village, on their way to the garrison, where they were to hold a council with the Cherokees. There was some degree of urbanity, though nothing at first very pre- possessing, in the appearance of Clarmont. He wore a hat ornamented with a band of silver lace, with a sort of livery or regimental coat, and appeared proud of the artificial distinctions bestowed on him by the government. He asked, familiarly, if I had ever heard of him before, and appeared gratified at my an- swering in the affirmative. I am told, however, that, of late years, his influence at *home* has been greatly superceded by that of Tá-lai, the true hereditary chief. Tá-lai was now also present, but destitute of any exterior decorations, though on his way to the general council; I did not consequently recognise him until pointed out to me. In excuse for laying aside the honourable distinctions of the government, he said, there was no necessity, he thought, of parading the medal, his people knew him to be the chief, and the major could not be ignorant of his station. This natural unassuming behaviour, which we so seldom witness in life, surprised and prepossessed me in fa- vour of this legitimate chief. His aspect was uncom- monly benign, and bespoke the man of candor and benevolence.

Last summer a general council of the natives, friendly disposed towards the Osages, took place at

their village; amongst them were Shawnees, Delawares, Creeks, Quapaws, Kanzas, Outigamis, &c.
Their ostensible object was not known ; it would appear, however, that they had been invited by the
Osages, who on this occasion gave away more than
300 horses. The Outigamis told them in an unlimited manner, that they would be always ready at the
first notice, to join them at any time, against any nation. With the Creeks they were dissatisfied, and al-
ledged that they had undervalued their hospitality by
bringing spoons in their pockets, which was probably
turned into a sinister omen.

Preparatory to undertaking a warlike expedition,
the Osages, in common with many other of the aborigines, practised rigid fasts, which were frequently
continued from three to seven days together, forming,
with other privations and inflictions, a kind of penance,
by which they disciplined themselves for disasters,
and supplicated the pity and favour of heaven. Their
invocations to the Good Spirit, and their lamentations,
are incessant About sunrise the whole village re-
echoes with the most plaintive tones of distress,
uttered at the doors of their lodges, or at the tombs
of those whom they loved and esteemed while living.
Indeed, all their affections, uncontrolled by the mask
of affectation, are sincere and ingenuous. Of the sin-
cerity of their conjugal attachment, notwithstanding
the coldness of temper which has been alleged
against the aborigines generally, I have witnessed,
among them and others, many unequivocal proofs.
The expression of affection, perhaps, as in other so-
cieties, where it is so studiously concealed, is more
tender and assiduous on the part of the female. A
few days ago we were near upon witnessing something tragical, in the conduct of an Indian woman,
who had been several years married to a French hunter, living with the Osages. Soon after Mr. Bougie's
arrival, intoxication taking place in the camp, a quarrel

ensued between the husband of this woman and another of the French hunters. Their altercation filled her with terror, and she gave way to tears and lamentations, not doubting but that the antagonist, who was the aggressor, intended the death of her husband, as threats among the Indians are the invariable preludes to fatal actions. When, at length, they began to struggle with eaeh other, without any more ado, she seized upon a hatchet, and would instantly have dispatched the man who fought with her husband, if not prevented by the bystanders.

That curious species of polygamy, which prevails among some other Indian nations, is likewise practised by the Osages, by which, the man who first marries into a family, from that period possesses the controul of all the sisters of his wife, whom he is at liberty either to espouse himself, or to bestow upon others. The maid, as amongst the Quapaws and others, is distinguished from the matron by the method she employs in braiding her hair into two cylindric rolls, which are ornamented with beads, silver, or wampum, and inclined to either side of the head near the ears. After marriage the hair is unloosed and brought together behind. This is one of those little arbitrary distinctions which is quite as invariable as the general costume of the people who employ it.

A practise no less notorious among the young men of the Osages, and the natives generally, is the careful extraction of the marks of pubescence from every part of the body. These Indians even pluck out their eyebrows, shave their heads, and leave only a small scalp upon the crown. Of this, two locks left long, are plaited and ornamented with silver, wampum, and eagle's feathers. The tonsure and ears, as well as the eye-lashes, are painted with vermillion on ordinary occasions, but blackened to express grief or misfortune. Sometimes, apparently out of fancy, they fantastically

24

decorate their faces with white, black, or green stripes.
The use of calico or shirts is yet unknown among
them, and their present fashions and mode of dress
have been so long stationary, as now to be by themselves considered characteristic.   In their dress, fairish
tawney red colour, and aquiline features, they resemble the Outigamis.

The Osages are more than usually superstitious.
With them an ominous dream is often sufficient to
terminate the most important expedition.   After per-
forming an exploit, instead of pursuing their success,
scarcely any consideration can deter them from instantly returning to bear the welcome intelligence to
their band.   Their communion with each other is so
frank, that nothing can remain a secret.   In this way
their intentions of war and plunder are long anticipated, however sudden and secret may be their actual
operations.   They are no strangers to dissimulation,
when it will answer their purpose in their intercourse
with others, but falsehood among their friends or fel-
lows would be looked upon as unnatural and unpar-
donable.   They entertain unconquerable prejudices
against hunters.   While in the village, or in their
company abroad, the stranger is sure to be protected
and treated like themselves in every particular; but
if he is found in their country as a foreigner, and pursuing a different interest from their own, he can
scarcely be distinguished from an enemy and an in-
truder, and must calculate on meeting with chastisement accordingly.   To be found upon their war-paths
is likewise considered criminal.   These particular
routes which they pursue in quest of their enemies,
are recognised by beacons, painted posts, and inscribed hieroglyphics, commonly set up near the
boundaries of their range; and those whom they
chance to find in this direction, are at best considered
as ambiguous friends, and trespassers on the neutral
character which is expected to be maintained.

The miserable fate which, last autumn, befel Mr.
M'Farlane (who is mentioned by Wilkinson, in his
descent of the Arkansa, as then taken prisoner by
the Osages) is a sufficient proof the danger of intrud-
ing on their war-path.* The Osages had taken this
hunter into custody near to a Pawnee village, with
whose inhabitants they were at war, and were about
to proceed with him to their town on the Verdigris.
He was, however, very desirous of returning to the
village for his son who remained behind, to which
the Indians at last consented, and two of them offered
to accompany him back towards the Pawnees; but
after proceeding some distance they seized upon him,
put out his eyes, and then goaded him along for several miles with sharpened canes, thus protracting his
death by torture, until one of them, through compassion, put an end to his existence by the tomahawk.
Although this fact was now well known in the territory, and not denied by the Osages, no steps had
been taken to avenge the death of this unfortunate
hunter. The Osages indeed disavowed the deed as
that of their nation, but contented themselves by saying, that the action had been committed by two bad
men, who were beyond their control. The property
of the white hunter generally, whom they discover in
their country, without special permission, is considered as an indisputable perquisite; and after perhaps
(as I have heard related) breaking his gun in pieces,
and flogging him with the ram-rod, they will turn him
out into the wilderness nearly naked, and leave him to
perish, unless, like a prisoner, he consents to adoption or affiliation, when every thing is again restored
to him, and he is received as one of their people.

28th.] To-day I accompanied one of the hunters
about 9 or 10 miles over the alluvial lands of Grand

* Charlevoix remarks, "Every one is an enemy found in the warrior's path," p. 155.

river, which were fertile, and covered in great part
with cane.   The river lands are no less extensive and
luxuriant betwixt the Verdigris and Arkansa, and
would apparently support a condensed settlement;
but the prairies will only admit of settlements along
their borders, in consequence of the scarcity of wood
and water.   Coal, however, in this country appears
abundant, as fragments are to be seen commonly deposited along the borders of the rivers.

On the 30th and 31st an irregular remittent fever
began to show itself in our camp, with which myself
and five or six others were affected.   With me it
came on towards evening, unaccompanied by any
sensible chill, but attended with the most excruciating head-ache and violent heat.

August 2d and 3d.] These two days in succession
I experienced the same fever, but now more moderate, and preceded by chills.

4th.] Last evening the chiefs of the Osage village
arrived from fort Smith, without effecting an interview with the Cherokees, who, under the pretext of
attending to their harvest, had postponed the meeting
until the month of September.   The chiefs, not without reason, appeared to be considerably perplexed and
disappointed at the conduct and apparent evasion of
the Cherokees.

Yesterday, whilst I lay sick, some Indian contrived
to rob me of the only penknife in my possession, and
my pocket microscope.   I immediately suspected the
thief to have been a fellow who had the same morning,
out of amusement, mounted my coat and hat, but he
constantly denied the theft, and suffered himself to
be searched by the soldier of police, who is generally
some trusty warrior appointed by the chief to keep
order in the camp or village, and to punish offenders
in a summary way.

The chiefs addressed the Indians present concerning the theft, and seriously admonished those who

had the articles to give them up. Tálai reproved the
Indians in general terms for their injustice, which he
asserted to be the means by which they had made themselves so many enemies. "Why will you," says he,
"steal things which are useless to you, and which are,
at the same time, of importance to others. To-day,
while we were travelling, we heard the report of a gun,
which might, indeed, have been that of white people,
who are our friends, but it might likewise have been
some party of those enemies by which we are every-
where surrounded, who could so easily have destroyed
a handful of old and almost defenceless chiefs. How
much better, my friends, would it be if we could
learn to do right and be honest. We should then
have friends instead of enemies; but as long as we
violate justice, we shall continue to live in fear and
shame. When did the white people steal from us?
yet you have both plundered and killed those who
have always been your friends and benefactors. This
evening we arrived here fatigued and hungry, and the
white people have fed us. We ought to return this
kindness by presents of provision; but, instead of
that, the Osages sell their tallow, and corn, and meat,
give nothing, and come and eat of that which they
have sold. The Osages are always a bad people, and
so have many enemies."

The candour of this speech surprised us, although
it well accorded with the honest and benevolent character of the speaker. I am told that he was quite
assiduous in attempting the reform of the village, and
inculcating amongst them the necessity and advantage of maintaining peace with their neighbours. It
is gratifying to learn that this chief, Tálai, whose example so well accorded with the just principles which
he preferred, was now gaining the ascendancy over
Clarmont, whose conduct had always been tinctured
by rapacity. Tálai, indeed, well deserved the chief
medal of the nation.

It is, I think, to be regretted, that the Indians should not be made sensible of the impropriety and illegality of executing summary and unlimited punishment upon the citizens of the United States, who are found travelling or hunting in their country. Ought they not rather to be taught that the government would be ever willing and ready to do them justice, by punishing their own citizens, rather than submiting them, in this way, to the cruel pilfering, and castigation of savages! If the frontier garrisons are not capable of effecting this beneficial purpose, for what were they established? but could not even this be better executed by the governor and the militia of the territory, than by the arbitrary commander and the soldiers of a garrison?

This morning, about day-break, the Indians, who had encamped around us, broke out into their usual lamentations and complaints to the Great Spirit. Their mourning was truly pathetic, and uttered in a peculiar tone. Amongst those who first broke forth into lamentation, and aroused the rest to their melancholy orisons, was the pious Tà-lai. The commencing tone was exceeding loud, and gradually fell off into a low, long continued, and almost monotonous base. To this tone of lamentation was modulated, the subject of their distress or petition. Those who had experienced any recent distress or misfortune, previously blackened their faces with coal, or besmeared them with ashes. This lamentation and abasement, in unison with oriental customs, recalled to mind the penance of the Jews, their " sackcloth and ashes," and Jeremiah their weeping prophet.

4th.] Last evening two very handsome young men of the Osages arrived from the village, with some tallow to barter, and while Mr. Bougie and the rest of the camp were amusing themselves at cards, these Mercuries contrived to carry off a small brass kettle, and endeavoured, though ineffectually, to hook off a musquetoe bier, after which they took the advantage of the night to make their escape. They appeared to have been very well satisfied with the trader, but could not postpone their dexterity at thieving, which being scarcely considered as a dishonourable action, is rarely punished further than by the restitution of the articles.

On the evening of the 5th, we were visited by an-other of the Osages, bringing the usual commodities of the season, tallow, dried bison meat, and sweet corn, being dried while in the milk, and thus forming an agreeable ingredient in the soup of the prepared bison beef. It is a dish which the Indians, from time immemorial, 'have been accustomed to prepare, and consider a luxury coeval with their annual festival of the "Green-corn Dance."

In the morning, I was informed, that this Indian wished to exchange a horse with me, for the mare which I had purchased of Mr. Lee; I desired them to tell him, that I requested to have nothing to say to him; knowing him, by report, to be a consummate thief and rascal; but, as he insisted on the subject, I went to see the animal offered me in exchange, and was truly surprised at the impudence and knavery of the demand. The horse which he proffered, was not worth possession, as lean as Rosinante. It may easi-ly be supposed that I rejected his offer, which was nothing better than an insult. My mare was at this time feeding across the Verdigris. The Indian said no more, concluded his barter with the trader, and left us; but instead of proceeding directly towards the village, by the usual route, he kept down the Ver-digris. I now suspected that he was intent on thieve-ry, and two of us directly followed him by land, and two by water. We saw him and his wife now cross-ing the river, and then walking hastily across the beach; by the time we came up with him, he had seized my horse, loaded it with his baggage, and would in a minute or two more, with all the dexterity of an Arab, have carried him off, and so by force and robbery have effected the exchange he so much desired. Daring villains seldom want excuses; he pretended, that the man of whom Mr. Prior bought the horse, had told him to bring it away, and leave the one he offered in its stead. His first depredation, this morning, was stealing a case of razors, which being discovered in his shot pouch, were taken from him; these he said, he only wanted to shave his head, and would then have returned them.

Circumstanced as we were, it was not politic to chastize him, as he would probably, out of revenge, have lurked about a week, in order to have stolen my horse. After some persuasion, and, above all, a hint that if his conduct were made known at the garrison, from whom I had received permission to proceed up the country, he need not expect the restitution of his wife and three children, from the hands of the Cherokees, if that was to be his line of conduct; he now began to speak in a submissive tone, and ordered his squaw to unpack my horse. I was still, however, mortified to find that it was necessary, prudentially, as suggested by the trader, not only to desist from administering punishment, but even to bestow a present upon the villain by way of encouragement. Such is the indulgent method of dealing with Indians employed by the traders!

As among most other nations of the aborigines, the principal labour, except that of hunting, devolves upon the women. Accustomed to perpetual drudgery, they are stouter and lower in stature than the men. They appear scarely to inherit the same condition. Considered almost as slaves and creatures of appetite, their lives are always secured as prisoners. It is to their industry and ingenuity, that the men owe every manufactured article of their dress, as well as every utensil in their huts. The Osage women appear to excel in these employments. Before the Cherokees burnt down their town on the Verdigris, their houses were chiefly covered with hand-wove matts of bulrushes. Their baskets and bed matts of this material, were parti-coloured and very handsome. This manufacture, I am told, is done with the assistance of three sticks, arranged in some way so as to answer the purpose of a loom, and the strands are inlaid diagonally. They, as well as the Cherokees and others, frequently take the pains to unravel old blankets and cloths, and re-weave the yarn into belts and garters. This weaving is no modern invention of the Indians. Nearly all those whom De Soto found inhabiting Florida and Louisiana, on either side of the Mississippi, and who were, in a great measure, an agricultural people, dressed themselves in woven garments made of the lint of the mulberry, the papaw, or the elm ; and, in the colder seasons of the year, they wore coverings of feathers, chiefly those of the turkey. The same dresses were still employed in the time of Du Pratz.* These feather mantles were, within the recollection of the oldest men, once used by the Cherokees, as I learnt whilst among them. There is,

* "Many of the women wear cloaks of the bark of the mulberry tree, or of the feathers of swans, turkies, or India ducks. The bark they take from young mulberry shoots that rise from the roots of trees that have been cut down ; after it is dried in the sun, they beat it to make all the woody part fall off, and they give the threads that remain a second beating, after which they bleach them by exposing them to the dew. When they are well whitened, they spin them about the coarseness of packthread, and weave them in the following manner : they plant two stakes in the ground, about a yard and a half asunder, and having stretched a cord from the one to the other, they fasten their threads of bark double to this cord, and then interweave them in a curious manner into a cloak, of about a yard square, with a wrought border round the edges." Du Pratz. Hist. Louisiana. p. 363. Lond. ed.

According to Adair also, the Choctaws formed blankets of the smaller feathers of the turkey. "They twist the inner end of the feathers very fast into a strong double thread of hemp, or the inner bark of the mulberry tree, of the size and strength of coarse twine, and they work it in the manner of fine netting." Adair's History of the American Indians. p. 423.

therefore, nothing extraordinary in the discovery of these garments around the bodies which had been interred in the nitre caves of Kentucky. Presents of these " mantels" as they are called by Purchas, now superceded by European blankets, were perpetually offered to Soto, throughout the course of his expedition, and are still made use of by the natives of the north-west coast. Nor is there any thing in this invention beyond the common ingenuity of man, guarding himself against the inclemencies of climate. To assert that all men were of the same race, because they had all invented a somewhat similar clothing, is quite as futile, as the same conclusion would be in consideration of their all being born naked.*

The principal food of the present Indians, who inhabit the west side of the Mississippi, is the bison, which they prepare in a very commodious way, without the use of salt, by cutting it up into broad and thin slices, which are dried on a scaffold over a slow fire, and afterwards folded up in the manner of peltries, so as to be equally portable. The tallow is rendered into skins or cases, like the utriculi, or leathern bottles of the ancients, the whole animal being skinned through the aperture of the neck. In this way, they also collect with convenience the honey and bear's oil, which is the produce of their forests.

From the general absence of religious ceremony, and the unostentatious character of devotion among the Indians, it has always been a difficult matter to inspire them with any thing like correct ideas of the Christian religion. As we have already remarked, they are not, however, void of superstition, such as a belief in the warnings of dreams, the observ-

---

* See Archæologia Americana, vol. i. p. 320, &c. in which there is an attempt to prove that the ancient inhabitants of the western states originated from the Malays.

ance of omens, the wearing of amulets, and the dedi-
cation of offerings to invisible or miraculous agents,
supposed to be represented in the accidental forms of
natural objects. But these objects, calculated to inspire a momentary homage, are never addressed for
any thing beyond temporal favours.

Although they generally believe in the immortality
of the soul, they have no steady and distinct concep-
tion of a state of reward and punishment. The future state, believed to be but little different from that
which they now enjoy, is alike attainable by every
hunter, and every warrior. It is on a conviction of
this belief, that the implements of war, and the decorations and utensils employed by the living, are en-
tombed with the dead. Their jealousy of the whites,
and suspicion of sinister designs, render them cold
and cautious in the adoption of Christianity, and it
has ever been those who have said the least on religion, and who, like the Society of the Friends and
the Moravians, have preached rather by their benevolent example, and by the introduction of useful arts,
that have made the most durable and favourable impression on the minds and morals of the natives.

To show how little can be anticipated among the
Osages, by the inculcation of the mere dogmas of
Christianity, may be seen by the following anecdote.
Mr. Bougie, informed me, that last winter, while accidentally engaged in reading the New Testament,
two or three young men, of the Osages, coming into
his store, enquired of him what was said in that book.
He answered, that it informed him of the descent of
God upon the earth, who was seen by men, convers-
ed with them, and wrought miracles. If that was
true, they asked, why did he not come down now
among men as he did then? To which Mr. B. replied, because the world was now so wicked. They
looked at one another, held their hands to their mouths,
as they always do in token of surprise, and, smiling,

said, "the book may tell you so, but we don't believe it."

Independent of some resemblance in language,
discoverable betwixt the aborigines of North America, and the Tartar tribes of the Russian empire, there
is, likewise, something very similar in their habits and
morals.   They are equally erratic and unsettled in
their abode, and have ever been so, according to He-
rodotus, for thousands of years.   The Hamaxobii, of
that author, still live in their travelling houses, and
occupy the same country without any sensible diminution or increase of numbers.   Both people are separated into numerous bands or tribes, characterised
by a diversity of language, acknowledging no other
rule than that which is patriarchal, and no other alliance than that of fraternity.   They are alike insensible to the wants and comforts of civilization.   They
know neither poverty nor riches; vice nor virtue.
Their simple condition appears to have perpetually
partaken of that of the first family of the human race,
and they have been alike exempt from the luxuries of
ephemeral grandeur, and the mournful vicissitudes of
fortune.   Happy equality, which knows neither the
sins of ambition, nor the crimes of avarice!

The picture of the Samoyades,* drawn apparently
by a careful hand, might almost pass for that of the
North American Indians.   Alike they acknowledge
the existence of a supreme and invisible Being, the
author of all things.   The sun and moon they also
adore as superior beings of the creation.   They both
in their invocations address the four quarters of the
earth.   Their priests or elders administer to them
charms when sick or unfortunate in hunting.   They
submit with apathy (or resignation) to misfortunes,
and express no violent passions.   Their insensibility
is such, as to prevent all surprise or curiosity at the

* Vide Pinkerton's collection of Voyages and Travels, vol.i. in loco.

sight of novelties. They fear, but do not adore bad spirits. Unacquainted with laws, and governed by customs, they acknowledge no ruler beyond the senior of the common family or tribe. To religious ceremonies they are strangers. Anticipating the contingencies of a future state of existence, they also inter with the warrior his bow and arrows. They allow polygamy, but avoid consanguinity in marriage. Their wives are purchased (to evince their esteem), and the marriage, consummated at an early age, is no longer binding than the continuance of mutual friendship and affection. Their names are taken from the animals of the forest, or the phenomena of nature. Their hair is coarse, lank, and black, and they have little or no beard, or marks of pubescence on other parts of the body, and, whenever it does appear, it is carefully eradicated. Such is the character, and such the manners of those Asiatics, inhabiting the very same parallel as that which includes the most proximate and occidental point of the North American continent, the same parallel, which in both continents afford the *Ovis Ammon*, or wild sheep, the rein deer, the white wolf, the chacal, the silver fox, the sable, and the ermine.

CHAPTER XIV.

*Journey by land to the Great Salt river of the Ar-
kansa—Proceed across the prairies to the Little
North Fork of the Canadian—Detained by sickness—Continue up the Little North Fork, arrive
at Salt river, and afterwards at the Arkansa—Molested and pursued by the Osages—Arrive again at
the Verdigris, and proceed to the garrison—Conclusion of the treaty between the Osages and Cherokees.*

August 11th.] To-day I left the trading establishment of the Verdigris to proceed on a land journey
up the Arkansa, accompanied by a trapper and hunter named Lee, who had penetrated across this country nearly to the sources of Red river, and followed
his present occupation for upwards of eight years.
We crossed the river, and proceeding through the alluvion, entered the prairie, over which we continued
in a westwardly course, encamping in the evening
upon the banks of a small creek, about 12 miles from
our place of departure.   The prairies or grassy plains
which we entered upon a mile from the river, exhibited the same appearance as below, and on the opposite side of the river.   The rock of the hills, like
those of the prairies near the garrison, consisted of a
ferruginous sandstone.   To the south of our encampment, we had in view a low ridge of hills very abruptly broken into fantastic contours.   In these prairies, I found a second species of *Brachyris,* pungent-
ly aromatic to the taste, and glutinous to the touch;
its aspect is that of *Chrysocoma.*   Our route was
directed towards the Salt river, or first Red river of
the Arkansa, called by Pike the Grand Saline, and
about 80 or 90 miles distant from our encampment.

12th.] We continued our journey about sunrise, proceeding over the plain in a south-west direction. About 10 miles from the brook of our last night's encampment we passed another, but destitute of running water, which is at this season of the year exceedingly scarce. The Arkansa, several miles to our right, appeared to make an extensive sinus to the northwest, as is designated in Pike's map, where it is continued up to the 100th degree of longitude, the dividing line from the possessions of Spain. We found the prairies full of grass about knee deep, although all the gullies and smaller streams were perfectly dried up ; it was only when we arrived at a brook or rivulet that we could obtain a draught of water, and that always stagnant, and often putrid. The day being oppressively hot and thirsty, I very imprudently drank some very nauseous and tepid water, which immediately affected my stomach, and produced such a sickness, that it was with difficulty I kept upon my horse, until we arrived at the next creek for shelter, where we encamped and remained for the rest of the afternoon. Our horses were still tormented with the clegs or green-headed flies of the prairies, which goaded them without intermission.

About 10 o'clock this morning, we crossed the trace which the Osages had made, going out to hunt in a body of 2 or 300 men and their families. Its direction was south, or towards Red river. Two or three miles further we crossed their returning track. We were no way anxious to meet with Indians, as they would, probably, rob us of our horses, if not of our baggage, and ill-treat us besides, according to the dictates of their caprice and the object of their party.—To-day we came about 20 miles.

13th.] We were again on our way soon after sunrise, and still continued through plains destitute of timber. After proceeding about four miles, we passed another insignificant brook, and about six miles further a second of the same magnitude. We observed very little game. Yesterday, Mr. Lee pointed out to me the burrow of a badger, about the size of those made by the prairie wolf. Still proceeding, a little to the north of west, about 10 miles further, we came to a considerable rivulet of clear and still water, deep enough to swim our horses. We kept for about two miles through the entangled thickets, by which it was bordered, in search of a ford. Both above and below it was bordered by wooded hills, which appeared almost to shut up our course, and terminate the prairies. This stream was called the Little North Fork (or branch) of the Canadian, and emptied into the main North Fork of the same river, nearly 200 miles distant, including its meanders, which have been ascended by the trappers of beaver. Having encamped, without crossing the rivulet, towards evening, I was about to bathe, but was sufficiently deterred by the discovery of a poisonous water snake, lurking a few yards from the spot I had chosen. No change yet appears in the vegetation; and the superincumbent rock continues arenaceous. No mountains or picturesque prospects present themselves to amuse the eye. Occasionally, indeed the monotonous plain is diversified by the view of low and broken ridges, often presenting isolated hills, deserted by the more friable materials with which they were once surrounded, and now presenting the fantastic appearance of artificial tumuli, and piles of ruins. In the course of the day we passed three or four of these hillocks, of considerable elevation. About six miles from our encampment, to the right, there are two of them nearly together, and two also which are separated from each other, nearly opposite to the others on the left. The Indians remark them in the regulation of their routes, and, on some of them, they have made elevated interments. This fondness for burying in high places has not subsided among the aborigines, and, probably, gave rise to the erection of artificial hills over the remains of the dead. Blackbird, the chief of the Mahas, was interred, at his particular request, on the summit of a hill which overlooked the village; and both the Mahas and the Arikarsees made choice of the summit of a neighbouring ridge for their general place of sepulture.

The day was very warm, though occasionally relieved by a breeze from the south-west; and the dazzling light of the prairies proved oppressive and injurious to the eyes. We passed a place where the Indians appeared to have been killing numbers of deer, though not recently.

14th.] We remained to-day on the banks of the Little North Fork, to recruit our horses, that of my companion being from the first totally unfit to travel from a large wound upon its back. I now experienced a relapse of the remittent fever, attended with delirium. Being about 3 o'clock in the afternoon when it came on, I was exposed to a temperature of between 90 and 100°. It was with difficulty that I could crawl into the shade, the thin forest being every where pervious to the sun, so that I felt ready to burn with heat; by forcibly inciting a vomit, I felt relieved. Mr. Lee, profiting by our delay, began to trap for beaver, and the last night caught four of these animals. Scarcely any thing is now employed for bait but the musk or castoreum of the animal itself. As they live in community, they are jealous and hostile to strangers of their own species, and following the scent of the bait, are deceived into the trap.

15th.] At night I again experienced an attack of the fever, without any preceding chill, and attended with diarrhœa. It continued 36 hours, the paroxysm being only divided for a short space by an intermediate chill. The heat of the weather continued excessive; and the green blow-flies, attracted by the meat brought to our camp, exceeded every thing that can

26

be conceived. They filled even our clothes with maggots, and penetrated into the wounds of our horses, so as to render them almost incurable.

16th.] Still at the same encampment, and still afflicted with the fever.

17th.] This morning, at the suggestion of my companion, for the purpose of trapping, we went about five miles lower down the rivulet. In proceeding this short distance, I fainted with the effort, and was near falling off my horse. All the remainder of the day and the succeeding night, I experienced the fever under the exposure of a burning sun and sultry air. Shade was not to be obtained, and the night brought with it no alleviation but darkness.

In the evening Mr. Lee suggested the propriety of our returning to the Verdigris, before I became so weak as to render it impossible ; but the idea of returning filled me with deep regret, and I felt strongly opposed to it whatever might be the consequences.

18th.] To return, was again urged to me in plainer terms than before. I therefore complied, on the condition of trying the event of one or two days longer, and that then, if no better, I would return. I remarked to him, however, that these small distances from one trapping place to another, would, at this hot season, be far less difficult for me to accomplish, than to enter back again upon the prairies.

19th.] We proceeded to another place of encampment, through ponds and dry gullies, crossing the prairies from point to point, for about 10 miles, instead of a supposed five or six, until it became dark, when, not finding the place where Mr. Lee had deposited his baggage, we stopped in a very eligible situation, compared with the rest of the wilderness through which we had been toiling. The preceding night we had experienced a slight rain, and had reason to suspect it again, but we lay down unprepared ; and about midnight were caught in a thunder storm

of great violence, and continued till daylight under
pelting torrents of rain.

20th.] Mr. Lee now said nothing more about returning, as his horse was become incapable of carrying either himself or his baggage. We had no
method left of proceeding, at present, but by making
double journeys, and employing my horse to convey
the whole. The flies still continued to annoy us, filling our blankets, linen, and almost every thing about
us with maggots. To compensate, however, in some
measure, for these disgusting and familiar visitors, we
had the advantage of the bee, and obtained abundance
of excellent honey, on which, mixed up with water,
I now almost entirely subsisted, as we had no other
food but venison, and were without either bread or
vegetables.

21st.] We again proceeded five or six miles further over stoney hills, with great fatigue, and again
encamped on a branch of the Little North Fork. Lee
was now in a great dilemma about our falling into the
way of the Indians; he observed to-day (22d) their
general encampment quite contiguous.

The fever had now rendered me too weak to bear
any exercise; and it was become impossible to find
any thing which would suit my feeble appetite. In
the commencing coolness of the weather, I had, however, a reasonable hope of recovery.

23d.] We continued about three miles further up
the banks of the rivulet, and again encamped amidst
gloomy prospects.

24th.] To-day, Mr. Lee having contrived to place
a great part of his baggage upon his own horse, we
proceeded about 10 miles, alternately along the borders of the rivulet and over the bases of the adjacent
hills, which we had now the satisfaction to find more
open and less rocky. We passed by three or four
enormous ponds grown up with aquatics, among
which were thousands of acres of the great pond lily

(Cyamus luteus), amidst which grew also the *Thalia dealbata*, now in flower, and, for the first time, I saw the *Zizania miliacea* of Michaux.   At length we gained sight of the prairies, which were doubly interesting after being so disagreeably immured amidst thickets and ponds.   In our way we struck across the desiccated corner of the pond ; here the *Ambrosias* or bitter weeds were higher than my head on horseback, and we were a considerable time in extricating ourselves from them.   Clearing the thicket, we ascended a hill of the prairie, and continued across it to the first creek, where we encamped.

26th.] While Mr. Lee was absent this morning examining the beaver traps, which he had set, to my surprise I observed, on the opposite side of the creek, an Indian busily examining our horses ; after viewing them a few minutes, he chased them down the creek in a gallop towards our encampment, and after looking at me also with caution, instantly disappeared without paying me a visit.   I need not say, how unwelcome this intelligence was to my cautious companion, who had not now to learn the rapacity of the savage hunters, having nearly lost his life, and all his property, last autumn, by falling in with the Cherokees near the banks of the Canadian.   We delayed not a moment to leave our encampment, expecting nothing more certain than an unfriendly visit or clandestine theft. My own situation was indeed extremely critical, as I could not possibly walk, and even required assistance to get on and off my horse: thus to have had it stolen would have been to leave me to perish without hope. As we passed along, something which I imagined to be an Indian, dodged near us twice, from amidst the high grass, like some unfriendly animal of the forest, and slunk from our observance.   This evening I felt extremely unhappy, and became quite delirious; when reclined, it was with difficulty that I could rise; a kind of lethargy, almost the prelude of death, now interposed, affording an ominous relief from anxiety and pain.

27th.] Three days were now elapsed since I had been able to taste any kind of food, and to add to the miseries of sickness, delirium, and despondence, we experienced as many days of unremitting gloom, in which the sun was not visible even for an hour.

30th.] Being a little recovered, we now ventured out some distance into the prairie hills; but, after travelling a few miles without much pain, my mind became so unaccountably affected with horror and distraction, that, for a time, it was impossible to proceed to any convenient place of encampment. This evening my companion killed two bison, the first we had seen on the route, but neither of them were fat, or any thing like tolerable food. I here spent a night of great misery and delirium, and felt exceedingly cold from the sudden decrease of the temperature.

31st.] We moved onwards a few miles, but encamped at an early hour.

September 1st.] We proceeded about 10 miles over wooded hills, with the expectation of soon arriving at the Salt river, which we imagined to lie before us, either to the west or south-west, but were entirely deceived, and my companion now appeared to be ignorant of the country. We saw nothing far and wide but an endless scrubby forest of dwarfish oaks, chiefly the post, black, and red species.

2d.] We now travelled about 15 miles nearly north, in the hope of arriving, at any rate, on the Arkansa, and passed through oak thickets, like those of Red river, for most part of the day. The land was poor and hilly, but abounded with clear and cool springs, issuing through rocks of a fine grained sandstone. We found the small chinquapin oak by acres, running along the ground as in New Jersey. The *Portulaca* resembling *P. villosa*, which I had seen below in a solitary locality, Mr. Lee picked up for me to-day, grow-

ing in arid rocky places, where the soil had been nearly washed away. The general aspect of the vegetable kingdom still, however, continued nearly the
same.

3d.] We continued on about 26 miles through the
same kind of deeply undulated country, abounding
with clear grit springs, but the land poor, and covered with scrubby oak, except occasional prairie openings and narrow valleys. At length we arrived on
the banks of a small clear brook dammed up by the
beaver, where we obtained a ford. Towards evening,
greatly fatigued, and with our course directed more
towards the west, we observed clouds of sand to arise
at a distance, which we were satisfied must originate
from the beach of some neighbouring river, and, in
about an hour after, we came upon the rocky bank
of the First Red Fork or Salt river, which, though
very low, was still red and muddy, bordered with an
extensive beach similar to the Arkansa, and not greatly differing from it apparently in point of magnitude.
Along the argillaceous banks I observed saline in-
crustations, and, on tasting the water, I found it to be
nauseous and impotably saline. Our horses, however, naturally fond of salt, drank of it with the utmost
greediness. Though gratified by the sight of this
curious stream, which we had so tediously sought, I
now lamented the loss of the fine spring water lately
afforded us by the barren hills. This extensive stream
constitutes the hunting boundary of the Pawnees and
Hietans. Its first view appeared beautifully contrasted with the broken and sterile country through which
we had been travelling. The banks of cotton-wood
(*Populus monilifera*), bordered by the even beach,
resembled a verdant garden in panorama view. A
few days journey to the west, Mr. Lee informs me,
that there are extensive tracts of moving sand hills,
accompanied by a degree of sterility little short of the
African deserts.

4th.] We continued a few miles up the banks of this saline stream, crossing it from point to point. But the following day (5th) we concluded on leaving it, studying our safety from the Osages, whose traces became now more and more evident. We pursued our course along the sand beaches of the river, now oppressively hot, and about noon turned out into a shade. Here, unfortunately, while Mr. Lee was busied about his beaver traps, his horse got into a mirey gully, and could not be extricated. In this dilemma, no resource for proceeding remained for my companion, but to construct a canoe, and so descend by water. From the general diminution and deterioration of the forest, it was not even an easy matter to find a tree of sufficient size for this purpose. The largest timber was the cotton-wood (*Populus angulata*). After an unexpected and irksome privation, I was now again gratified by the taste of fresh water, which we found in a small stagnant rivulet contiguous to our encampment.

On the 8th, my companion launched his canoe, which so exactly answered his purpose that it would have sunk with any additional loading. Although I had now so far recovered as to possess a little appetite, we were, for several days, destitute of any kind of food, except the tails of the beaver, the flesh of this animal being now too lean and musky to be eaten. The game appeared to be driven out of the country by the approach of the Indians. I still continued my route along the beaches of the river, which proved almost insupportably hot, and I severely felt the want of fresh water, though it now, from necessity, became possible for me to swallow this tepid brine, which always proved cathartic. As we proceeded, the river appeared continually bordered by sandstone hills, like the Arkansa. Amongst several other new plants, I found a very curious *Gaura*, an undescribed species of *Donia*, of *Eriogonum*, of *Achyranthes*, *Arundo*, and *Gentian*. On the sandy beaches grew several plants, such as the *Uralepsis arıstulata* (*Festuca procumbens*, Muhlenberg), an *Uniola* scarcely distinct from *U. spicata* and *Sesuvium sessile,* which I had never heretofore met with, except on the sands of the sea coast.

9th.] About noon we arrived at the entrance of the Arkansa, and were once more gratified with the taste of fresh water. Here the stream, now at its lowest depression, was almost colourless, and scarcely any where exceeding the depth of three feet. We travelled down it 9 or 10 miles, and saw the ascending smoke of the general encampments of the Osages, whom, if possible, we wished to avoid. By the multitude of traces upon the sand, it was easy to perceive that the whole village and its accompaniments were in motion.

10th.] We still saw the smoke of the Osage fires in all directions, and hourly expected a discovery. As I passed along contiguous to the river, now alone, one of the Indians saw me in the wood, but did not venture to come up, dodged out of sight, and then ran along with haste towards his encampment. This wolfish behaviour, it may be certain, was not calculated to give me any very favourable anticipation of our reception. I could not help indeed reflecting on the inhospitality of this pathless desert, which will one day perhaps give way to the blessings of civilization. The scenery was not without beauty ; wooded hills of gentle slope every where bordered the river ; and its islands and alluvions, still of considerable extent, are no way inferior to the lands of the Ohio.

11th.] To-day, with all our caution, it became impossible to avoid the discovery of the Indians, as two or three families were encamped along the borbers of the river. They ran up to us with a confidence which was by no means reciprocal. One of the men was a blind chief, not unknown to Mr. Lee, who gave him some tobacco, with which he appeared to be satisfied. About the encampment there were a host of squaws, who were extremely impertinent. An old woman, resembling one of the imaginary witches Macbeth, told me, with an air of insolence, that I must give her my horse for her daughter to ride on; I could walk;—that the Osages were numerous, and could soon take it from me. At last, the blind chief invited us to his camp to eat, but had nothing to offer us but boiled maize, sweetened with the marmalade of pumpkins. When we were about to depart, they all ran to the boat, to the number of 10 or 12, showing symptoms of mischief, and could not be driven away. They held on to the canoe, and endeavoured to drag it aground. Mr. Lee tried in vain to get rid of them, although armed with a rifle. At length, they got to pilfering our baggage; even the blind chief, who had showed us a commendatory certificate which he had obtained at St. Louis, also turned thief on the occasion. We had not got out of the sight of these depredators, before another fellow came after us on the run, in order to claim my horse, insisting that it was his, and I could no way satisfy his unfounded demand, but by giving him one of my blankets.

Mr. Lee, as he descended, now observed two men on the shore, who hid themselves at his approach, and began to follow him as secretly as possible. They continued after us all the remainder of the day, till dark. We knew not whether they intended to kill or to rob us; and, endeavouring to elude their pursuit, we kept on in the night, amidst the horrors of a thunder storm, the most gloomy and disagreeable situation I ever experienced in my life. In consequence also of the quicksands and the darkness, it was with the utmost difficulty that I could urge my horse to take the river, which it was necessary repeatedly to cross. In one of these attempts, both myself and it were on the point of being buried before we

27

could extricate ourselves. Dressed in leather, I came out of the water drenched and shivering, almost ready to perish with cold. After some persuasion, I prevailed upon Lee to kindle me a handful of fire, by which I lay alone for two or three hours, amidst the dreary howling of wolves, Mr. Lee not wishing to trust himself near such a beacon. Nothing, however, further molested us, and, after cooking and eating a a portion of a fat buck elk, which my companion had contrived to kill in the midst of our flight, we continued our journey by the light of the moon. After proceeding about 20 miles farther down the Arkansa, unable to keep up with Lee and his boat, at noon we agreed to part. I took with me some small pieces of the boiled elk, with a portion also uncooked, and furnished myself, as I thought, with the means of obtaining fire, but, when evening arrived, I was greatly mortified to find all my attempts to obtain this necessary element abortive. My gun was also become useless, all the powder having got wet by last night's adventure.

14th.] Fatigued with the sand-beaches, as hot and cheerless as the African deserts, I left the banks of the river ; and, after travelling with extreme labour through horrible thickets for three miles, in which the *Ambrosias* were far higher than my head on horseback, I, at length, arrived amongst woody hills, and a few miles further came out, to my great satisfaction, into the open prairies, from whence, in an elevated situation, I immediately recognised the Verdigris river. At night, though late, I arrived on its wide alluvial lands, lined with such an impenetrable thicket, that I did not attain the bank, and had to lie down alone, in the rank weeds, amidst musquetoes, without fire, food, or water, as the meat with which I had been provided was raw, and spoiled by the worms.

15th.] With all the advantage of day-light, it was still difficult to penetrate through the thicket, and ford the river. Towards evening, I again arrived at the trading establishment of Mr. Bougie, an asylum, which probably, at this time, rescued me from death. My feet and legs were so swelled, in consequence of weakness and exposure to extreme heat and cold, that it was necessary to cut off my pantaloons, and at night both my hands and feet were affected by the most violent cramp.

I remained about a week with Mr. Bougie, in a very feeble state, again visited by fever, and a kind of horrific delirium, which perpetually dwelt upon the scene of past sufferings. I now took the opportunity of descending to the garrison with an engagée, but continued in a state of great debility, my hands and feet still violently and frequently affected with spasms.

In about five days slow descending, from the feebleness of my invalid companion, we arrived at the garrison.

The Indian councils now pending betwixt the Osages and Cherokees filled the fort with a disagreeable bustle. The Osages, according to the stipulation of the treaty signed at St. Louis, were assembled to receive their prisoners from the hands of the Cherokees. The captives, chiefly female, were, however, kept back, and they wished to retain them on the score of adoption. Tálai and Clarmont insisted on their compliance with the treaty; and the government agents now ordered the Cherokees to produce the prisoners in 10 days. The 11th day, however, arrived without any appearance of the Cherokees, excepting five of their hunters. The chiefs of the Osages were exceedingly mortified. Captain Prior told them to demand of the commander the liberty of seizing upon the five Cherokees in the fort as hostages. To this the chief, called the Mad Buffalo, objected, saying, "if we take these Cherokee prisoners to our village, the warriors, and those who expected the return of their own people, would say, who are these strangers and enemies? we wanted our own captives, not Cherokees, and so they would instantly kill them."

In the evening the Osage chiefs left the fort, and proceeded towards their village; but next morning the Cherokees began to assemble, and the Osages were sent for to receive their prisoners, now arrived. Tálai and Clarmont sent the lesser chiefs, and remained behind, but the Cherokees insisted on the presence of the whole, and after a second message they came as desired.

Tikitok, one of the principal Cherokees, a very old and venerable looking man, presided on the occasion, and every appearance of friendship and satisfaction, accompanied by the usual smoking, prevailed on either side. The prisoners, after some little talk, were now produced, and given up according to the treaty. There was, however, a chief sitting next to Tikitok, who undertook to propose, that the prisoners should be permitted to use their own will, and go to either party as they should chuse, but this unfair and equivocating proposal was not made known to the Osages, some private conversation with the Cherokees putting a stop to it. It appeared that, in the interval of captivity, one of the young women had contracted marriage with a Cherokee of her own age. Their parting was a scene of sorrow; the Cherokee promised to go to the village, and ask her of her father, she also plead with the chiefs to stay, but Clarmont, unmoved by her tears and entreaties, answered, "your father and mother lament you; it is your duty to go and see them. If the Cherokee loves you, he will not forget to come for you." In this way terminated the treaty of peace between the Osages and Cherokees, in September, 1819.*

* Since this period, as might readily be foreseen, hostilities have again commenced between these restless and warlike tribes, who can

CHAPTER XV.

*Proceed from the garrison to the Pecannerie settle-
ment—Hot-springs of the Washita—Phenomena of
the seasons.*

In consequence of sickness, and an extreme debility, which deprived me of the pleasure of my usual
excursions, I remained at the garrison until the 16th
of October. A nervous fever had now for ever separated me from the agreeable company of Dr. Russel,
and amongst my associates in affliction were numbered two missionaries, who had intended to proceed
to the Osages. One of them, (Mr. Viner), after the
attacks of a lingering fever, paid the debt of nature.

From July to October, the ague and bilious fever
spread throughout the territory in a very unusual
manner. Connected apparently with these diseases,
was one of an extraordinary character. It commenced
by slight chills, and was succeeded by a fever, attended with unremitting vomitings, accompanied with
blood, and bloody fœces. Ejecting all medicine, it
became next to impossible to administer internal relief. The paroxysms, attended with excruciating pain,
took place every other day, similar to the common
intermittent. One of the soldiers who descended with us, was afflicted in this way for the space of
six days, after which he recovered. On the intermitting
days he appeared perfectly easy, and possessed a
strong and craving appetite. I was credibly in-

perhaps never be prevailed upon to live in friendship, as they will be
perpetually transgressing each other's hunting bounds. At a very recent
date (1821), 400 Osage warriors appeared before the garrison of Belle
Point, on their way against the Cherokees, accompanied by a party of
the Sauks and Fox Indians, and killed four Quapaws hunting in the
neighbourhood. Such is the effect of the imprudent and visionary
policy of crowding the natives together, in the hopes of keeping them
at peace.

formed that not less than 100 of the Cherokees, settled contiguous to the banks of the Arkansa, died
this season of the bilious fever.

On the 3d of November, I at length got down in
a perogue of the garrison as far as Major Wilborne's
in the Pecannerie settlement.   Here, though the
bilious fever and ague had been unusually prevalent,
no instance of mortality had taken place.

In this settlement there was a succession of heavy
rains down to the month of September.   Above, we
had experienced no rain beyond the month of June.
Perhaps the unusual prevalence of rain, on the banks
of the Arkansa, might have been conducive to the
extraordinary sickness of this season.   As a proof of
the locality of this rain, the river was now so exceedingly low, that no boats drawing more than 10 or 12
inches of water could possibly navigate it from the
Dardanelles to the Verdigris.   All along the banks, the
clay and pebbles of the beaches were whitened with
an efflorescence of salt (muriate of soda), deposited
from the water of the red freshes.   We also remarked that all the sandstone rocks, scattered confusedly
on the borders of the river, blacken by exposure, and
assume a metallic tinge, probably arising from an admixture of manganese.

The Pecannerie, now the most considerable settlement in the territory, except Arkansas, derived its
name from the Pecan nut-trees *(Carya olivæformis)*,
with which its forests abound ; in a few years it will
probably form a county, containing at this time about
60 families, all, in regard to circumstances, living in
a state of ignorance and mediocrity of fortune : many
of them indeed were renegadoes from justice who
had fled from honest society, to seek refuge in these
fertile alluvial forests, where, indulging themselves in
indolence, they become the pest of their more industrious and honest neighbours, and are encouraged in
their dishonest practices by the laxity of the laws, and

the imperfect manner in which they are administered. Thus the settlement was now oppressed by gangs of horse thieves, who carried their depredations even among the neighbouring savages.

The soil throughout this settlement, after three or four years working, is found to be extremely favourable for the growth of cotton, as appeared by the crops of the present year, but the price was fallen to 3 dollars per cwt. in the seed, with little or no demand, so that the settlers, for want of a market, were really indigent, and most of them lived in a very poor and uncomfortable manner. The alluvial lands, here about two miles wide, are flanked by a range of wooded hills, and a somewhat broken country of considerable fertility.

A number of families were now about to settle, or rather take provisionary possession of the land purchased from the Osages, situated along the banks of the Arkansa, from Frog bayou to the falls of the Verdigris; a tract in which is embraced a great body of superior alluvial land. But, to their disappointment, an order recently arrived, instructing the agent of Indian affairs to put the Cherokees in possession of the Osage purchase, and to remove them from the south side of the river. It appeared, from what I could learn, that the Osages, purposely deceived by the interpreter, at the instigation of the Shoutous, had hatched up a treaty without the actual authority of the chiefs, so that in the present state of thing sa war betwixt the Cherokees and the Osages is almost inevitable, unless the latter relinquish the banks of the Arkansa, as Messrs. Shoutou wish them. The Osages in a recent council said, they would have no objection to dispose of their lands, provided the whites only were allowed to settle upon them.

I understand that the hot springs of the Washita are situated about a mile from that river, contiguous to the

bank of a brook. At the springs, a ridge of between
five and six hundred feet, from whence smoke had
been seen to issue, appears, by the massive rocks that
fill this stream, to have been broken through, or un-
dermined by its torrents. Many thermal springs, besides those employed by visitors, are seen boiling out
of the side of the hill, and mingling with the cool
water of the brook. The principal fountain, issuing
from amidst huge masses of black rocks, apparently
bituminous and calcareous slate in thick laminæ, has
a stream of near a foot in diameter at its orifice, and
hot enough to boil eggs or fish; a steam arises from
it as from water in a state of ebullition, attended with
a considerable discharge of bubbles. It is only after
mixing with the cool water of the brook, at some distance from this spring, that it becomes of a temperature in which it is possible to bathe. There is, however, a kind of rude inclosure made around the spring,
as a steam bath, which often probably debilitates, and
injures the health of ignorant and emaciated patients.
Major Long, who visited these springs in the month
of January, found their temperature to vary from 86°
to 150° of Fahrenheit. Hunter and Dunbar ascertained the temperature of five different springs, to be
at 150°, 154°, 140°, 136°, and 132°. The water, as
near Onondago, in the state of New York, at the tepid baths of Matlock in Derbyshire, and in many
parts of Italy, charged with an excess of carbonic
acid, holding lime in solution, deposits a calcareous
tufa, which incrusts leaves, moss, or any other substance which it meets in its course, to the great surprise of the ignorant, who commonly pronounce them
petrifactions. Indeed, the exploring party of the
Washita assert, that a mass of calcareous rock,
100 feet perpendicular, had been produced by this
aqueous deposition. Eruptions of argillaceous mud
in small quantities have also been observed, which in
time become considerably indurated.

Among the more remarkable features of the autumnal season in this country, is the aspect of the atmosphere, which in all directions appears so filled with smoke, as often to render an object obscure at the distance of 100 yards. The south-west winds at this season are often remarkably hazy, but here the effect is greatly augmented by the burning of the surrounding prairies, annually practised by the savages and whites, for the benefit of the hunt, as the ground is thus cleared of a heavy crop of withered grass, prepared for an early vegetation in the succeeding spring, and also assisted in its growth by the stimulating effects of the alkaline ashes. Indeed, ever since the beginning of September, the prairies had appeared yellow and withered, with a prevailing mass of dying vegetation. The autumnal Asters and Solidagos, are but a faint gleam of the mid-summer splendour of these flowery meadows. Throughout this territory, there are no grasses nor other vegetables of consequence in agriculture (except the cane), which retain their verdure beyond the close of September. 'Tis true, that in the sheltered alluvions, verdure may be protracted, and it is here that the cattle, left to nature, now seek their food, and, as the winter advances, finally repair to the sempervirent cane brake. That delightful and refreshing verdure one naturally expects to see in a garden, regales not the eye of the Arkansa farmer beyond the vegetating period assigned by nature. From the month of September to February (except in the lowest and richest alluvions), every enclosure, in common with the prairies, appears a dreary waste of withered herbage, with the exception of the biennial turnip, the radish, and the cabbage, which still retain their freshness. The month of February, however, scarcely closes before vegetation again commences, and the natural meadows, thickets, and alluvions, in March, are already enamelled with the flowers of May;

28

The aridity of the autumnal atmosphere, which be-comes more and more sensible as we advance towards the west, or recede from the ocean, may be perceived to modify many of the natural productions of the country, and deserves to be studied by those who re-side on the spot. Amongst the *Cucurbitaceæ*, every species of melon, which attain such enormous bulk and perfection east of the Mississippi, are here often of diminutive size, notwithstanding the heat of the climate ; and by the increasing dryness of the air, the plants, full of young fruit, wither and prematurely die. The diminution of the forest, and at length its total disappearance, is also, in all probability, attributable to the same source of infertility.

The natural phenomena of the seasons appear no less corroborative of a distinction of climate betwixt the eastern and western territories. From the Pecan-nerie settlement eastward, heavy rains were experienc-ed for most part of the summer down to the begin-ning of September ; while from the garrison upwards, scarcely any rain except the slightest flying showers had fallen since the month of June. It might, indeed, be reasonably conjectured, that the further any coun-try was removed from the ocean, the great reservoir of rains, and the more it was elevated above that level, the more it would have to depend upon the win-ter or rainy season for irrigation ; and that, in such a country, rain can hardly be expected in the sum-mer, especially if the temperature be elevated. Facts bear out these conjectures, for the higher we ascend toward the great platform of the Andes, the more arid becomes the climate; and at length, approach-ing the mountains, nothing is to be seen but a barren and desert region, tantalized with numerous streams, which flow only in the winter, and then with such force and velocity, as to tear up frightful ravines, and, sweeping away thousands of acres of friable materials, which to a considerable depth constitute the more an-

cient incumbent soil, leave behind, upon the denudated plains, colossal masses insulated in the most fantastic forms, so as to appear like piles of artificial
ruins. Such is the appearance of the saline plains of
the Arkansa, and many extensive tracts towards the
sources of the Missouri, from Fort Mandan westward to the basis of the Northern Andes.

CHAPTER XVI.

*Cadron settlement—Arrive at Arkansas—Continue to
the Mississippi—The wandering fanatics—Pirates
—Natchez—stratification of its site, and remarks
on its agricultural productions—The Choctaws—
Fort Adams—Point Coupé—Baton Rouge—Opulent Planters—New Orleans.*

On the evening of the 18th of December, I again
arrived at the Cadron,* where four families now resided. A considerable concourse of travellers and
some emigrants begin to make their appearance at
this imaginary town. The only tavern, very ill provided, was consequently crowded with all sorts of
company. It contained only two tenantable rooms,
built of logs, with hundreds of crevices still left open,
notwithstanding the severity of the season.

Every reasonable and rational amusement appeared
here to be swallowed up in dram-drinking, jockeying,
and gambling; even our landlord, in defiance of the
law, was often the ring-leader of what it was his duty to
suppress. Although I have been through life perfectly steeled against games of hazard, neither wishing to rob nor be robbed, I felt somewhat mortified

* Or Quadrant, a name applied to the neighbouring creek by the
French hunters, probably in commemoration of some observation made
there by that instrument, to ascertain the latitude.

to be thus left alone, because of my unconquerable aversion to enter this vortex of swindling and idleness.

From the 18th to the 27th we had frosty nights ; and on the 28th a fall of snow that continued throughout the day, and which still (*January* 3d) remained on all northern exposures; considerable sheets of ice, near three quarters of an inch in thickness, now began to invade the still water of the river, but were generally broken up by evening.

In one of the beds of grauwacke slate, which form the picturesque cliffs of the Cadron, I observed articulations of a species of orthoceratite, apparently belonging to the genus Raphanister of Montfort. Above this bed, and forming the summit of the hills, occurs a massive laminated sandstone of a grey colour and inconsiderable dip.

On the 4th of January, 1820, after waiting about a month for an opportunity of descending, I now embraced the favourable advantage of proceeding in the boat of Mr. Barber, a merchant of New Orleans, to whose friendship and civility I am indebted for many favours.

5th.] This morning we again passed the outlet of the river called La Feve's Fork, coming in on our right. It sources with the Pottoe, the Kiamesha, Little river of Red river, and with the Petit John forms an irregular and acute triangle, affording a large body of good land and, as well as the latter, is said to be navigable near 200 miles, including its meanders. Its entrance is marked by a concomitant chain of hills and cliffs, which border the Arkansa, and proceed in a north-westerly direction. For about a mile and a half, these hills, of grauwacke slate, present the appearance of an even wall coming up to the margin of the river, and owe this singular aspect to their almost vertical stratification. Their summits are tufted with pine, and the opposite alluvial point, which was sandy, and to appearance scarcely elevated above inundation, possessed also a forest of similar trees.

This evening we again arrived at Piat's, and in view of the pyramidal Mamelle; its extraordinary appearance, elevation, and isolation arises from the almost vertical disposition of its strata, which are probably of the same nature as those we passed to-day near the Petit John. Not far above inundation, on the same side of the river, three miles above Piat's, these vertical rocks form a very curious and crested parapet.

6th.] This evening we arrived at Mr. Daniel's, an industrious farmer, and provided with a rough-looking, but comfortable winter cabin. About two miles from hence, Mr. D., who lives upon a confirmed Spanish right, had erected a grist mill. Saw-mills were also about to be built at the Cadron, and two or three other places. The establishment of a town was now contemplated also at the Little Rock, by colonel Hogan, and some others. They had not, however, sufficient capital, and no doubt expected to derive some adventitious wealth from those speculators who were viewing various parts of the newly-formed territory.

7th.] We again arrived at the lower end of the Eagle's-nest bend, from whence commenced the uninhabited tract of 60 or 70 miles.

8th.] To-day we passed seven bends, making about 28 miles. The water at this, its lowest stage, appears to be perfectly navigable for the larger boats from the Little Rock to the Mississippi. By the cane which occurs in all the bends, and indeed by the apparent elevation, there are here great bodies of good land, free from inundation. The soil in some of the banks consists of an uncommonly rich dark Spanish brown loam.

9th.] This forenoon we passed the fourth Pine Bluff, at the base of which we observed abundance of earthy iron ore, in flattened, contorted, and cellular masses, scattered about in profusion ; much of it appeared to be pyrites, other masses more or less argillaceous and siliceous. Here, on the portions of the high bank which had sunk down by the undermining of the current, we saw the wax-myrtle of the Atlantic sea-coast.

10th.] This evening we arrived near to the termination of the second Pine Bluffs, which continue along the river for nearly two miles. We passed through seven bends of the river, and came about 27 miles. The frost was now succeeded by mild and showery weather, and the bald eagles *(Falco leucocephalus)* were already nestling, chusing the loftiest poplars for their eyries.

11th.] Soon after breakfast we came again in sight of the houses of the French hunters Cusot and Bartolemé, and found also two families from Curran's settlement encamped here, and about to settle. I here obtained two fragments of fossil shells, apparently some species of oyster, one of which was traversed with illinitions of crystallized carbonate of lime, and contained specks of bovey coal, from which I concluded them to have been washed out of the Bluffs above. Besides these I was also shewn a small conch-shell, not apparently altered from its natural state, and probably disinterred from some tumulus. Some time after dark we arrived at Mr. Boun's, a a metif or half Quapaw, and interpreter to the nation, who lived at the first of the Pine Bluffs. Two or three other metif families resided also in the neighbourhood.

On the 12th we arrived at Monsieur Dardennes', and to-day experienced a keen north-western wind. Water froze the instant it touched the ground.

13th.] The weather still freezing. In the evening we passed Mr. Harrington's, a farmer in very comfortable circumstances. Betwixt Morrison's and this place, the river makes two cuts, through two bends of about eight miles each.

14th.] This evening we arrived at the residence of the late Mr. Mosely, and about 20 miles below Harrington's. His estates were said to be worth not less than 20,000 dollars, which had all been acquired during his residence in this territory. A proof that there is here also scope for industry, and the acquisition of wealth.

About noon we landed at one of the Quapaw or Osark villages, but found only three houses constructed of bark, and those unoccupied. In the largest of them, apparently appropriated to amusement and superstition, we found two gigantic painted wooden masks of Indians,* and a considerable number of conic pelt caps, also painted. These, as we learnt from an Indian who came up to us from some houses below, were employed at festivals, and worn by the dancers, a custom which was also probably practised by the Natchez, in whose temple Charlevoix observed these marmosets. At the entrance of the cabin, and suspended from the wall, there was a female figure, with a rudely carved head of wood painted with vermillion. Being hollow, and made of leather, we supposed it to be employed as a mask for one of the musicians, having in one hand a pendent ferule, as if for the purpose of beating a drum. In the spring and autumn the Quapaws have a custom of making a contribution dance, in which they visit also the whites, who live in their vicinity, and the chief alms which they crave is salt or articles of diet.

On the 15th we again arrived at the post of Osark, or as it is now not very intelligibly called, Arkansas, a name by far too easily confounded with that of the river, while the name Osark, still assumed by the

* The Tuscaroras also wear masks at set times, for the purpose, as they pretend, of driving away evil spirits, and accompany these ceremonies by the sacrifice of two white dogs.

lower villagers of the Quapaws, and in memory of whom this place was first so called, would have been perfectly intelligible and original.

In the evening we had a storm of melting snow and hail, which, on the following morning was succeeded by a north-west wind, accompanied by a severe frost. The river was now, however, beginning to rise and assume a muddy tinge from the influx of the lagoons, and lower rivulets. A more extensive fresh cannot now be expected before the commencement of milder weather, and the thawing of the river towards its sources. The oldest settlers affirm, that the Arkansa had not, during their knowledge of it, ever been so low as before the present rise. The Ohio and Mississippi also continued too low for the navigation of the steam-boats.

16th.] This morning we observed the newly appointed governor, general Miller, going up to the town from his boat, which appeared to be very handsomely and conveniently fitted up, bearing for a name and motto " I'll try," commemorative of an act of courage for which the general had been distinguished by his country.

On arriving in the town, we found the court engaged in deciding upon the fate of a criminal, who had committed a rape upon the unprotected, and almost infant person of a daughter of his late wife. The legal punishment, in this and the Missouri territory, for this crime, castration! is no less singular and barbarous, however just, than the heinous nature of the crime itself. The penitentiary law of confinement, so successfully tried in the states of Pennsylvania and New York, for every crime short of murder, is an improvement in jurisprudence, which deserves to be adopted in every part of the United States. It often reclaims the worst of the human race, learns them habits of industry with which they had been unacquainted, and corrects those vices which perhaps ignorance and parental indulgence had fostered. There is certainly a flagrant want of humanity in the multiplicity of sanguinary and stigmatizing punishments. To sacrifice all that portion of the community to infamy, who *happen* to fall beneath the lash of the law, is incompatible with the true principles of justice. Maim a man, or turn him out with the stigma of infamy into the bosom of society, and he will inevitably become a still greater scourge to the world, in which he now only lives to seek revenge by the commission of greater but better concealed crimes.

Interest, curiosity, and speculation, had drawn the attention of men of education and wealth toward this country, since its separation into a territory; we now see an additional number of lawyers, doctors, and mechanics. The retinue and friends of the governor, together with the officers of justice, added also essential importance to the territory, as well as to the growing town. The herald of public information, and the bulwark of civil liberty, the press, had also been introduced to the Post within the present year, where a weekly newspaper was now issued. Thus, in the interim of my arrival in this country it had commenced the most auspicious epoch of its political existence.

17th and 18th.] I again paid a visit to the prairie, which, as well as the immediate neighbourhood of the town, is in winter extremely wet, in consequence of the dead level, and argillaceous nature of the soil. The interesting plants and flowers which I had seen last year, at this time, were now so completely locked up in the bosom of winter, as to be no longer discernible, and nearly disappointed me in the hopes of collecting their roots, and transplanting them for the gratification of the curious.

On the 19th, I bid farewell to Arkansas, and proceeded towards the Mississippi, in the barge of Mons. Notrebé, a merchant of this place, and the day following, without any material occurrence, arrived at the confluence of the Arkansa, a distance of about 60 miles. The bayou, through which I came in the spring, now ran with as much velocity towards White river, as it had done before into the Arkansa, its current and course depending entirely upon the relative elevation of the waters of the two rivers with which it communicates. The large island, thus produced, possesses extensive tracts of cane land, sufficiently elevated, as I am told, above inundation, as does also the opposite bank of the Arkansa. About 12 miles above the mouth, the site first chosen for the Spanish garrison, and which was evacuated in consequence of inundation, was pointed out to me. A house now also stands on the otherwise deserted spot, where once were garrisoned the troops of France, at the terminating point of the river. We now found ourselves again upon the bosom of one of the most magnificent of rivers, which appeared in an unbroken and meandering sheet, stretching over an extended view of more than 12 miles, and decorated with a pervading forest, only terminated by the distant horizon.

21st.] I now embarked for New Orleans in a flat boat, as the steam boats, for want of water, were not yet in operation.

Not far from this place, a few days ago were encamped, the miserable remnant of what are called the Pilgrims, a band of fanatics, originally about 60 in number. They commenced their pilgrimage from the borders of Canada, and wandered about with their wives and children through the vast wilderness of the western states, like vagabonds, without ever fixing upon any residence. They looked up to accident and charity alone for support; imposed upon themselves rigid fasts, never washed their skin, or cut or combed their hair, and like the Dunkards wore their beards. Settling no where, they were consequently deprived of every comfort which arises from

the efforts of industry. Desertion, famine, and sickness, soon reduced their numbers, and they were
every where treated with harshness and neglect, as
the gypsies of civilized society. Passing through
Ohio, Indiana, and Illinois, they at length found their
way down the Mississippi to the outlet of White river and the Arkansa. Thus ever flying from society
by whom they were despised, and by whom they had
been punished as vagabonds, blinded by fanatic zeal,
they lingered out their miserable lives in famine and
wretchedness, and have now nearly all perished or
disappeared. Two days after my arrival in the territory, one of them was found dead in the road which
leads from the Mississippi to Arkansas. If I am
correctly informed, there now exists of them only one
man, three women, and two children. Two other
children were taken from them in compassion for
their miserable situation, and the man was but the
other day seized by a boat's crew descending the river, and forcibly shaved, washed, and dressed.

Down to the year 1811, there existed on the banks
of the Mississippi, a very formidable gang of swindling robbers, usually stationed in two parties at the
mouth of the Arkansa, and at Stack island. They
were about 80 in number, and under the direction of
two captains. Amongst other predatory means of
obtaining property, was that of purchasing produce
from boats descending the river, with counterfeit
money. Clary and his gang of the Arkansa, had,
some time in the autumn of 1811, purchased in this
way some property from a descending flat boat.
The owner, however, before leaving the shore, discovered the fraud, and demanded restitution, but was
denied with insolence ; and they proceeded, at length,
so far as to fire upon his boat. These circumstances
being related to the companies of several other flats
who very opportunely came up at this time, and 12
of them being now collected, they made up a party to

apprehend this nest of pirates. It was nearly night when they landed, and were instantly fired upon by the robbers. They at last arrived at the house which they occupied, broke it open, and secured Clary and two others who had attempted to hide themselves. A court martial was held over them, which sentenced Clary to receive a number of lashes from the crew of each boat, and the two other delinquents were condemned to confinement, and to work the boat in the place of two of the boatmen who were wounded. These men, on arriving at Natchez, were committed to prison, but no one appearing against them, they were of course acquitted. Clary confessed, that he and his crew had, within the week previous to his apprehension, bought and transmitted up the Arkansa, with counterfeit money, 1800 dollars worth of produce. It was also known that he had been a murderer, and had fled to the banks of the Mississippi from justice. The Stack island banditti have never been routed, and some of their character were still found skulking around Point Chicot and the neighbouring island, always well supplied with counterfeit money.

22d.] This morning we were visited by three Choctaws in quest of whiskey. Their complexions were much fairer than most of the Indians we meet with on the Mississippi. Two of them were boys of about 18 or 19, and possessed the handsomest features I have ever seen among the natives, though rather too effeminate. About 20 miles below the Arkansa, in the Cypress bend, we saw the first appearance of *Tillandsia* or Long moss.

On the 24th, we arrived at Point Chicot, which is included in the Arkansa territory ; the boundary being the Big Lake, about 20 miles below. From one of the settlers, living a few miles below Point Chicot, I learn, that on the eastern side of the Mississippi, the high lands are here from 15 to 20 miles distant.

The reaches and bends, in this part of the river, are hardly less than six miles in length. Toward the centre of the bends considerable bodies of cane appear, indicative of an elevation above the usual inundations; it is, however, probable that these tracts are narrow, and flanked at no great distance by lagoons and cypress marshes subject to the floods. Many bends indeed presented nothing but cypress and black ash.

From the Chicasaw Bluffs downward, along the banks of the Mississippi, we perceive no more of the Tulip tree *(Liriodendron tulipifera)*, and but little of the *Platanus*, greatly reduced in magnitude, compared with what it attains along the Ohio. The largest tree of the forest here is that which is of the quickest growth, the Cottonwood poplar *(Populus angulata)*.

27th.] The whole country, generally speaking, along the river, appears uninhabited, though vast tracts of cane land occur in the bends. I am, however, informed that the cane will withstand a partial inundation. Since we left Point Chicot the river presents us with several magnificent views, some of 8, some of 12, and even 15 miles extent; but the absence of variety, even amidst objects of the utmost grandeur, soon becomes tiresome by familiarity. As above the Arkansa, the river still continues meandering. The curves, at all seasons washed by a rapid current, present crumbling banks of friable soil more or less mixed with vegetable matter. By the continued undermining and removal of the earth, the bends are at length worn through, the former tongue of land then becomes transformed into an island, and the stagnation and partial filling of the old channel, now deserted, in time produces a lake. Some idea of the singular caprice of the Mississippi current may be formed, by taking for a moment into view the extraordinary extent of its alluvial valley, which below

the Ohio is from 30 to 40 miles in width, through all
which space it has from time to time meandered, and
over which it will never cease to hold occasional possession.   On the opposite side of all the bends there
are what are called bars, being platforms of sand formed by the deposition of the siliceous matter washed
out of the opposite banks by the force of the current.
These sand flats, sometimes near a mile in width, are
uniformly flanked by thick groves of willows and poplars, the only kind of trees which survive the effects
of the inundation to which these bars are perpetually
subject.]

28th.] This morning we passed the settlement
called the Walnut Hills, a situation somewhat similar
to that of Natchez, consisting, however, of a cluster of
hills of 150 or 200 feet elevation, laid out in a chain
of agreeable farms.   The banks, along the river,
though not near so elevated as those of the Chicasaw
Bluffs, are still far enough above the reach of inundation, and present a stratification and materials entirely
similar :   the same friable ferruginous clays, and
also one or two beds of lignite, the lower about a foot
in thickness, very distinct at this low stage of the
water, and about three feet from its margin.   The
declivity for near half a mile back presents innumerable slips parallel with the river, and in one of the
ravines large masses of sandstone were washed out
towards the river.

In the evening we arrived at a small town called
Warrington, containing two inns and as many stores.
The land appeared low, but was secured from inundation by a levee or embankment carried out for two
or three miles below the town.   Out of its small quota
of population, 37 individuals last summer died of the
yellow-fever, said to have been introduced by the
steam-boat Alabama.   The gloomy mantling of the
forest communicated by the *Tillandsia usneoïdes* or
long moss, which every where prevails, is a never-fail-

ing proof of the presence of an unhealthy humidity in the atmosphere. The stagnating lagoons and bodies of refluent water also largely contribute to the un-healthiness of the climate. The vast extent and depth of this inundation is sufficiently evident by the marks along the banks of the river, which in places exhibited a rise of 50 feet above the present level !

29th.] To-day we passed the grand Gulf or eddy, near to which enters Big Black river. Here again the friable hills of the high land make their appearance on the borders of the river, on and around which there are settlements. At the base of the hills loose heaps of sandstone lie scattered. A thin stratified bed of the same was now also visible. In high water a violent and dangerous eddy sweeps along these rocks. On the declivity of this hill we see the first trees of the *Magnolia grandiflora*. The small palmetto *(Sabal minor)* commences about Warrington. The dis-tance to high land on the opposite or western side of the river is said to be little less than 30 miles.

30th.] This morning we came to what is called the Petit Gulf, where another cluster of hills appears scat-tered with settlements. Here the banks present noth-ing but friable materials, still also similar to the Chica-saw Bluffs. Beds of very white sand, intimately mixed with argillaceous earth, appear in prominent cliffs. One of the houses which we visited is apparent-ly built upon an aboriginal mound, and there are two others about a mile distant, in which have been found bones and pot-sherds. Last evening we passed bayou Pierre, 30 miles up which stream, and 15 by land, is situated the thriving town of Gibsonport.

31st.] To-day we arrived at the well known and opulent town of Natchez, situated on the summit of a hill which forms part of the same range and primitive soil as the Petit Gulf. The port was crowded with flat-boats, produce bearing a re-

duced price in consequence of the low rate of, and
small demand for, cotton.

The cliffs of Natchez appear more elevated than
those of the Petit Gulf. The lands, of an inferior soil,
are also remarkably broken and deeply undulated.
The crumbling precipice, of about 150 feet elevation,
is continually breaking, by the action of springs and
rain-water, into gullies and frightful ravines ; the whole
visible matter which composes the hills consisting of
clays, ferruginous sand, and quartzy gravel.   A few
years ago, the undermining of the current swept down
a considerable part of the bank with several houses
upon it.   From the irregularity in the thickness of
this ancient maritime alluvium, arises the great difference of depth at which water is here obtained.   In
the same vicinity water has been found at 35, and
then again at 110 feet from the surface.

The day after my arrival I waited upon Saml. Post-
lethwaite, Esq. related by marriage to the late Mr.
Dunbar.   From Mr. P. and his amiable lady, I met
with every attention and kindness which friendship,
hospitality, and politeness could have possibly dic-
tated.

To my enquiries concerning the horticulture and
agriculture of Natchez, Mr. P. informed me, that
the peach and fig, as well as the pear and the quince,
succeed extremely well.   The apple trees also, introduced from Kentucky, afforded nearly equal success.
The cherry, the gooseberry, and the currant, though
thriving, scarcely produce at all.   The pomegranate,
and the myrtle, grow and fruit almost as in their native climate.   The orange and lemon require some
shelter from the prevailing winter.   Grapes attain to
tolerable perfection, but the clusters are often blighted,
apparently by the humidity of the atmosphere.   The
kernels of dates which have been planted, germi-
nate and grow with considerable vigour.   The olive,

which so many years ago was introduced by the first
French settlers, and said, by Du Pratz, to have succeeded, is now entirely lost.

Cotton, which constitutes the staple commodity and
wealth of this country, has, like all other crops, a considerable tendency to impoverish the soil ; before the
settlement became so much condensed, and land so
advanced in value, no method of improving the worn-
out lands was ever thought of. Such fields were
then left waste, and new lands still continually cleared.
Of late years some attention has been paid towards
renovating the soil, by plowing in the herb of the cotton, after being thrashed to pieces as it stands in the
field. A much more convenient and expeditious
method, however, is that which Mr. P. has practised,
who employs a loaded harrow or a roller armed with
knives, which divides the plant also into much smaller
pieces. The seed, which forms three-fourths of the
crop in weight, being very oleaginous, would likewise return to the soil a considerable share of nourishment, as appears by the experiment of applying it to
maize, which, thus treated, grows as luxuriant as
when manured with gypsum. The seed of the cotton also, when scalded, and mixed with a little salt,
forms a nourishing and agreeable food for cattle.

Of late years, a prevailing disease has injured the
crops of this plant. From what I learn, it appears to
be of the same nature as that which destroys the
grapes, and depends apparently upon the state of the
atmosphere, progressing with more or less rapidity in
proportion to its humidity. The disease in question
attacks the extremity of the peduncle, appearing, at
first, like a moist or oily spot, which is succeeded by
a sphacelous state of the integuments, and an abortion
of the capsule.

Although we perceive but little attention paid to
science or literature in this territory, it does not by

30

any means appear to be destitute of public patronage, as there is a very handsome endowment in lands appropriated by the state for the building and support of a college. Some difficulty, now nearly obviated, as I understood, had been the means of retarding the progress of the institution. The inhabitants of Natchez, generally speaking, as in most of the southern states, live in ease and affluence.

To my enquiries concerning the aboriginal Natchez, Mr. P. said, he was inclined to believe them now extinct, as some years ago he had heard that only two or three individuals of them then remained. Their first flight, after the cruel defeat and massacre which took place in their fort, was across the river, to what is now called Sicily island, a body of land at this time settled, of about five miles in width, partly insulated by the overflows of the Tensaw, and rising into a hill considerably above the reach of inundation. The unfortunate Natchez were not, however, suffered to remain in peace, and being again routed by the French and their Indian allies, were, on the verge of extermination, driven to seek refuge among the neighbouring Indians. From my friend, Mr. Ware, of the Mississippi Territory, I learn, that there still exists a small village of the Natchez on the banks of the Tallipoosee, in Alabama, governed by a chief, named Coweta, who joined the United States against the Lower Creeks in the late war.

Mr. P. informs me, that in digging, some time ago, into a neighbouring mound, to the depth of a few feet, fragments of a sword blade, and some other relics of European warfare, were found, together with beads and remains which appeared to have accompanied an aboriginal interment. From these circumstances, it would appear, that some courageous opponent of the French had made a desperate stand upon this sacred ground, in order to annoy his enemies,

and to sell his life as dear as possible upon the tomb
of his ancestors.   I am the more inclined to hazard
this opinion, not only from the circumstances related
(of the broken fragments of European weapons, and
the decorations of a warrior), but likewise from the
assertion of the aged Illinois chief, made at Kaskaskia,
who, on being interrogated as to the use and origin of
the lofty mounds in that neighbourhood, answered,
that his forefathers had employed them as situations
of defence against their enemies the Iroquois.

Mr. Ware informs me, that aboriginal remains
abound in the vicinity of Natchez.   Twelve miles
above the town there is a square fort of three or four
acres area, furnished with several gateways, and
erected on a commanding situation.   About 12 miles
below the town there is likewise a group of mounds.

Considerable numbers of Choctaws appeared at this
season straggling through the streets of Natchez, either
begging or carrying on some paltry traffic, but chiefly
for the sake of liquor.   I am informed that civilization is making some advances among those who live
in the nation, and who have consequently abandoned
their ancient wandering habits.   Those of them we
see here are meanly dressed and of a swarthy complexion.   Their ancient mode of exposing the dead
upon scaffolds, and afterwards separating the flesh
from the bones, is falling into disuse, though still
practised, as Mr. Ware informs me, by the six towns
of the Choctaws on the Pascagoula.   They still entertain the same tradition of their origin which was current in the time of Du Pratz, though he believes
them to have emigrated into the country which they
now possess.   The legend is, that they sprung out
of a hill, situated contiguous to Pearl river, which,
Mr. Ware tells me, they still visit and venerate.
The Creeks entertain a tradition of coming from the
west side of the Mississippi, and that too at so recent a
date, as to have heard of the landing of White people

on the Atlantic coast soon after their arrival. The
Seminoles, Utchis, and Yamasees are a portion of
those more ancient people whom they found in possession of the country, and with whom they carried
on an exterminating warfare. Indeed, many of the
people of that country discovered by Soto, and some
of them numerous and powerful, are now no longer
in existence. Those whom he calls the Cutifa-chi-
qui, then governed by a female, held a court equally
as dignified as that of Powhatan in Virginia.

The Choctaws possess in an eminent degree that
thirst for revenge, which forms so prominent a trait in
the disposition of the man of America. By far too indiscriminate in its object, murder and accidental death
are alike fatal to the perpetrator, and scarcely any lapse
of time, or concession short of that of life, is taken. It
is but a few years ago, that two Choctaws in the town
of Natchez, firing at each other, in the same instant,
fell both dead on the spot: one of them, in defence
of a life which he had forfeited ; the other, in quest of
revenge for the death of a relative.

By a recent treaty, effected through the influence
of general Jackson, the Choctaws are now about to
relinquish the east side of the Mississippi, and to exchange their lands for others in the territory of Arkansa, situated betwixt Arkansa and Red rivers, and
extending from the Quapaw reservation to the Pottoe. In consequence of this singular but impolitic
measure of crowding the aborigines together, so as to
render them inevitably hostile to each other, and to
the frontier which they border, several counties of the
Arkansa territory will have to be evacuated by their
white inhabitants, who will thus be ruined in their
circumstances, at the very period when the general
survey of the lands had inspired them with the confi-
dent expectation of obtaining a permanent and legal
settlement.

February 4th.] To-day we left Natchez, and in the distance of 15 miles passed Ellis's Cliffs, another portion of re-entering high land, broken into a very picturesque landscape, decorated with pines and magnolias. These cliffs, no way essentially different from those above, present here, immediately above the carbonaceous bed, a very thick stratum of white sandy clay, so far indurated as to withstand the washing which has carried away the superincumbent soil.

In the course of the night we arrived at Fort Adams, another spur of the high land ; a term which can only be used in reference to the alluvion, as the apparent undulation is here nothing more than an adventitious subsidence or washing of the soil, the ravines and gullies being occasioned by its friable nature. Rock, however, appears at the base of the lofty hill, on which stands a block house of the late garrison.* A tavern, a store, and two or three other houses are here established for the convenience of the interior.

7th.] To-day we arrived at the settlement of bayou Sarah, a mile up which stream is situated the town of St. Francisville, and passed a line of opulent plantations on the Louisiana bank of the river called Point Coupée. From hence we begin to perceive the orange, though not very thriving. Sugar is also planted thus far, and appears to succeed. Mons. Poydras, a bachelor 80 years of age, owns and employs in this settlement betwixt 4 and 500 negroes, which, together with property in New Orleans, amounts to an estate of several millions of dollars. His plantations at Point Coupée are principally employed in the lucrative business of planting and making sugar.

8th.] We again obtained sight of the high land in

---

* Some of this rock is an impure argillaceous limestone ; but the principal part consists of an indurated and parti-coloured clay, subject to disintegration, in which state it resembles the pink-coloured clay heretofore noticed.

the cliffs near Thompson's creek, and, as usual, on the eastern side of the river. About three feet above the present level, we also observed the occurrence of the bovey-coal or lignite, overlaid by massive beds of ferruginous clays and gravel. This high land, without again approaching to the immediate margin of the river, continues at no great distance from hence to Baton-Rouge.

9th.] Early this morning we passed the thriving town of Baton-Rouge, where a garrison has been established ever since its cession. Not far from hence, the high lands or primitive soil terminates, beyond which, to the sea, the whole country is alluvial and marshy. Continued lines of settlements still present themselves on either bank, and cotton and sugar are the great articles of their agricultural opulence.

About 3 o'clock in the morning, we experienced a heavy squall from the north-east, accompanied by torrents of rain, and were in considerable danger of losing the flat, with all our property and baggage. Ever since leaving Natchez, we have had weather like summer, and vegetation already advances.

10th and 11th.] We have in view an almost uninterrupted line of settlements on either hand which continue to New Orleans. These planters are nearly all of French or Spanish extraction, and, as yet, there are among them but few Americans. Their houses are generally built of wood, with piazzas for shade in the summer. Notwithstanding their comparative opulence, they differ little either in habits, manners, or dress from the Canadians. Dancing and gambling appear to be their favourite amusements. The men, as usual, are commonly dressed in blanket coats, and the women wear handkerchiefs around their heads in place of bonnets. The inhabitants do not appear to be well supplied with merchandize, and the river is crowded with the boats of French and Spanish pedlars, not much larger than perogues, but fitted up with a cabin, covered deck, and sails.

Another vast monopolizer of human liberty, along the coast (as the borders of the Mississippi are termed by the French), is general Wade Hampton, who possesses upwards of 400 slaves, and has obtained at one crop 500 hogsheads of sugar, and 1000 bales of cotton, then collectively worth upwards of 150,000 dollars: in the United States an immense fortune, without any additional property, and equal to that of almost any English nobleman. But, with the means of being so extensively useful, I do not learn that either this gentleman or Mons. Poydras,* expend any adequate part of their immense property to public advantage. And, more than that, these unfortunate slaves, the engines of their wealth, are scarcely fed or clothed in any way bordering on humanity. Their common allowance of food, is said to be about one quart of corn per day ! Thus miserably fed, they are consequently driven to theft by the first law of nature, and subject the country to perpetual depredation. How little wealth has contributed towards human improvement, appears sufficiently obvious throughout this adventitiously opulent section of the Union. Time appears here only made to be lavished in amusement. Is the uncertainty of human life so great in this climate, as to leave no leisure for any thing beyond dissipation? The only serious pursuit, appears to be the amassing and spending of that wealth which is wrung from the luckless toil of so many unfortunate Africans, doomed to an endless task, which is even entailed upon their posterity. "O slavery, though thousands in all ages have drank of thee, still thou art a bitter draught!"

An evil, however, which has been so long establish-

---

* Mons. P. has, I understand, endowed a place in New Orleans for the education of female orphans.

ed, cannot be eradicated at a single blow. The abolition of domestic slavery must be a work of time.
Let an age be chosen at which it shall cease to operate; say a limit of 28 or 30 years. Let the negroes
be sent into the civilized world with the rudiments of
education, and the means of obtaining a livelihood.
After acquiring their freedom, it is highly probable,
that they would still continue to seek the employment of their former masters, and the neighbourhood
in which they were born. The project of transport-
ing the free negroes to the country in which they
originated appears extremely rational, and ought to
be promoted by every means in the power of the
public. We are sensible that the negroes who remain in the society of the whites, must ever be subjected to the degradation of an inferior cast. They
were not formed to mingle indiscriminately amongst
us; but though they may be inferior to us in intellect and civilization, they were undoubtedly born to
the possession of rational liberty.

In the contiguous country of Opelousa, so called
from the Indians who formerly lived in it, there are
extensive and fertile prairies, where great herds of cattle are raised for the market of New Orleans. A
year ago, about 12,000 head were sold on the banks
of the Mississippi, at the rate of from 30 to 35 dollars each.

From hence to New Orleans, now 86 miles distant, the whole coast is defended from inundation by
an embankment or trench of earth, thrown up with
about the same labour as that which is bestowed upon a common ditched fence. In this simple way,
millions of acres of the richest land, inexhaustible by
crops, is redeemed from waste, and we have now the
pleasure of viewing an almost uninterrupted line of
opulent settlements continued from Baton-Rouge, to
more than 50 miles below New Orleans.

Among the more common reptiles of this country, already beginning to appear abroad, I know of none more curious, than a kind of Cameleon lizard, of frequent occurrence, and in some measure related to that celebrated species, excepting that the colours which it assumes are only those with which it is familiar in nature; such as ash-colour in the vicinity of a pale object, dark brown upon the ground, or on the trunks of trees, and a brigʰt green amidst verdant herbage.

17th.] After another dete.tion of two days by the prevalence of a strong south-west wind, we continued our voyage, and early this morning passed the great plantation of general Hampton, situated about 70 miles from New Orleans, at Ouma poini, the name of a nation or tribe of Indians now nearly extinct, and who, with the remains of the Chetimashas, once living nearly opposite to bayou la Fourche, are at this time existing in a partly civilized state on the bayou Plaquemine. The learned Peter S. Duponceau, Esq. informs me, that the language of the Chetimashas, a people said, by Du Pratz, to be a branch of the Natchez, appears to be radically distinct from that of the other aborigines of the southern states. From hence the banks of the river are lower, and the labour of keeping up the levees greater, though the rise of the river is slower, its width and uniformity of channel more considerable, and now almost destitute of islands or bars. The river is very probably influenced in this respect by the embankments, which are continued almost without interruption from Fort Adams nearly to Fort Placquemine. We had now in view a perpetual succession of the habitations of the richest planters, surrounded with groups of negro cabins. They are almost exclusively engaged in the planting of sugar, and possess establishments no way inferior to those of the West India Islands, some of them being valued at as much as 100,000 dollars, every

31

thing included. As the settlements are chiefly in single lines along the bank of the river, the land is commonly sold by the measurement in front, running back about 40 arpents,* and have been disposed of at as much as 3000 dollars per arpent in front, or 75 dollars per arpent actual measurement.

Notwithstanding the fearful tyranny exercised over the slaves on these large plantations, the annals of this settlement are not without the remembrance of seri-ous symptoms of revolt. About nine years ago, a party of negroes, equipped with arms, liberated them-selves, after destroying their master with two or three other individuals who attempted to oppose them, and were not subdued until totally destroyed by the neigh-bouring militia. There were of them 300, who were routed near to Red Church, about twenty-four miles above New Orleans; so that, betwixt the fears of inundation, the efforts of the enslaved Africans to emancipate themselves, and the fatality of the climate, the opulent planters of Louisiana possess no enviable advantage over the happy peasant, who dwells in the security which honest industry and salutary frugality afford him.

The excessive attachment to gambling which cha-racterises the inhabitants of Louisiana, and the love of speculation, exhibited in the great and transitory influx of foreigners and citizens from the northern states, is now ostensibly checked by a species of taxa-tion called license. Thus, every store-keeper pays an annual assessment of 110 dollars to the common-wealth. Every pedlar 12 dollars. Every Pharo bank and Roulette table 500 dollars a year, and every Bil-liard table 50 dollars. In excuse for thus tolerating the Pharo bank and the Roulette, the legislature affirm their inability to check the evil by punishment.

* The *arpent* of Paris is less than the English and United States sta-tute acre, as 512 is to 605. The arpent is used in Louisiana, and other places in America inhabited by the French, as a measure of length; each arpent is equal to 29.1 Gunter's chain, very nearly; consequently, 40 arpents amounts to 116.4, Gunter, or 2660.8 yards.—*Note by Mr. Darby.*

18th.] This morning we arrived at New Orleans, now said to contain about 45,000 inhabitants, a great proportion of whom are of French extraction and retain their mother tongue. The situation of the town, which was begun in 1718, is rendered unhealthy by the swamp which circumscribes its western suburb, and which continues at all seasons totally impassable. A short canal crosses it, forming a communication with the bayou St. John, and lake Ponchartrain, by which means a commercial communication is opened to Mobile, Pensacola, and the Alabama territory.

In the neighbourhood of the city, and along the coast, the beautiful groves of orange trees, orchards of the fig, and other productions of the mildest climates, sensibly indicate our approach to the tropical regions, where the dreary reign of winter is for ever unknown. But little pains as yet have been taken to introduce into this country, though so thickly settled, the ornamental and useful plants which it is calculated to sustain. We yet neither see the olive, the date, nor the vineyard, notwithstanding the adaptation of the climate to their culture. That the date itself would succeed, an accidental example in the city renders probable. This palm, which grows in Orleans street, has attained the height of more than 30 feet, with a trunk of near 18 inches in diameter, and has flowered annually for the space of several years. The period of inflorescence appears to be about the commencement of April, but being only a staminiferous plant, it has not consequently produced any fruit.

That fatal epidemic, the yellow fever, was last summer unusually prevalent, and carried off probably 5 or 6000 individuals, a great part of whom were, as usual, emigrants from the northern states, and different parts of Europe. By what I can learn, the hospital in this place is very ill suited to the recovery of those patients who are hurried to it during the rage

of this disease.   They are crowded almost to contact;
so that the contagion acquires force and fatality in the
very institution formed for its recovery.   Many, however, flock to this last refuge for the indigent and
miserable, in a state which precludes all hopes of recovery.

The expense of medical assistance, the difficulty of
obtaining attendance, and the selfish and fearful supineness which seizes upon all classes at this awful season,
serves to increase the fatal gloom which surrounds the
unhappy stranger, thus often inhumanly abandoned
by all society, and left, before the approach of the fatal
moment, like a carcase to the vultures !

The scene of crowded graves which appals the eye
in the general burying ground, marked by boards, or
covered tombs, inscribed with mournful remem-
brances ; the hosts which are swept off, also, interred
in forgotten crowds, and consigned to relentless oblivion, appeared thickly to chequer the whole surface
of the earth, and warn the stranger, in no ambiguous
phrase, of the fatal climate in which he sojourns.
These crowds of sepulchres are not the slow accumulation of an age, as a section of these remains is
frequently dug up and consumed, to give place to the
renewed harvest of death.

The prevailing religion is that of the Catholics ;
though there is also a handsome church erected by
the Presbyterians.

Science and rational amusement is as yet but little
cultivated in New Orleans.   There are only three or
four booksellers to supply this large city and populous
neighbourhood.   The French inhabitants, intermingled
with the African casts in every shade of colour,
scarcely exceed them, generally speaking, in mental
acquirements.   Every thing like intellectual improvement appears to be vitiated in its source, nothing exists to inspire emulation, and learning, as in the West

Indies, has no existence beyond the mechanism of reading and writing. Something like a museum was begun in the city a few years ago, but by a protean evolution it has been transformed into a coffee-house for gambling. In another part of the city, an assemblage of specimens of the fine arts, busts, medallions, mosaics, and paintings, is also associated with the dice and bottle.

The market, at this season, by no means dear, or bearing any thing like a reasonable proportion with the extravagant charges of the public entertainers, appeared to be tolerably well supplied, though singularly managed, and that entirely by negro slaves, who spread out the different articles in petty quantities, like the arrangement of an apple stall, charging, however, at the rate of about 100 per cent for the trouble. Superfine flower now sold at the low rate of six dollars per barrel; bacon and cheese at 10 cents the pound, salt butter at 25 cents; sugar at seven dollars per cwt.; coffee 25 to 30 dollars per cwt.; rice seven dollars per cwt. Fresh beef, however, and that by no means good, sold at 25 cents per pound. As in the West Indies, the principal market appears to be on Sunday in the forenoon. In the afternoon the negroes assemble in the suburbs of the city, and amuse themselves by dancing. When thus assembled by common friendship, if they have any reflection, they must be convinced of the efficient force which they possess to emancipate themselves; they are, however, strictly watched by the police, and the sole object of their meeting appears to be amusement.

Some idea of the extensive commerce carried on in the western states and territories with New Orleans, may be formed from the number of steam-boats alone, now 75 in number, besides other craft and shipping, which navigate the Mississippi and its numerous tributary streams. But in consequence of the general and unfavourable fluctuation in the commerce of the United States, the number of these vessels is become greater than their actual employment will warrant. A majority also of the steam-boats have this year lain unemployed for more than six months, in consequence of the extraordinary lowness of water; but the valuable staple produce of Louisiana, must always insure to its inhabitants a preponderating balance of wealth.

APPENDIX.

SECTION I.

AN ACCOUNT OF THE ANCIENT ABORIGINAL POPULATION OF THE BANKS OF THE MISSISSIPPI, AND THE CONTIGUOUS COUNTRY.

THIS wilderness, which we now contemplate as a dreary desert, was once thickly peopled by the natives, who, by some sudden revolution, of which we appear to be ignorant, have sunk into the deepest oblivion. In the abridged account of the great enterprize of Ferdinand de Soto by Purchas, begun in the year 1539, we read of numerous nations and tribes, then inhabiting the banks of the Mississippi, of whom, except the Chicaças, the Cherokees (called more properly Chelaques), and the small remnant of the Kaskaskias, and Tonicas, not an individual remains to reveal the destinies of his compatriots. Their extinction will ever remain in the utmost mystery. The agency of this destruction is, however, fairly to be attributed to the Europeans, and the present hostile Indians who possess the country. It is from these exterminating and savage conquerors, that we in vain inquire of the unhappy destiny of this great and extinguished population, and who, like so many troops of assassins, have concealed their outrages by an unlimited annihilation of their victims.

As this part of the American history is very obscure and neglected, I shall probably be excused for introducing it at greater length than would otherwise have been necessary.

De Soto, after encountering considerable difficulty and hardship, in his progress through the interior of what then was called Florida, arrived, at length, amongst the Chica-ças, who occupied pretty near the same country in which we find them at present. The principal object of the commander, and those who had embarked with him from the island of Cuba, of which he was governor, appears, as usual, to have been a search for the precious metals; and the natives, ever willing to rid themselves of those whom they feared and hated, kept perpetually instigating the adventurers to distant pursuits. The plain, on which we find them encamped, previous to their proceeding across the Mississippi (which did not at that time bear this name), and to which they had been conducted by their native guides, could have been no other than one of the Chicasaw Bluffs, or ancient crossing-places, and apparently the lowest. While busied here in providing boats for crossing, they were visited by a party of the natives who descended the river,* and declared to the governor (Soto), that they were the subjects of a great lord (or chief), whose name was *Aquixo*, who governed many towns, and a numerous people on the west side of the Great River (or Mississippi), and they came to inform him, that the chief with all his men would come to await his commands. The following day, the cazique† arrived with 200 canoes full of Indians,

* Purchas's Pilgrims, vol. IV. p. 1546.

† This Peruvian title for chieftain is employed throughout the narrative, by Garcilasso de la Vega, the author of the history, and himself a descendant of the Incas, who chose to follow the fortunes of Soto, one of the conquerors of his country.

armed with their bows and arrows, painted and decorated with feathers of various colours, and defended with shields made from the skins of the bison; the warriors were numerously arranged from the head to the stern of the boats. The canoe of the cazique was furnished with a tilt over the stern, beneath which he sat, and gave his commands. The canoes of the lesser chieftains were also equipped in the same manner. Approaching the bank, the cazique addressed the governor, saying, he came to visit, to honour, and obey him, inasmuch as he was the greatest lord upon earth, and that he now waited his commands. The governor returned him thanks, and desired him to come on shore to hold some further communication. Without, however, attending to this request, the chief sent a present to the governor of three canoes loaded with fish, and loaves made of the pulp of persimmons.* Receiving this present, the governor again invited him to the shore, but without success. The cazique, baffled in his purpose of deceiving Soto, whom he found in readiness, began now to row off, on which, the governor instantly ordered the cross-bow-men to fire a volley at the natives, in which five or six of them fell. Still they retired in good order, not a man deserting his oar, though his fellow warrior dropped at his side. They afterwards attempted several times to land, but as often fled to their canoes on the approach of the Spaniards. The canoes were very large and well made, being also decorated with tilts, plumes, paveses and flags.

The river (Mississippi) de Soto found to be almost a mile broad. A man who stood still could scarcely be discerned from the opposite shore. The current was strong and deep, with the water always muddy, and continually charged with floating trees.

* Called Prunes by the Spaniards.

32

Having passed the Rio Grande (as he calls it), and travelled up the bank about three miles, he came to a great town of *Aquixo*, from whence the inhabitants had fled. They discovered a party of 30 Indians coming over the adjoining plain to reconnoitre their movements, but on perceiving the Spaniards they instantly fled. They were, however, pursued by the cavalry, who killed 10 of them, and took 15 prisoners. As the town to which Soto proceeded was situated near to the bank of the river, he left a detachment to bring up the boats, and proceeded with the rest of his armament by land, but finding it difficult to keep along the bank, which was obstructed by the entrance of creeks, left the boats exposed to the annoyance of the natives, but understanding which, he instantly dispatched a party of cross-bow-men to their defence. Here he broke up the boats, but saved the iron for future contingencies. The following day, he proceeded up the river in quest of the province called Pacaha, which he was informed lay contiguous to Chisca, where the Indians had told him of the existence of gold. On his way he passed through great towns of Aquixo, from all of which the inhabitants had fled at his approach. Here he was informed, by some of the natives whom they had taken, that three days journey further up the river there dwelt a great cazique named Casqui.* He crossed a small river upon a bridge,

---

* The same apparently with Kaskaskia, spelled Kaskasquia by Father Charlevoix, and Caskaquia by Du Pratz. This band, as well as the Kahoquias, Tamaroas, Peorias, and Pimeteois, formed part of the Illinois nation, now nearly all extinct, though they could once enumerate as many as twenty thousand souls. They were found inhabiting the rivers which still retain their name, and have fallen before the Iroquois, and the Chicasa nations, with whom they waged war. Their name of Illinois, or Illinese of La Hontan, so much like Leni-Lenape, or that of the Delawares, and signifying, in common with that appellation, the

and the rest of the day, until sun-set, they were continually wading in water either waist or knee deep. At length, they gained the dry land, and congratulated themselves, as they were under some apprehension of passing the night in that dismal situation. At noon they arrived at the first town of Casqui, and found the Indians unprepared for resistance. Here the Spaniards took many of both sexes prisoners, and considerable stores of garments* and skins, as well in the first town, as in a second, which was surprised by the cavalry, and lay about half a league distant. They found this country to be higher, drier, and more champaign than any part which they had yet seen contiguous to the river ; from which we are fully satisfied, that the country thus described, can be no other than the Little Prairie, and that chain of high lands which continues to New Madrid, in the vicinity of which, there are also many

original or *genuine men*, besides the tradition of their having come in company with the Miamies from the borders of Hudson's bay or the North Pacific, and their speaking nearly the same language, as related by Charlevoix,† appear as so many proofs of the common origin of these two people. It is also related by the same author (before their arrival in the country, which they so extensively occupied in the time of Soto's incursion, and in which they lived till the period of their approaching extinction), they had settled along the borders of the river des Moins, or Moingona, of the Mississippi, which gave name to one of their tribes. The friendship which they cultivated, about a century ago, with the Osages, and the Arkansas, who are the same people, and some incidental resemblances between them, lead us to believe them also commonly related by language and descent.

* These "mantels," as they are called by Purchas, were fabricated from coarse threads of the bark of trees and nettles.

† Fifty years ago (1720) the Miamis were settled at Chicago, and were, at this time, "divided into three villages, one at the river St. Joseph, a second on Miami of Lake Erie, and the third called the Watanons of the Wabash." "There is scarcely a doubt," adds Charlevoix, "but that this nation and the Illinois were not long since one people, considering the affinity of their languages." *Charlevoix, Hist. Journ.* p. 114.

aboriginal remains. The neighbouring fields abounded with walnut trees, bearing round nuts with soft shells, and with leaves which they considered to be smaller than usual ;* of these nuts the Indians had collected a store for use. Here they also found mulberries, and red† and grey plumbs.‡ The trees appeared as fruitful as if they had been protected in orchards, and the woods generally were very thin. De Soto continued travelling two days through the country of Casqui before he arrived at the town inhabited by the cazique ; most part of the way was over champaign country, *filled with great towns, always within view of each other.* Soto sent an Indian to announce his arrival to the cazique, desiring his friendship and fraternity. To which he answered, by graciously bidding him welcome, and making an offer of his services to accomplish all that he requested. The chief also met him with a present of skins, garments, and fish. After which compliments de Soto found all the inhabitants of the towns peaceable and friendly, and their chiefs and elders coming out to congratulate him with presents. The cazique, attended by a numerous train of his people, respectfully awaited the approach of the governor, about half a league from the town.

Friendly compliments were again exchanged, and the cazique made an offer of his houses for de Soto to lodge in ; he, however, excused himself from accepting this civility on prudential motives, and encamped in the adjoining fields.

The cazique went to the town, and afterwards returned again accompanied by many Indians singing. As soon as

---

* Probably Pecans (*Carya olivæformis*).
† *Prunus chicasa ?* ‡ *P. hiemalis.*

they arrived in the presence of the governor, they all pros-
trated themselves upon the ground. After which, the
cazique besought him, as he was the son of the Sun, and
a great lord, to restore two blind men to their sight, which
he had brought along with him. The governor, however,
excused himself, and referred him to the Supreme Being
and author of health, and, on the occasion, had a cross set
up for them to worship, in remembrance of Jesus Christ,
who died thereon.

The governor now inquired of the chief the distance to
Pacaha, and was told, that it was one day's journey ; that
at the termination of the country of Casqui, there was a
lake like a brook, which ran into the Mississippi (or Rio
Grande), and that he would send men before him to construct a bridge for his convenience in passing it. The
same day the governor took his departure, he lodged at a
town belonging to Casqui ; the following, he passed some
other towns, and came to the lake, which was half a cross-
bow shot over, deep, and running with a considerable current. The bridge, constructed of logs, was completed on
his arrival. The cazique of Casqui attended upon the
governor, accompanied by his people.

The cazique of Pacaha, it appears, was at enmity with
the Casqui, and fled at the approach of Soto and his supposed allies, notwithstanding his endeavours to pacify
them. Some of them, whom he took prisoners in an adjoining town, would have fallen victims to their natural
enem⸱⸱s but for his interposition. In the town which they
sacked, they found great store of woven garments, besides
deer skins, lion skins (panther skins, in all probability), as
well as bear and cat skins. They also found targets of bison hides.

De Soto, at length, entered into Pacaha, and took up his lodging in the town where the chief was accustomed to reside ; which is described as large, walled, and defended with towers, through all which were cut loopholes for arms. The town was well supplied with maize, besides a promising harvest then in the field. Within from a mile and a half to three miles, were also other large towns, surrounded with enclosures of pickets. That now occupied by de Soto, was situated contiguous to a large lake, which filled a ditch thrown up nearly round the town. By a weir thrown over the outlet of the lake, abundance of fish were continually ready for the use and amusement of the chief, and with the nets which the Spaniards found in the town, they supplied themselves to their utmost satisfaction. Amongst them we readily recognize the *Silurus* or Cat-fish, which the natives called Bagres ; those of the lakes were about the bigness of pikes, but in the river (Mississippi), they occasionly found some which weighed upwards of 100lbs. There was another which they called the Pele-fish, destitute of scales, and with the upper jaw extended in front a foot in length, in the form of a peel or spatula.*

From this place, De Soto despatched a troop of 30 horse and 50 foot to the province of Caluça, to ascertain the practicability of proceeding to Chisca, where the natives, it may be remembered, had informed him of the existence of a mine of gold and of copper. The country over which

---

* Of this singular fish, I received circumstantial accounts at the Post of Arkansa. It also exists in the Ohio, and is the *Platyrostra edentula* of Lesueur, described in the Journal of the Academy of Natural Sciences of Philadelphia, vol. i. part 2, pp. 227, 228, and 229, and allied to the *Polyodon* of Lacepède. The plain description of this very local and curious animal, affords additional evidence, if it were necessary, of the truth of the relations of Garcilassa de la Vega, notwithstanding the scepticism of some of the later French writers.

they proceeded, for seven days, was an uninhabited desert
(probably in consequence of inundation), and they returned almost exhausted with famine and fatigue, existing almost entirely upon green plums, and stalks of
maize, which they found in a poor town of six or seven
houses.* From thence, towards the north, they learnt
that the country was very cold and thinly settled, and so
overrun with herds of bison, that it was scarcely possible
to defend their maize from depredation ; they also afforded the principal article of provision on which the natives
subsisted.

Perceiving no possibility of supplying his troops in
marching over this desert country, de Soto, from the information of the Indians, determined to change his course
and proceed towards the south, where he had information
of the existence of a great province called Quigaute, affording abundance of provision. To this country the governor now directed his march, and, at length, arrived in
the town usually occupied by the chief ; by the way he
received presents, of numerous skins and woven garments,
but the cazique, justly afraid to meet the invaders of his
country, absented himself from them. This town is re-
corded by La Vega, to have been the largest which they
had yet seen in Florida.

According to their custom, the Spaniards took all the
men and women whom they could conveniently seize as
their prisoners. This arbitrary step produced the desired
effect, and they now all came forward to prove their obedience to the mandates of the general. The cazique and
his two wives were detained in the house of the governor,
who made inquiry of them concerning the neighbouring

---

* This inundated country appears to be the Great Swamp, which
commences below Cape Girardeau, said to be 60 miles long.

country and its inhabitants. They said, that towards the south, down the river, there were large towns, and chiefs who governed extensive countries and numerous people ; and that, toward the north-west, there was a province, contiguous to certain mountains, called Coligoa. To this place the governor and all his officers resolved to go, supposing that, as a mountainous country, it might, in all probability, afford mines of the precious metals. The country, which they had yet seen on the western borders of the Mississippi, was low and alluvial, and promised nothing but agricultural wealth, which had never entered into the sinister views of these El Dorado adventurers. The distance from Pacaha to Quigaute they considered to be about 200 miles.

They now proceeded for seven days through desolate forests, abounding in shoal lagoons, affording an abundance of fish. The Indians of Coligoa had never before seen Europeans, and at their approach fled up the river, near to whose banks their town was situated. The chief, however, and a number of both sexes, were taken prisoners by the orders of Soto. Presents of garments and deer skins were brought in to the governor, and among them were two robes of the bison,* which, within 10 or 12 miles of their town, were said to be abundant, and that the country was cold and thinly inhabited.†

Here our adventurers were again informed of a fertile and well inhabited country, called Cayas, still lying towards the south. From Quigaute to Coligoa, they supposed the distance to be about 80 miles. The soil here

* Called ox-hides.

† This mountainous country and province of Coligoa, was, in all probability, situated towards the sources of the St. Francis, or the hills of White river.

appeared to be extremely productive, and was planted with
maize, kidney beans, and pumpkins.   The chief of Coligoa provided them with a guide to Cayas, but did not accompany them in person.   After a journey of five days,
they came to a province called Palisema.   The chief left
his house for de Soto in a state of preparation, but did not
wait an interview.   A party of horse and foot were sent
to detect him, but returned without success ; they met
with many people, but, in consequence of the roughness of
the country, detained none of them as prisoners, except a
few women and children.   The town was small and scattered, and but ill supplied with maize.   He afterwards
proceeded to another town called Tatalicoya, and carried
with him the chief, who conducted him in four days to
Cayas.   De Soto was disappointed by the scattered appearance of the population in this province, and imagined
he had been deceived, but was informed, that the space
inhabited was very considerable, and the land fertile.   The
town which they arrived in was called Tanico,* and was
situated near to a river.   The governor spent a month in
the province of Cayas, which abounded with maize and
pasturage for their horses.   In the neighbourhood there
was a lake of very hot and somewhat brackish water.
Here the party provided themselves with salt, which they
had long been in want of, and which they found the natives in the practice of using and fabricating from this
water.†

From Cayas, de Soto proceeded to Tulla, but here he
found the town abandoned at the news of his approach.
The chief, however, came accompanied by 80 Indians,

---

* The same people with the Tunicas, called also Tonicas, by Charlevoix and Du Pratz.

† These are evidently the salt waters of the Washita.

who brought with them a present of bison robes, which, at this advanced season of the year, proved very acceptable to the party.   La Vega greatly admired the decorum and propriety with which these natives behaved in their intercourse and addresses to the governor.   Towards the west, de Soto was informed of a thinly inhabited country, but that towards the south-west, there were great towns, especially in a province called Autiamque, ten days' journey from Tulla, or about 160 miles, and a country well supplied with maize.   To this place they proceeded, after dismissing the two caziques of Cayas and Tulla, with an intention of spending the winter which now approached, and which they expected would detain them for the space of two or three months.   They proceeded five days over very rough mountains, and at length came to a town called Quipana,* situated between hills.   Here awaiting in ambush, they succeeded in taking two Indians, who told them that Autiamque was six days' journey distant, and that there was another province towards the south, eight days' journey off, abounding in maize and well peopled, which was called Guahate ; but, as Autiamque was nearer, the governor proceeded in that direction.   After travelling three days, they came to a town called Anoixi ; previous to entering, he surprised it by a troop of horse and foot, and took many men and women prisoners. Within two days after, they entered another town called Catamaya, and lodged in 'he adjoining fields.   Two Indians came with a pretended message from the chief, to learn the intention of the Spaniards.   Soto desired them to tell their lord, that he wanted to hold a conference with him.   But the Indians never returned, nor any other mes-

* Probably the same as the Quapaws.

sage from the cazique. The following day they entered
the town, which was deserted by its fearful inhabitants,
and in it they found as much maize as they wanted. That
day they lodged in a forest, and the following they arrived
at Autiamque. Here they found abundance of maize,
French beans, walnuts, and prunes (or persimmons dried);
they also took some of the natives busied in carrying off
the provision which their wives had hidden. The surrounding country was open and well inhabited. The governor lodged in the best part of the town, and fortified
his troops by a strong picket fence after the manner of the
natives. Near to the town, there was a river (the Washita), which passed through the province of Cayas, and
which was every where well peopled. They spent three
months in Autiamque, and were well supplied with provision, amongst which La Vega enumerates conies (or
hares), some of which were larger than those of Spain;
these the natives caught by means of spring traps. The
snow was here so considerable, that for one month they
never left the town, except for fire-wood, and were obliged
to follow the path which was beaten on purpose by the
horsemen.

On the 6th of March, 1542, de Soto departed from Autiamque, and proceeded to Nilco, which the Indians said
was contiguous to the Mississippi (or Rio Grande), from
whence it was his determination to proceed to the sea,
and procure a reinforcement of men and horses, as now
he had but 400 men left out of the thousand with which
he landed, and 40 horses, some of which were become
lame. De Soto here experienced an irreparable loss in
the death of John Ortiz, a Spaniard, who had accompanied the previous expedition of Pamphilo de Narvaez,
being taken prisoner by the natives of the bay of Spirito

Santo, in East Florida, amongst whom he had acquired
much of the manners and language of the Indians. Besides his loss as an interpreter, they were likewise bereft
of a guide, and made many unnecessary wanderings and
errors in their route. They spent 10 days in travelling
from Autiamque to a province called Ayays ; and came
again to a town situated near to the Washita (or the river
of Cayas and Autiamque). Here he passed the river by
means of a boat which they built on purpose, but for four
days after they could not travel for snow. When the snow
had now ceased, they went through a wilderness, and a
country so enswamped and full of lakes, that they travelled one time a whole day in water from the knee to the
stirrup, and sometimes they were obliged to swim. At
length, they arrived at a town called Tutelpinco, which
was abandoned, and destitute of maize ; near to it there
passed a lake communicating with the river, by an outlet
which now ran with a considerable current.

De Soto spent a whole day in seeking a passage across
this lake, and all without success. Returning at night to
the town, he met with two Indians, who showed him the
passage, which they effected the following day by means
of hurdles or rafts of cane. After travelling three days,
they came to a town of the territory of Nilco, called Ti-
anto. Here they took 30 natives, and among them two
chiefs. De Soto, according to his custom of levying contribution on the natives, dispatched a party beforehand to
Nilco, to prevent the Indians from gaining time to carry
away their provision. The party passed through three or
four large towns, and in the town where the chief resided,
which was four miles from where the governor had remained, they found many Indians armed with their bows and
arrows, standing apparently on the defensive. But as soon

as the Spaniards began to approach, without more ado, they set fire to the house of the chief, and fled over a contiguous lake, which was not fordable for the horses.

The next day they arrived at Nilco, and lodged in the cazique's town, which stood in a prairie, and was inhabited for the space of half a mile. Within three miles were other large towns, well stored with the usual kind of provision. The Spaniards considered this as the best inhabited country which they had seen in Florida, except Coça and Apalache. A deputation came to Soto in the name of the chief, with a present of a garment of fur, and a string of pearls, to which the commander made a suitable return. This Indian promised to return in two days, but never fulfilled his promise, and in the night, the Indians were perceived carrying away their maize, and erecting cabins on the opposite side of the river.

This river, which ran by Nilco, was again recognized as the same which passed by Cayas and Autiamque, and from its contiguity to the Mississippi, appears to have been the Red river. Near to its confluence, was situated what La Vega calls the province of Guachoya. Three days after his arrival at Nilco, the commander came to Guachoya, where he hoped to hear of the sea, and recruit his men while the brigantines should be building, which he intended to dispatch to the Spanish settlements. He took up his residence in the town of the chief, which was fortified with pickets, and situated about a cross-bow shot from the Mississippi.

The chief of Guachoya came to the commander, accompanied by many of his people, who brought presents of fish, dogs, deer skins, and woven garments. He was asked concerning the distance from hence to the sea, to which he could receive no answer, and was, moreover, informed that no more towns or settlements were to be met with on that side of the river in descending.   Soto suspecting the truth of this disagreeable information, sent one of his officers with eight horsemen down the river to acquire more certain intelligence, and to learn, if possible, the distance and practicability of proceeding to the sea.   This messenger travelled eight days through sunken lands, and was not able to proceed in all that time more than about 30 miles, in consequence of the obstruction of bayous, cane brakes, and almost impenetrable forests, which were entirely destitute of habitations.

At this news, as well as at the desperate situation of his affairs, the commander fell sick with despondence.   But previous to taking to his bed, he sent an Indian messenger to the chief of Quigalta, to declare to him, that he was of the offspring of the sun (a pretention which was supported by the princes of the Natchez), and that, as such, he had been every where obeyed and served ; that he requested him to accept of his friendship, and visit him, as he would be gratified by his presence ; and that, as a mark of his esteem and obedience, he hoped he would bring something with him, of that which was most esteemed in his country ; to which, however, the chief returned the following independent answer :

" That as to his relation with the sun, he would believe it if he would dry up the river.   He paid no visits, but, on the contrary, received obedience and tribute, either willingly or by force, from all the people with which he was acquainted.   Therefore, if he desired an interview, it would be most proper for him to pay the visit. If his intentions were peaceable, he would be received with hospitality, but if he wished for war, he could attend him in the town where he now resided, but that, for him, or any other mortal, he would not step back a foot."

When the messenger returned with this unexpected answer, the governor was confined to his bed, and sick of a fever, but expressed a mortification that he was not immediately prepared to cross the river (Mississippi), which was here very rapid, and chastise the pride of this chief of Quigalta.* The river is here described as being a mile in width, and 16 fathoms deep, having both banks thickly inhabited by the natives.

The enterprising Soto, sensible of the approach of death, called around him the officers of his ruined army, and, in their presence, appointed Louis de Mososco de Alvarado their succeeding captain general and governor. The following day, the 21st of May, 1542, Ferdinand de Soto died, near to the confluence of Red river with the Mississippi. Mososco, now reduced to stratagem, determined to conceal his death from the natives, because that Soto had made them believe that the Christians were immortal, and because they were impressed with a high opinion of his vigilance and valour, and, seeing him now removed by death, they might be instigated to take up arms against the miserable handful of troops that remained. Knowing the inconstancy of their friendship, and their credulity, de Soto made them believe he possessed the art of prying into their inmost secrets, without their knowledge ; and, that the figure which appeared in a mirror, which he showed them, disclosed to him all their intentions, by which means they were often deterred from practising treachery against him.

* From the geographical situation, this aboriginal province must have been that of the Natchez.

Mososco, after concealing the body of Soto for three days, had him at length removed and buried in the secrecy of the night, near one of the gates of the town within the wall. The Indians, however, having seen him sick, suspected what in truth had happened ; and, passing by the place of his interment, where the earth was fresh, the circumstance became a matter of conversation among them, in consequence of which, Mososco had the body disinterred in the night, and wrapt up with a ballast of sand, and committed to the deep of the river. At length, the chief of Guachoya inquired for Soto, and was informed by Mososco, that he was gone for a while to heaven, as he had often done before, and because his stay was now to be protracted for a considerable time, he had appointed him to fill his place in the interim. The chief, still, however, believed that he was dead, and ordered two handsome Indians to be brought and sacrificed, according to their custom on the death of a chief, in order that they might wait upon him hereafter. Mososco still insisted, that de Soto was not dead, but gone to heaven, and that of his own soldiers, he had taken such as were necessary to serve him, and desiring the Indians to be loosed, advised the chief hereafter to desist from such an inhuman practice. Upon this, the intended victims being set at liberty, one of them refused to return with his chief because of his inhumanity, and attached himself to Mososco.

After some deliberation concerning their intended route, they came, at length, to the conclusion of attempting a passage to New Spain over land, as more practicable than the way by sea. After passing through several Indian towns whose names are now unintelligible, we find him, at length, among the Naguatex (or Natchitoches).

After proceeding in a western direction, about 300 miles from the Mississippi, they came to a river called Daycao, which Purchas conjectures to be the Rio del Oro of Cabeza de Vaca. From hence, after encountering the inclemencies and hardships of the commencing winter, they found it necessary to return to the confluence of Red river and the Mississippi, as it was impossible for them to subsist among the wandering natives of the sterile wilderness they were approaching, and over which, the natives themselves merely migrated and hunted, being destitute of any supply of maize, and spending a wandering life, like that of the Arabs, subsisting upon the Tunas (prickly pears), and roots of the plains.

Having returned to Minoya, considerably reduced by a sickness, which bordered on the typhus fever, they commenced building boats for the purpose of descending the Mississippi to the sea. In the month of March, though there had not been rain previous for a month, the river took such a rise, that in its overflow it reached to Nilco, 18 miles distant, and from the natives, Mososco understood that the flood was equally extensive on the opposite side. In the town occupied by the Spaniards, which was somewhat elevated, the water reached to the stirrups on horseback; and for two months they never stirred out of their houses, except on horseback or in canoes.

From an Indian, who was tortured for the purpose, Mososco learnt, that the caziques of Nilco, Guachoya, Taguanate, and others, to the number of about 20 chiefs, commanding many people, had determined to fall upon him by treachery. The signal for the destruction of the Spaniards on which they had agreed, was the time of making a present to the commander. The Indian, who gave this information, was detained in close confinement, and the day arriving for the delivery of the first presents, 30 Indians appearing with fish, Mososco ordered their right-hands to be cut off, and sent them back in this condition to their chief.   He also sent word to the cazique of Guachoya, that he and the rest of the conspirators might come when they pleased, as he was prepared for them, and could readily divine all their intentions as soon as thought of.   This circumstance threw them into consternation, and the chiefs respectively came forward to excuse themselves.

Their boats being finished in the month of June, the summer flood again visited the town, and without any farther trouble, the boats were now launched and conveyed into the Mississippi.   They shipped 22 of the best horses which they had in the camp, and of the rest they made provision.   They left Minoya on the second of July, 1543, being now reduced to 320 men, who occupied seven brigantines.   They were 17 days in descending to the sea, which they considered to be a distance of about 500 miles from the place of their departure ; and, indeed, pretty well corresponding with the present estimated distance.   In the course of their descent, they were repeatedly attacked by the natives.

On the 18th of July, they arrived in the gulf with a fair wind, and continued with a moderate breeze for two days, to their great astonishment still in fresh water, and were greatly tormented by musquetoes.   After coasting two and fifty days, they at length arrived in the river of Panuco the 10th of September, 1543, and were in all 311 men.

Such is a brief sketch of this memorable expedition, which opened the northern hemisphere of the New World to the enterprize and industry of the Europeans, and whence civilized society has derived far more lasting and important advantages, than could ever have accrued from the mere discovery of the precious metals.

SECTION II.

THE HISTORY OF THE NATCHEZ.

WE see nothing, says Charlevoix, in their outward appearance that distinguishes them from the other savages of Canada and Louisiana.   They seldom made war, living in quiet possession of their country, and having no ambition to distinguish themselves by conquering their neighbours.   Their despotic form of government, accompanied by some taste for parade and courtly magnificence, and the great servility of their subjects, appeared to be the shadow of a departing power, and concomitant population, such as had been unparallelled in the history of the northern natives.

Their great chief pretended to derive his origin from the Sun, which was likewise the principal object of their adoration.*   He was always chosen from the family of the nearest female relative of his predecessor, and his mother was also invested with considerable power,† and consider-

---

* The Hurons also, according to the same author, pretended that their hereditary chiefs were descended from the Sun, and continued the descent by the females in the same manner.

† In a speech made to governor Clinton, in 1788, by Domine Peter, a native orator, on the part of the Senecas and Cayugas, the authority of the female chieftains is acknowledged, by the speaker, and thus apologized. " Our ancestors considered it a great offence to reject the counsels of their women, particularly (that) of the female governesses (or chieftains).   They were esteemed the mistresses of the soil (as they solely attended to the labours of agriculture).   Who, said they, bring us into being ? Who cultivate our lands, kindle our fires (or ad-

ed as an auxiliary chief.   She, no less than the Great Sun,
dispensed with the lives and liberties of their subjects.
The lesser chiefs and the people never approached them
without uttering three salutations, in a loud and mournful
tone, which it was necessary to repeat on retiring, and also
to walk out from their presence backwards.   Even when
they happened to meet them, they were obliged to arrange
themselves on either side of the path, and repeat the customary salutation as they passed.   Their subjects likewise
brought them the best of their harvest, of their hunting,
and their fishing.   And no person, not even their nearest
relatives, or those of noble families, when invited to eat
with them, had a right to put their hand to the same dish,
or to drink out of the same vessel.

Every morning, as the sun appeared, the great chief
came to the door of his cabin, and turning himself towards
the East, bowed to the earth, and howled three successive
times.   A pipe dedicated to this purpose was then brought
to him, out of which he smoked tobacco, blowing the fume
towards the sun, and the other three quarters of the world.*

minister food to the calls of hunger), but our women? &c." *Governor*
Clinton's Discourse, December, 1811, *App. p.* 80.

As the mothers of the slain in battle, the women had the controul of
prisoners, either to adopt or destroy them at will, and their interposition
to procure peace, and stay hostilities, was universally acknowledged.
We have a remarkable example of this in the history of the Delawares,
who, at the instigation of the Iroquois, became a nation of mediators,
and were thus said to have assumed one of the distinguishing functions
of the female sex, and were, consequently, debarred from active war
and masculine distinction.   *See Heckewelder's History of the Delawares,*
in the report of the Historical Committee of the American Philosophical
Society.

* This, which Sir William Jones considered as the ritual of the Tartars, is also employed by the Sioux or Naudowessies, as I have repeatedly witnessed.

The actions of the Great Chief were allowed to be without impeachment; and his life, according to an ancient and solemn compact, could never become forfeited by his crimes. Indeed the death of the Great Sun was considered the greatest national calamity which could happen, and superstition had brought it to be considered as an omen of the cessation of their theocracy, and of the destruction of the world. Their sons were termed nobles, an honour which was likewise attainable by the meritorious of inferior rank. The common people laboured under a de-

According to the observations of Mr. Wm. Bartram, the Creeks likewise practised the same ceremony.

An invocation not very dissimilar to this sacred ceremony, is that of Agamemnon in the Iliad; thus translated by Pope:

> Then loudly thus before th' attentive bands
> He calls the gods, and spreads his lifted hands:
> O first and greatest power! whom all obey,
> Who high on Ida's holy mountain sway,
> Eternal Jove! and yon *bright orb* that rolls
> From east to west, and views from pole to pole!
> Thou mother *Earth!* and all ye living *Floods;*
> Infernal Furies! and Tartarian Gods;
> ———————— Hear and be witness.

> *Pope's Iliad,* Book III. lines 344—354.

According to Humboldt, in his Monumens de l'Amerique, vol. ii. pp. 54 and 55, the Mexican cycle of 52 years was divided into four indictions of 13 years, in reference to the *four seasons* of the year, the *four elements,* and the *cardinal points.* The most ancient division of the zodiac, according to Albategnius,[*] is that into four parts. "These four signs," he adds, "of the equinoxes and the solstices, chosen from a series of 20 signs" (the number of days in the Mexican month), "recal to mind the four *royal stars,* Aldebaran, Regulus, Antares, and Fomahault, celebrated in all Asia, and presiding over the seasons.[†] In the new continent, the indictions of the cycle of 52 years, formed, as we would say, the four seasons of the *grand year,* and the Mexican astrologers were pleased to see presiding over each period of 13 years one of the four equinoctial or solstitial signs."

[*] De Scientia Stellarum, cap. 2. (ed. Bonon. 1645,) p. 3.
[†] Firmicus. lib. vi. c. 1.

grading appellation, not indeed very different from the
French epithet of *canaille*, or our own term the mob, or
the vulgar. They carried this distinction even into their
language, as there were different modes of addressing the
vulgar and nobles.*

When either the male or female sun died, all their *al-
louez*, or intimate attendants, devoted themselves to death,
under a persuasion that their presence would be necessary
to maintain the dignity of their chief in the future world.
The wives and husbands of these chiefs were likewise immolated for the same purpose, and considered it the most
honourable and desirable of deaths. More than a hundred
victims were sometimes sacrificed to the manes of the
Great Chief.† The same horrible ceremonies, in a more

* The following example of the noble and common language of the
Natchez, is given by Du Pratz.* In calling one of the common people he
would say, *aquenan*, that is, "hark ye;" if to a sun or one of the nobles,
the address would be *magani*, which also signifies the same. To one of
the common people, calling at his house, he would say, *tachte-cabanactc*,
"are you there," or "I am glad to see you." To a sun the same thing is
expressed by the word *apapegouaiché*. Again, according to their custom, I say to one of the common people, *petchi*, "sit you down;" but
to a sun, *caham*. In other respects the language is the same; as the
difference of expression seems only to take place in matters relating to
the persons of the suns and nobles, to distinguish them from the people.

† Among the Mexicans, prisoners, rather than domestics and attendants, were devoted to death at the obsequies of the great, as victims
to that spirit of revenge so deeply cherished by savage or barbarous
nations. So even Achilles, lamenting over the body of Patroclus, says,

> Ere thy dear relics in the grave are laid,
> Shall Hector's head be offer'd to thy shade;
> That, with his arms, shall hang before thy shrine;
> And twelve the noblest of the Trojan line,
> Sacred to vengeance, by this hand expire:
> Their lives effus'd around thy flaming pyre.
>   *Pope's Iliad*, Book XVIII. lines 391—396.

* Hist. Louisian. p. 328.

limited degree, were also exercised at the death of the lesser chiefs.

At the death of one of their female chiefs, Charlevoix relates, that her husband not being noble was, according to their custom, strangled by the hands of his own son. Soon after, the two deceased being laid out in state, were surrounded by the dead bodies of 12 infants, strangled by the order of the eldest daughter of the late female chief, and who had now succeeded to her dignity. Fourteen other individuals were also prepared to die and accompany the deceased. On the day of interment, as the procession advanced, the fathers and mothers who had sacrificed their children, preceding the bier, threw the bodies upon the ground at different distances, in order that they might be trampled upon by the bearers of the dead. The corpse arriving in the temple where it was to be interred, the 14 victims now prepared themselves for death by swallowing pills of tobacco and water, and were then strangled by the relations of the deceased, and their bodies cast into the common grave, and covered with earth.

The Natchez, together with the remains of the Grigras and Thioux, who had become incorporated with them, did not, in 1720, amount to more than 1200 warriors.* Only six or seven years prior to this period, their warriors were estimated at 4000. This rapid decrease they attributed to the prevalence of contagious diseases, by which they had been wasted, for it does not appear that they were ever addicted to war, having long lived in peace with the neighbouring nations, who venerated their sacred institutions, and acknowledged their political ascendancy and power. Their dominion once extended from the borders of bayou

* Du Pratz Hist. Louisian. p. 313. (*Ed. Lond.*)

Manchac to the banks of the Ohio, and they numbered not less than 500 suns or caziques. Descended from, and confederated with them, were the Taensas of the Mobile, and the Chetimashas of bayou Placquemine, remnants of whom still exist, not far from the sites where they were first found by the French colonists, and against whom they waged an unsuccessful war.

The Natchez had a distinct tradition of migrating to the Mississippi, from the coast of the Gulf of Mexico, at two distinct periods of time. A part of the nation (probably about the period of the first establishment of the Mexican monarchy) fled from the threatening oppression of their natural enemies, and living in undisturbed tranquillity for several generations in their newly acquired territory, they became very populous, and were only joined by the Great Sun after the arrival and invasion of the Spaniards, with whom at first they had entered into an alliance. As to their ultimate oriental origin, it appears to be merely connected with their presumption of a descent from the sun, which first illuminates the eastern hemisphere. It was this superstition which proved so fatal to the Mexicans, who venerated as a celestial race the Spanish conquerors, because they had arrived from the region of the rising sun. Traces of the natural worship of the two great luminaries of day and night, were every where visible throughout the regions of the New World, and continue to be practised by those who are still unbiassed by the influence of the European nations.* The Hurons, no

---

* The great Deity of the savages of the river Bourbon, and the river St. Therese, Hudson's Bay, is the sun. When they deliberate on any important affair, they make him, as it were, smoke. They assemble at day-break in a cabin of one of their chiefs, who, after having lighted his pipe, presents it three times to the rising sun ; then he guides it with

less than the Muyscas of the plain of Bogota, in the
equatorial regions, personified the moon in their female
deity, Atahentsic, who was the mother of the fratricide

both hands from the east to the west, praying the sun to favour the nation. This being done, all the assembly smoke in the same pipe.
Charlevoix, Hist. Journ. p. 108 (Ed. Lond.) The Sioux also practise
the same rites.

Gookin, in 1674, says, " Some, for their God, adore the sun; others
the moon; some the earth, others the fire, and like vanities. Yet,
generally, they acknowledge one great supreme doer of good; and him
they call Woonand or Mannitt; another, that is, the great doer of evil
or mischief; and him they call Mattand, which is the Devil, &c." Com-
pare this relation with the invocation of Agamemnon, already quoted,
from which it scarcely differs in any particular.

Traces of the adoration of the sun are discoverable also in Colden's
History of the Five Nations, not only among the Iroquois, but also with
the neighbouring nations: thus among the attestations to a treaty of
peace made with the Iroquois, by a band of the Utawas, we find the following. " Let the sun, as long as he shall endure, always shine upon
us in friendship." With which apostrophe was delivered a figure of
the sun, sculptured of red marble.* A similar figure was again presented to the Five Nations by the Utawas and a branch of the Hurons
(called Dionondadies) jointly, in another treaty concluded between
them.†

At a treaty in which general Harrison assisted, towards the commencement of the last war, the council-house being crowded, a chief
arriving late was suffered to stand some time unheeded, until the general sent him a chair, as from his father. He refused the offer, saying, probably in allusion to their ancient belief, " The sun is my father, the
earth my mother, and my seat is the ground."

The sacred, or eternal, fire is also decribed in the following incidental
remark, made by a chief speaker of the Five Nations: "Before the
Christians arrived amongst us, the general council of the Five Nations
was held at Onondago, where there has, from the beginning (or from
the remotest time) been kept a fire continually burning, made of two
great logs whose flame was never extinguished."‡

---

* Colden's Hist. Five Nations, third edition, i. p. 115.   † Ibid. i. p. 185.
‡ Ibid, vol i. p. 176.

Jouskeka, or the sun,* betwixt whom were divided the powers of good and evil. The moon possessing the attributes of Hecate, and the sun those of Phœbus, Apollo, or Osiris the brother of Isis, or the moon.†

---

* Charlevoix, Hist. Journ. p. 249. *(Ed. Lond.)*

† In ancient times, before the moon accompanied the earth (says the mythology of the Muyscas or Mozcas Indians), the inhabitants of the plain of Bogota lived like barbarians, naked, without agriculture, without laws, and without worship. Suddenly there appeared among them an aged man, who came from the plains east of the Cordillera of Chingasa : he seemed to be of a different race from that of the indigenes, for he had a long and tufted beard. He was known by three different names ; under that of *Bochica, Nemquetheba,* and *Zuhè.* This aged person, after the manner of Manco-Capac, taught men to clothe themselves, to construct dwellings, to cultivate the earth, and to unite in society. He brought with him a woman, to whom tradition gave also the three names of *Chia, Yubecayguaya,* and *Huythaca.* This female was of an uncommon beauty, but exceedingly wicked, counteracting her husband in every thing which he undertook for the good of men. By her magic art she swelled the river Funzha to such a degree, that the water inundated the whole valley of Bogota. This deluge destroyed the greatest part of the inhabitants, a few only escaping upon the summits of the neighbouring mountains. The old man, irritated, drove the beautiful Haythaca from the earth ; she then became the moon, which, from that period, commenced to enlighten our planet during the night. Afterwards Bochica, son of the sun, taking pity on the men who were dispersed upon the mountains, broke, with his powerful hand, the rocks which close the valley on the side of Canaos and Tequendama. By this opening he carried off the water of the lake of Funzha, reunited again the people of the valley of Bogota, constructed towns, introduced the *worship of the sun,* nominated two chiefs, between whom he divided the ecclesiastic and secular power, and then retired, under the name of *Idacanzas,* into the sacred valley of Iraca, near to Tanja, where he devoted himself to exercises of the most austere penance, for the space of two thousand years. *Humboldt's Vues des Cordillères, et Monumens des Peuples indigènes de l'Amérique.* Vol. I. pp. 87, 88. (Ed. Octavo.)

The Jouskeka, who destroyed his brother, and the Atahentsic of the Hurons, also, in some measure, resemble the Cihuacohuatl or woman of

The great ritual of this religion, which obtained throughout America, is the pipe which was filled with the ine-
briating tobacco, and smoked in offering to this great luminary, and to the four quarters, or the surrounding horizon
of the visible world, which it illuminates. Associated
with this adoration, as simple as natural, was that of preserving an eternal fire in some sacred place appropriated
to this purpose, as well as for the celebration of their festivals and deliberative councils. The pipe was brought forward on every solemn occasion, and to ratify every serious
pledge of peace, integrity, and friendship. The rites of
hospitality, sanctioned by this ceremony, were irrefraga-
ble, as well as every commercial and political contract.
The Hurons say, that the Indian nations derived the
sacred pipe from the great luminary to whom it is dedicated, and, that it was first presented to the western nation
of the Pawnees,* a tradition which I have found corroborated by the nation of the Mandans and the Minitarees.
Those people, as well as the Naudowessies, influenced by
an idolatrous regard for the sun, make offerings of their
most valuable effects,† and, occasionally, even of the lives
of their prisoners. The Mexicans immolated hosts of
human victims to their cruel and imaginary deities.

If the Natchez refrained from cruel offerings to their

the serpent, adored by the Mexicans, and figured in their hieroglyphic
paintings. This goddess was regarded as the mother of the human race,
and in the painting alluded to, published by Humboldt, she is accompanied familiarly by a serpent, and in the same symbolical sketch there
are two smaller figures engaged in combat, as if to designate the Cain
and Abel of the Hebrews, and which were considered in Mexico as the
children of the female deess. *Humboldt,* vol. I. pp. 235, 236.

* Charlevoix, p. 133.

† They present robes of the bison painted with the rays of the sun,
exposing them upon poles, set up in the prairies.

gods, they failed not to sacrifice many human victims at
the death of their caziques, who pretended to derive their
origin from the sun.

In their other superstitions, manners, and customs, they
differ too little from the rest of the aborigines to tolerate
the repetition. Their peculiar usages are in some degree
still kept up by those confederated tribes which we call
the Creeks or Muskogolgees, to whom they appear to have
been more intimately related, than any other of the remaining aborigines. Among these people fire is still venerated, and the appearance of the new moon announced
with festivity and gladness. According to the relation of
my venerable friend, Wm. Bartram, there existed also
among them a language of distinction and of honour, and
an aristocratic acknowledgment of superior and inferior
order in their society.

The occasion of that signal depopulation which the
Natchez had experienced, when first discovered by the
French, must ever remain in unaccountable uncertainty.
The prevalence of fatal and contagious diseases at one
period more than another, is scarcely admissible in a
country which had ever exhibited the same aspect,
and amongst a people who had never inhabited crowded
towns or cities. From the migratory and unsettled character of the more northern natives, and their acknowledged superiority in arms, particularly the Iroquois, with
whom they warred,* may be with more probability deduced the real cause of this destruction. The valley of
the Ohio, and the interior of Kentucky and Tennessee,
still exhibit unequivocal and numerous remains of a vast

* When La Salle was among the Natchez, in 1683, he saw a party
of that people, who had been on an expedition against the Iroquois
Tonti's account of La Salle's Expedition (Ed. Lond.), p. 112.

population, who had begun to make some imperfect advances towards power and civilization. Works were constructed for public benefit, which required the united energy, skill, and labour of a devoted multitude. We, in vain, look for similar subordination among the existing natives; by their own tradition they destroyed this race, as foreigners, and gained possession of their country and their fortresses, abandoning them as the barbarians of the north did the cities of Europe, and thus prostrating every advance which had been made beyond the actual limits of savage life.

These devoted people, the Mexicans of the north, were not, however, relieved by their acquaintance with the civilized world. They had peaceably suffered the French to settle around them, and assisted them when in the utmost want and necessity. They thus saved the lives of those, who were about to prove their mortal enemies and oppressors.

The first quarrel which took place betwixt the French and Natchez, in the year 1722, was occasioned by the insolence and injustice of a common soldier of the fort, who, demanding in an unreasonable manner a debt from an aged warrior of the White Apple village, proceeded by unjust pretences to instigate the guard to shoot him, which proved mortal, and for which rashness he received from the commander nothing more than a reprimand.

The village, determined on revenge, fell upon two Frenchmen in their neighbourhood, and at last upon the settlement of St. Catharine. The great chief, however, called the Stung Serpent, at the intreaty of the commandant of Fort Rosalie, succeeded in producing a cessation of hostilities, and soon afterwards a peace.

Notwithstanding this favourable posture of affairs, M.

De Biainville, the governor, violating every principle of honour and of justice, a few months afterwards, in the midst of peace, surprised the unfortunate Natchez of the offending village, and falling upon them in cold-blooded treachery, obliged them to give up their aged chief, whose head he had demanded of his people.

Some years after this affair, the tyranny and injustice of the Sieur de Chopart, who commanded the post of Natchez, had nearly proved fatal to the whole of the French settlement in Louisiana. Soon after arriving at the post, he projected forming an eminent settlement, in order to gratify his ambition, and amongst all the situations which he examined, none could satisfy him but the village of the White Apple, which was not less than a square league in extent. The commandant, without further ceremony, ordered the chief to remove his huts and his people, as soon as possible, to some other quarter. To which the Sun of the Apple deliberately replied, that his ancestors had lived in that village for almost as many years as there were hairs in his head, and that therefore they had a just right to continue there unmolested.

The Sun, without making any impression on the mind of the inexorable Chopart, withdrew, and assembled the council of his village, who represented to the commandant that, at present, their corn was only shooting, and if now neglected, would be lost both to themselves and the French, who were not numerous enough to tend it. But this excuse, though just and reasonable, was menacingly rejected.

At length, the old men proposed to the commandant, to be allowed to remain in their village until harvest, and to have time to dry their corn, on condition, that each hut of the village should pay, at a time appointed, a basket of corn and a fowl, a measure which would also afford them time to deliberate on some method of delivering themselves from the tyranny of the French.

This proposal succeeded with the avaricious Chopart, who pretended to grant them this respite as a favour. The Sun and council of the village, now consulted together on the means of ridding themselves and their nation of the French. They entered into a secret conspiracy to destroy the whole settlement at a blow, on that odious day appointed for the delivery of the stipulated tribute. They were also to endeavor to gain over the other neighbouring nations into the plot, in order to complete their success, and accelerate the fatal project.

To obtain uniformity in the execution, bundles of rods, equal in number, were to be delivered to their several allies, and also retained by themselves in the recess of their temple ; one of which was to be withdrawn and broken each day, until the accomplishment of the stated period.*

The secret councils which were held among the nobles and elders, gave some alarm to the people, and aroused the curiosity of the Stung Arm, mother to the Grand Sun, who, at length, wrung from this chief the fatal secret. Influenced either by caprice or compassion, she destroyed the concert of the execution, which was to have been seconded by the Choctaws, by withdrawing a number of the rods, and so hastening the approaching time of the massacre. All the warnings which she gave to the commander and other individuals, were treated with disdain, as the effects of fear and cowardice.

On the eve of St. Andrew, 1729, the Natchez left their towns preparatory to the execution of their plot, and to show their contempt for the commandant, they had left his execution in the hands of one of the vulgar, who was

---

* This method of recording the lapse of time was also practised by the Chicasas and Muskogolgees, according to the relation of Adair.

armed with a wooden hatchet, no warrior deigning to kill him. At the time appointed, the massacre became general and instantaneous, and of about 700 persons, but few escaped to bear the fatal intelligence to New Orleans, the capital.

The Choctaws were greatly displeased at the acceleration of the period appointed for the accomplishment of the plot by the Natchez, and were, in consequence, easily induced, soon afterwards, to join the French against them. Arriving early in the following spring, the troops appointed by M. Perier, then governor of Louisiana, joined by the Choctaws, made their attack on the fort of the Natchez. After the lapse of several days employed in firing without any great effect, the besieged, fearing the worst, began to sue for peace, and offered as a condition to deliver up all their prisoners. The Natchez gaining time by these offers of pacification, took advantage of the following night, and evacuated their fort with all their families, baggage, and plunder.

After the Natchez had abandoned the fort, it was demolished to the ground.

A short time after their flight, determined on revenge against the Tonicas, who were allies of the French, they destroyed them by stratagem, under pretence of offering them terms of peace.

The Natchez had now abandoned the east side of the Mississippi, and fortified themselves near to Silver creek connected with the Washita.

M. Perier and his brother, with a considerable armament, penetrated to the retreat of the unfortunate Natchez, who, struck with terror at the sight of their relentless and formidable enemies, shut themselves up in their fort, and abandoned themselves to despair and desperation. Soon after the battery had commenced, a bomb happening to fall in the midst of their fort amongst the women and children, they were so struck with terror and grief at the cries of the helpless, that they instantly made the signal of capitulation. They, however, started diffi‑ culties again to obtain time. The night was granted them, and they attempted a second flight, but were, for the greatest part, checked and obliged to retire into the fort. Those who did escape, joined a party who were out a hunting, and they altogether retired to the Chicasaws.* The rest surrendered themselves prisoners, among whom were the Grand Sun, and the female chiefs; they were carried to New Orleans in slavery, and there consigned to prison, but were shortly after sold in the king's planta‑ tions. Bent upon their annihilation, the French after‑ wards transported them to St. Domingo, and in this way terminated the fate of the Natchez as a nation, whose only fault was that of patriotism, and an inviolable love of ra‑ tional liberty.

It appears that the small party who had sought refuge among the Chicasaws, still insecure from the bitter hos‑ tilities of the French, had at last retired into the country of the Creeks; and, at this time occupy a small village called Natchez, on the banks of the Tallipoosee, whose chief, Coweta, fought under the banners of general Jack‑ son. Their language (said to be destitute of the letter *r*), and their positive affinities to any existing nation of the aborigines, has never yet been ascertained, and remains open to the inquiries of the curious, who will not proba‑ bly long enjoy the advantage of contemplating the cha‑ racter of this feeble fragment of a once numerous, pow‑ erful, and rational people.

* Mr. Brackenridge adds, that, after the defeat by Perire, about 200 of the Natchez fortified themselves some distance up Red river, but were attacked and destroyed by St. Dennis. *Hist. Louisiana.* p. 44

SECTION III.

OBSERVATIONS ON THE CHICASAWS AND CHOCTAWS.

THE Chicasaws and Choctaws, who speak a language considerably related, entertain a tradition in common with the Iroquois, the Delawares, the Illinois, and most of the nations of North America, of having once migrated from the west, and crossed the Mississippi to their present residence. They are said to derive their name from two distinguished leaders, Choctawby and Chicasawby, who instigated their warlike and political movements. These personal appellations were frequently employed by the aborigines in the time of Soto, who speaks, for example, of the Kaskaskias and others by those who then held the rule, as the cazique or chief of Casqui, of Nilco, of Cayas, &c., all which, as far as still recognizable, have passed very improperly into so many epithets apparently national, but which were, in fact, as we discover both by language and confederation, merely so many bands of the same people receding from the residence of the original stock, either through ambitious caprice, enterprize, or necessity. This connection among the Delawares or Lleni-lenapés, affording an easy clue of origin, was always readily acknowledged under the epithets of grandfather, the original stock, and brothers or collateral descendants, by which were designated the receding tribes, and by a mere reference to which, never for a moment disputed, the paternal and ruling authority of the ancient household was universally acknowledged and venerated. From a neglect of this genealogical analysis has arisen that confusion of origin, and those fallacious ideas of Indian nations and languages which many suppose to exist; as if the human family in America, had ever consisted of as many paltry and radically dismembered fragments, as there were names employed to designate them.

It is not a little singular, that to all inquiries of ultimate residence which have ever been made among the American natives, they should so uniformly refer back apparently almost to the same period and the same country. The occasion of this simultaneous migration, however urgent and important, is now perpetually locked in mystery. It was, undoubtedly, instigated by some important human revolution, which appears to have set in motion a vast hive of the human race in search of some more commodious state of subsistence. They were too barbarous to have adventured in quest of pecuniary wealth, and could have had naturally no other object for separation greater than that which slowly dispersed the first patriarchs of the world. Their migrations, as described by the Mexicans, probably took up a period of ages, and the vicissitudes of fortune which attended their progress, unrecorded by the circumstantial pen of history, and limited by chronology, may, probably, contribute to that extraordinary appearance of simultaneous and uninterrupted movement, which was rather carried on through an extended cycle of time, than in the short space requisite to the completion of an expedition. There is one thing, however, certain in regard to the Chicasaws and their collateral bands, that they have for at least the three last centuries occupied the countries in which we still find them. For it was here that they were discovered by De Soto, and where they had not then apparently by any means recently established themselves. On what footing they had resided as near neighbours to the Natchez, I am unable to ascertain ; they appear from the first to have been a jealous and hostile nation, and became the bold, cunning, and successful ene- mies of the whites from their first interview with the Spaniards, who certainly, as wanton invaders, did not act in a way to conciliate the esteem of the natives. The Natchez asserted that they could once number no less than 500 Suns (or chiefs who pretended to derive their origin from that luminary which they adored), and that their possessions extended in a continual line from Nat- chez to the mouth of the Ohio. Whether they had been dispossessed and reduced to the feeble state in which they were discovered by the French, through the enmity of the Chicasaws, Iroquois, or the Illinois, we cannot now determine, though, from the contiguity of the latter, and their former strength, we should rather conclude them, or the northern confederates, to have been the destroyers of the Natchez, than the Chicasaws, as we find them and the Choctaws to have been the abettors of the Natchez, in their unfortunate contest with the French, yet of a cha- racter extremely versatile and revengeful, insomuch that the Choctaws, who had at one time proffered their assist- ance, withdrew it in favour of their enemies, in conse- quence of the unforeseen circumstance which to the Natchez prematurely hastened the secret attack they had concerted against their enemies, and which was to have been regulated by the consummation of a period of time, designated by a bundle of rods deposited in the temple, each of which counted for a day. The comple- tion of this fatal period was, however, secretly hastened, to destroy the concert with the Choctaws, by the revenge- ful sister of the Great Sun, who, resenting the secrecy her brother had observed towards her, withdrew a number of the tallies, and though by this means the main object was not defeated, yet it excited the fatal jealousy and enmity of the Choctaws, who were consequently disconcerted in completing the intended measure of vengeance.

From the high tone in which the chief of Quigalta answered the requisitions of Soto, (and who, occupying the identical spot where Natchez now stands, could, by the concurrence of their traditions, scarcely have been any other than the same people), we perceive their power and independence, although concentrated within narrower limits, still highly respectable.

In the time of Charlevoix, an active war was carried on betwixt the ever restless and rapacious Chicasaws and the Illinois, who, by them and the Iroquois, in the end appear to have been exterminated as a nation.

From the situation which the Chicasaws and their branches occupied on this continent, from the earliest period of history, we may, I think, consider them as among the most ancient of the existing aborigines. To give a more correct idea of their former extent and influence, considered in the most general point of view, I shall bring together their scattered branches, so as to afford a retrospect of the whole. Although we have chosen to speak of the Chicasaw as the principal band, which it now is, in consequence of the reduction or extinction of most of the rest ; yet, in point of numbers, the Mobilians, now, I believe, extinct, must have far exceeded the Chicasaws. They were discovered by De Soto, dwelling in the vicinity of the present bay and river of Mobile. Their name, by De Soto, is Mouvill. Unwilling to acknowledge the arbitrary usurpation of their Spanish discoverers, a battle ensued, which, in consequence probably of the inequality of arms and skill, proved very destructive to the Mouvillians, who lost 2500 men. From so considerable a loss at the first outset, and that without a surprise, it is evident that their numbers must have been considerable. They were nearly extinct in the time of Charlevoix, who, concerning their religious rite of preserving an eternal fire in a temple, remarks, that it appeared probable, the Mobilians had, over all the people of Florida, a kind of primacy of religion, for it was at their sacred fire that the others were obliged to kindle *that*, which, by accident or neglect, had been suffered to go out.* In the vicinity of the Mobilians lived also the Chatots, in the time of Du Pratz, occupying a village of about 40 huts. A little north of Fort Louis, on the Mobille, according to the same author, lived the Thomez, who were not more numerous than the Chatots.

To the north of the Apalaches, who gave name to the mountains so called, lived the Alibamas, and to the north of the Alibamas, were the Abeikas and Conchacs, apparently the same people. Their language was scarcely at all different from that of the Chicasaws, and their name of *conchac* is the Chicasaw word for the knives which they formerly made of sharpened splits of cane.

The Aquelou Pissas, formerly living within three or four miles of the site of New Orleans, had removed, in the time of Du Pratz, to the borders of lake Ponchartrain.

Upon the Yazoo river, lived the Chacchi-oumas (or Red Cray-fish), consisting of about 50 huts. Not far from them, also dwelt the Oufe-Ogoulas (or the Nation of the Dog), occupying about 60 huts. The Tapoussas likewise lived upon the banks of this river, and had not more than 25 cabins. These, as well as the Oumas of the

---

* Charlevoix's Hist. Journ. p. 323.

Mississippi, who still lived on the present site of the great plantation of General Wade Hampton, in the time of the author already mentioned, did not use the letter *r* in their language, and, as well as all the above named natives, appeared to be branches of the Chicasaws, as they spoke either that language or its dialects.

Most part of these small nations, after joining the Natchez in their unsuccessful plot against the French, retired among the Chicasaws, and were finally incorporated with them.

The language of the Chicasaws, it appears, was not unknown on the western side of the Mississippi : the Caddoes or Cadoda-quioux, divided into several extensive branches, as well as the Natchitoches, although possessed of a peculiar language, as well as all the Indians of Louisiana generally, were more or less acquainted with the Chicasaw or Mobilian.*   And it was, no doubt, from this circumstance that John Ortiz, who had escaped the fate of the adventurers of Pamphilo de Narvaez, and who was discovered by De Soto living among the Indians of East Florida, rendered himself so easily understood throughout the whole of that extensive route which was pursued by Soto.

From the earliest settlement of the French on the borders of the Mississippi, the Chicasaws evinced a hostile disposition, which, indeed, they had probably cherished from their ancestors, who had severely punished the little army of De Soto.   Their hostility is attributed by Charlevoix to the friendship which subsisted between the French and the Illinois, their enemies.   They appear, however, afterwards to have remained neutral, and would have con-

* Du Pratz's Hist. Louisiana, p. 318.

tinued so, had not the tyrannical Biainville commenced
hostilities against them, for the customary hospitality
which they had shewn to the unfortunate remains of the
Natchez, whom they had received and adopted. To the
requisitions of Biainville to give up the Natchez, whom
he was bent on exterminating, the Chicasaws answered,
that the Natchez having sought their protection, had been
received and adopted by them, so that they now constituted
but one people. If Biainville, said they, had received our
enemies, should we demand them ? or, if we did, would
they be given up?

Without listening to reason, Biainville commenced warlike preparations against the Chicasaws Supplies of ammunition were sent up the Mississippi to the post of Illinois, desiring the commandant to equip as many of the
Indians, inhabitants, and troops, as possible, to join him at
the Chicasaws, by the 10th of the following May. The
Indians attempted in vain to surprise the convoy, which,
proceeding in safety to the fort at the mouth of the Arkansa, left the gunpowder there without any manifest
reason, which Artaguette, the commandant at Illinois, understanding, from those who had neglected to convey it,
immediately sent down a boat for the purpose of obtaining
it, which was taken by a party of the Chicasaws, after
killing all the crew except two individuals, whom they
made slaves.

In the mean time, Biainville proceeding to fort Mobile, engaged the Choctaws to join him as mercenaries.

On the 10th of March, 1736, the troops being assembled,
began their march the 2d of April, and arrived at Tom-
becbee on the 20th, where they fortified their camp, and
remained till the 4th of May, detained by a conspiracy
among themselves to destroy the commandant and garri-

son. The Choctaws, who joined them, were about 1200 in number, and commanded by their principal chief.

On the 26th of May, they marched to the fort of the Chicasaws, crossing an adjoining rivulet of considerable depth; the fort defended the village, which was situated upon an agreeable plain. This defensive position was thrown up on an eminence with an easy ascent, around it stood several huts, and others at a greater distance, which appeared to have been put in a state of defence; and close to the fort ran a little brook, which watered a part of the plain.

On approaching the fort they observed four Englishmen enter it, and that the British flag was flying. The attack was made, and obstinately maintained for a considerable time on both sides, but greatly to the disadvantage of the French. The Indians, protected by a strong stockade, were under cover from every attack, and could have defended themselves by their loop-holes. In addition to which, they formed a gallery of flat pallisadoes quite round, covered with earth, which screened it from the effects of grenadoes. Thus the troops, after lavishing their ammunition against the wooden posts of the Indian fort, were obliged to retreat, with the loss of 32 men killed, and almost 70 wounded; and, abandoning the country, retired to fort Mobile, from whence the militia and Indians were disbanded.

Mr. Artaguette, with his Illinois troops and Indian allies, arriving in the Chicasaw country on the 9th of May, waited the arrival of the French until the 21st, when, hearing nothing of them, and fearful of the impatience of the Indians, made the attack with success, at first, having forced the Chicasaws to quit their village and fort. They also attacked another village with the same success, but hurried away in the pursuit, M. d'Artaguette received two wounds, which caused him and a small body of his men, 46 soldiers and two sergeants, to be abandoned by the Indians, and, after defending their commander all that day, they were at last obliged to surrender.   The troops under Biainville having retired, and the Indians consequently finding no opportunity of gaining a ransom for their prisoners, put them all to death by slow fire, except a sergeant, who, meeting with an indulgent master, found means to make his escape.

Biainville, desirous to take vengeance upon the Chicasaws, wrote both to France and Canada, requesting succours.

The reinforcements having arrived from France, proceeded up the Mississippi to the Cliffs of Prud'homme, now called the Chicasaw Bluffs, where they landed, and fortified their encampment, which was situated on a fine plain, and called fort Assumption, in commemoration of the day on which they landed.

They made wagons and sledges, and cleared out roads for the conveyance of cannon, ammunition, and every thing necessary for forming a regular siege.   They were also immediately reinforced by the forces which they had requested from Canada, consisting of a mixed multitude of French, Iroquois, Hurons, Episingles, Algonquins, and other nations, led by the commandant of the Illinois, with the garrison inhabitants and neighbouring Indians, as many as could be brought together, and furnished with a considerable number of horses.

This formidable army, the greatest that had ever been seen in the interior of America, remained in camp without undertaking any thing, from the month of August, 1739, to the succeding month of March.   Provisions, which were at first in plenty, became at last so scarce, that they were obliged to eat up the horses, which were intended to draw the artillery, ammunition, and provisions. They were also seriously attacked by sickness, which at length inclined M. Biainville to have recourse to mild methods. He therefore detached a small body of troops and Canadian Indians against the Chicasaws, with orders to make offers of peace to them in his name, if they were inclined to sue for it.

What the general had foreseen did indeed happen. For no sooner had the Chicasaws seen the French, followed by the Indians of Canada, than they apprehended the approach of the rest of the numerous army, and making signals of peace, came out of their fort in the most humble manner, hazarding all the consequences of such an exposure, in the hope of obtaining peace. They solemnly protested an inviolable friendship to the French, and avowed that they had been instigated by the English to take up arms against them, and seeing their error they had already separated from them, and had, at that very time, two of that nation whom they had made slaves, and of the truth of which assertion, they might, if they pleased, now satisfy themselves.

Lieutenant de St. Laurent, accompanied by a young slave, therefore, went in order to ascertain the truth of their professions; as he passed through the village, the women were heard to demand him as a sacrifice to their hatred, but were prevented by the men from offering him any injury. Peace was now instantly concluded, and a few days after, they accompanied the commander of the detachment in a considerable body, to carry the pipe of peace to the French governor, and to deliver up the two Englishmen. They behaved before M. Biainville with

the utmost submission, and offered, if necessary, to attest
their friendship by making war upon the English. Thus
concluded the war of the French with the Chicasaws,
about the beginning of April, 1740.

In the revolutionary war with Great Britain, they appear to have sided with the republicans ; and displayed
considerable fidelity and courage in the late war against
the Creeks, under the command of general Jackson.

After the Iroquois, we are not acquainted with any nation of the aborigines of North America, who have been
so restless and enterprising as the Chicasaws, and who
have better maintained their ground against every species
of hostility. They have not only, says Du Pratz, cut off
a great many nations who were adjoining them, but have
even carried their love of war and vengeance as far as
New Mexico, near 600 miles from the place of their residence, to exterminate a nation that had removed to that
distance from them. In this enterprise they were, however, deceived and cut off.

The Choctaws, still equally numerous, reckoned, in the
time of Du Pratz, 25,000 warriors. We know but little
of them more than a few detached customs, and the tradition, that they had made a sudden arrival in the country
which they now occupy. There is a small village of them
in the vicinity of the town of Arkansas, but made up principally of those, who had rendered themselves obnoxious
to the rest of the nation, who, probably, as well as the
Cherokees and Creeks, have found the necessity of introducing corporeal and general punishments, for the benefit
and security of society.

As we cannot discover any mention of them by the historian of De Soto, they were perhaps, at that period, included amongst the Chicasaws. And, from the extinction

of the Mobilians and other nations, met with by that adventurer, we are inclined to believe them the modern usurpers of the country which they now possess. Many of them live on the borders of the Yazoo, and other parts of the Mississippi and Louisiana territories. It is certain, as we have had already occasion to notice, that they made war against the Chicasaw , in aid of the French, and that, though they professed to aid the cause of the Natchez, yet that afterwards, through mere jealousy, they had joined with the French against them.

The Choctaws, till very late years, had a practice, not indeed peculiar, of exposing their dead upon scaffolds till such time as the flesh decayed, which was then separated from the bones by a set of old men, who devoted themselves to this custom, and were called "bone-pickers," after which, the bones were interred in some place set apart for the purpose.

This custom unquestionably arose out of a veneration for the deceased, and an attachment to their remains, which, among a wandering and unsettled people, were thus conveniently removed. A circumstance of this kind is related by Charlevoix,* where the Indians on removing their village, carried with them also the bones of their dead.

* Historical Journal, p. 334. (*Ed. Lond.*)

SECTION III.

THERMOMETRICAL OBSERVATIONS IN THE ARKANSA
TERRITORY, DURING THE YEAR 1819.

	A. M. deg.	P. M. deg.		A. M. deg.	P. M. deg.
January 20	12 67		April 12	7 54	2 74
21	12 67		13	7 62	3 76
March 9	12 50		14	7 64	2 74
10	12 50	P. M. deg.	15	7 64	3 78
12	8 66	3 76	16	7 64	3 66
13	48	3 60	17	7 54	3 70
14	48	3 56	18	10 56	4 65
15	56	3 73	19	8 54	2 70
16	8 28	5 34	20	6 60	1 74
17	8 34	3 48	21	6 62	3 76
18	8 42	3 50	22	66	6 70
19	8 38	2 50	23	6 56	1 76
20	8 48	3 58	24	6 62	3 72
21	6 22	5 48	25	6 56	2 78
22	8 48	3 66	26	7 63	3 70
23	7 60	3 72	27	6 56	3 77
24	6 60	2 70	28	6 66	9 75
25	7 54	4 78	29	7 69	1 80
26	7 42	5 64			5 80
27	8 46	1 66	30	6 66	12 75
28	7 52	3 54	May 1	8 68	
29	6 60	2 54	2	7 60	4 80
30	7 40	3 44	3	7 68	12 82
31	6½ 32	12 58			7 82
April 1	7 48	2 68	4	7 68	3 78
2	6½ 58	3 60	5	7 68	3 76
3	7 52	2 64	6	7 68	3 68
4	7½ 44	2 60	7	7 68	3 78
5	7 40	2 70	8	7 60	3 66
6	7 50	1 70	9	8 68	3 70
7	6½ 60	2 76	10	8 70	3 86
		at 7 76	11	6 77	4 86
8	7 64	2 74	12	8 76	2 86
9	7 56	2 66	13	7 78	4 68
10	7 60	1 64	14	7 62	4 66
11	7 52	3 76	15	7 54	

		A. M. deg.	P. M. deg.			A. M. deg.	P. M. deg.
June	23		4 80	August	11	8 76	3 86
	24	6 68	3 82		12	76	3 86
	25	7 74	3 80		13	7 76	3 86
	26	6 72	3 76		14	7 76	3 86
	27	7 74	3 76		15	7 76	3 86
	28	7 68	3 80		16	76	3 86
	29	7 70	4 84		17	76	3 86
	30	7 73	3 88		18	76	3 86
July	1	7 76	3-5 86		19	76	3 86
	2	7 72	3-5 84		20	76	3 86
	3	7 73	3 88		21	76	3 86
	4	8 72	3 74		22	74	3 82
	5	7 68	3 74		23	70	3 78
	6	7 68	3 78		24	70	3 78
	7	7 69	3 90		25	70	3 78
	8	7 74	3 88		26	70	3 78
	9	7 78	3 90		27	70	3 78
	10	7 80	3 90		28	70	3 78
	11	7 73	3 86		29	70	3 78
	12	7 72	3 92		30	70	3 78
	13	6 78	3 90		31	70	3 78
	14	7 78	3 90	Sept.	1	72	3 82
	15	7 80	3 91		2	72	3 82
	16	7 76	3 86		3	74	3 86
	17	6 70	3 84		4	74	3 86
	18	6 60	3 88		5	76	3 86
	19	6 64	3 86		6	76	3 86
	21	7 70	3 76		7	76	3 86
	22	7 72	3 82		8	76	3 86
	23	7 72	3 88		9	76	3 86
	24	7 78	3 86		10	76	3 86
	25	7 72	3 85		11	74	
	26	7 72	3 90		12	76	3 86
	27	7 70	3 88		13	70	3 86
	28	7 73	3 90		14	52	
	29	7 76	3 90		17	62	3 88
	30	7 76	3 90		18	64	3 86
	31	7 76	3 90		19	72	3 86
August	1	8 76	3 90		20	74	3 89
	2	8 72	3 90		21	68	3 84
	3	8 72	3 82		22	62	3 82
	4	8 72	3 76		23	60	3 80
	5	8 72	3 84		24	58	3 88
	6	8 76	3 84		25	49	3 70
	7	7 76	3 84		26	51	3 80
	8	7 76	3 84		27	54	3 84
	9	7 76	3 84		28	64	3 88
	10	7 78	3 86				